MALAWI

A GEOGRAPHICAL STUDY

MALAWI

A GEOGRAPHICAL STUDY

J. G. PIKE

Hydrologist, Department of Hydraulics, Malawi

AND

G. T. RIMMINGTON

*Assistant Professor of Education, Acadia University,
Nova Scotia, Canada. Formerly Education Officer,
Ministry of Education and Social Development, Malawi*

London

OXFORD UNIVERSITY PRESS

1965

Oxford University Press, Amen House, London E.C.4

GLASGOW NEW YORK TORONTO MELBOURNE WELLINGTON
BOMBAY CALCUTTA MADRAS KARACHI LAHORE DACCA
CAPE TOWN SALISBURY NAIROBI IBADAN ACCRA
KUALA LUMPUR HONG KONG

Printed in Great Britain
by Richard Clay and Company Ltd., Bungay, Suffolk

DEDICATED TO
THE PEOPLE OF MALAWI
AND TO
THE MEN AND WOMEN OF THE
MALAWI CIVIL SERVICE
WHOSE WORK HAS MADE THIS BOOK POSSIBLE

PREFACE

It is now more than a century since David Livingstone first set foot in Malawi. Travelling extensively around the shores of the lake, which he named Nyasa, although known to the Portuguese as Lake Maravi and by the people of Malawi as *Nyanja Nyenyezi*, he admired the beauty of its landscapes and at the same time deplored the horrors of the slave trade which took away so many of its people.

In 1891 Harry Johnston travelled from Port Herald to Karonga, a journey which was to culminate in the establishment of the British Central Africa Protectorate in 1892. On 6 July 1907, the country became known as the Nyasaland Protectorate. On the same date, fifty seven years later, the country will become the independent state of Malawi. Malawi was the name of a much older African nation, which existed before Europeans entered the area. It is a link with the past, symbolising a new interest among Africans not only in politics, but also in the bases of their own culture. Throughout this book therefore the country is referred to as Malawi, although in certain historical contexts 'Nyasaland' has been retained.

Since 1891 the administration has become settled, the tribes, with the spread of educational facilities and the growth of more legitimate trade, have become peaceful, and knowledge about the country's geography has accumulated. Much that is of a geographical nature has been written in *The Nyasaland Journal*, published by the Nyasaland Society, in papers published in the Annual Reports of Nyasaland Government Departments, and in other magazines and journals. No previous attempt has been made, however, to produce a systematic geographical account of Nyasaland from the information available.

It is hoped that this book will help to fill the present vacuum, although the authors are well aware that much information still remains hidden, and therefore not written about. Much remains to be done, for instance, in the field of social geography, especially in the analysis of settlement patterns and the relationship between agriculture and social customs. Nevertheless, with the prospect of political independence not far distant at the time of writing it has been thought worthwhile to present this study, bringing the patient research of many of our colleagues to the notice not only of the new elected rulers and leaders of Malawi, but also of the rest of the world, watching with interest the fortunes of a new nation.

For help with this work in its early stages the authors are indebted to Professor Frank Debenham, who, despite ill-health at the time, reviewed the first few chapters and offered valuable criticism. Grateful thanks are also due to Dr. Frank Dixey, who discussed geomorphological aspects with one of the authors, and also supplied valuable reference material; to Mr. G. Jackson for his helpful suggestions and permission to reproduce his vegetation map; to Mr. J. D. Chapman of the Nyasaland Forestry Department and Mr. F. Wright of the Imperial Forest Institute, Oxford, for material supplied on some aspects of vegetation; to Dr. A. Young, formerly Soil Surveyor of the Nyasaland Agricultural Department, for permission to use his provisional soil map; to Mr. Colin Baker of the Nyasaland Administration for his advice on historical aspects; to Dr. C. R. Hursh of the International Co-operation Administration for his interest and help in many directions; to Mr. J. R. Mayo, Draughtsman of the Nyasaland Geological Survey for the drawing of maps and diagrams; to Mrs. Enid Wolak, for many hours of typing kindly done voluntarily; and to Mr. B. E. Whitmore and Mr. R. Hopwood for photographic assistance and advice.

To the London offices of Sir William Halcrow and Partners, Hunting Technical Services, and Sir Alexander Gibb and Partners our thanks are due for making documents and reports available.

In other directions we have been assisted by many associates and colleagues in Nyasaland, among whom we would single out Messrs. J. C. N. Carver, F. Kharika, E. W. Latham, R. G. Gale, R. L. Kinsey, D. N. Patterson, R. D. Walshaw, and I. S. Macdonald. Many others, too numerous to be named here also helped in some small measure. To all of them the authors express their sincere thanks.

Finally, it seems fair to add that although the authors at the time of writing were members of the Nyasaland Civil Service any views expressed are personal, and have no official standing. Although we accept the entire responsibility for anything written we should be pleased if any reader in a position to do so would inform us of any errors which they happen to notice.

Blantyre & Dedza, Nyasaland   JOHN G. PIKE
November 1963   GERALD T. RIMMINGTON

The substance of chapter VIII has been taken from Professor Rimmington's thesis (*Population and Settlement Patterns in the Dedza District of Nyasaland*) presented for the degree of Doctor of Philosophy in the University of London.

CONTENTS

LIST OF ILLUSTRATIONS

Immediately preceeding Part One

ACKNOWLEDGEMENTS FOR PHOTOGRAPHS

The authors express their gratitude to the following: Mr. R. A. Kinsey, formerly of the former Federation of Rhodesia and Nyasaland Information Department, for plates 1–12, 19–24, 28, 29 and 31–33; The Chief Information Officer, Nyasaland Department of Information, and Provincial Information Officers, for plates 13–15, 18 and 25; The Editor, *The Nyasaland Journal*, for plate 30.

Photographs shown in plates 16 and 17 were taken by G. T. Rimmington.

FIGURES

TABLES

1. The broken, hilly foothill country of the Nkata Bay lake-shore area.

2. HORA MOUNTAIN, MZIMBA DISTRICT

A fine example of a hornblende-syenite inselberg rising above the well peneplaned
Miocene surface. The late Cretaceous (Vipya) surface in the left background.

3. LAKE NYASA FROM THE LIVINGSTONIA ESCARPMENT

Florence Bay, Youngs Bay, and Deep Bay in the foreground. Livingstone Mountains across the lake.

4. The Vipya Highlands Near Chikangawa.

5. The uninhabited Nyika Plateau.

6. Zomba Mountain from the North-East.

7. THE LICHENYA PLATEAU, MLANJE MOUNTAIN

This plateau stands at an elevation of some 6,500 to 7,000 feet. The patches of forest on the grassland are mainly of 'Mlanje Cedar'.

8. The Shire River flowing through the wide flat Upper Shire valley near Fort Johnston.

9. THE SHIRE RIVER AT CHIROMO LOOKING DOWNSTREAM

The Ruo River joins the Shire River from the left bank just beyond the palm trees. The Port Herald hills can be seen in the right background.

10. Ngoni warriors at Hora Mountain, Mzimba district.

11. A village set in a large clearing in the woodland (Visanza area).

12. Church of Scotland, Blantyre, built in 1895.

13. Street scene in Blantyre. The Town Hall is at the end of the road.

14. Traditional housing in a Land Resettlement Scheme at Zomba.

15. The Imperial Tobacco Company's African Village at Limbe.

16. A section of the Asian trading estate in Dedza.

17. The offices of the District Commissioner in Dedza.

18. The Colonial Development Corporation tung oil extraction factory at Mzuzu.

19. The women of the village return from the fields—subsistence gardens in the background.

20. A master farmer and his wife on their farm near Blantyre. Note the tobacco in the foreground and the maize in the background.

21. Experimental plots at Konsalendo, Cholo district. Note contour ridges with coffee, banana, sisal and pineapples growing.

22. Tobacco grading at Limbe.

23. TEA PLANTATION, MLANJE DISTRICT
Mlanje Mountain in the background.

24. The south-western flanks of Mlanje massif. Note tea plantation in the foreground, *Eucalyptis saligna* plantation in the middle distance and *Brachystegia* forest at the foot of the mountain.

25. Tea Processing at Cholo.

26. A Co-operative Society rice market, Kota Kota lake shore.

27. Afforestation with exotic conifers—Vipya Plateau.

28. Pine forests on Zomba Plateau. The Chilwa plain is visible in the distance.
29. Early morning catch at a beach on the shores of Lake Nyasa near Fort Johnston.

30. Fishing in Chiwandama Rapids

31. Blantyre railway station. The train is for migrant workers journeying to Southern Rhodesia.

32. The *M.V. Ilala II* calls at Deep Bay.

33. The beautiful harbour at Nkata Bay, Lake Nyasa.

PART ONE

PHYSICAL GEOGRAPHY

CHAPTER I*

GEOLOGY AND STRUCTURE

AFRICA, a vast continental shield, has been a land area since pre-Cambrian times and probably assumed its present outlines in the early Jurassic period. Over this long period of some 140 million years, the movements of this shield have been persistently in a vertical direction, giving a structural pattern of basins and swells that rise towards the east to form a system of coalescing plateaux extending from Abyssinia to the Cape Province. The East African 'swell' is traversed in a north–south direction by a system of rift valleys with which the great lakes of Africa are associated. These various plateaux have been uplifted and denuded in successive cycles of erosion resulting in the stripping of large areas of later sediments and softer rocks, thus exposing the ancient shield of pre-Cambrian rocks, some of which were originally very deep-seated. These pre-Cambrian schists and gneisses underlie the greater part of Malawi, the Palaeozoic, Karoo, Cretaceous, and Tertiary formations occurring only as relics of denudation in sheltered or down-faulted segments in the pre-Cambrian rocks.

The geological formations of Malawi may be considered in three main divisions: the pre-Cambrian or Basement Complex, the Karoo System, and the post-Karoo formations. Except for a minor outcrop in the Port Herald hills, the Palaeozoic formations are absent from Malawi, although there is evidence of their former greater extent.

THE GEOLOGICAL FORMATIONS

The Pre-Cambrian System

The most widespread system of rocks in Malawi are the various gneisses, schists, metamorphosed sediments, and igneous intrusions of pre-Cambrian age. The sub-divisions of this system are as yet unknown, but two broad divisions have been recognized. The Moçambique System underlying much of southern and central Malawi is composed of schists, migmatites, gneisses, granulites, and dolomitic marbles together with intrusions of syenites and associated rocks. The Mafingi System occurs in isolated areas of northern and central Malawi, notably the Mafingi mountains, the Mchinji hills in the Fort Manning district and to the north-east and west of the Nyika plateau, and is made up of quartzites, phyllites, and micaeous schists, clearly of sedimentary origin.

These two systems have been assigned an Upper and Middle pre-Cambrian age respectively. There is evidence however that both systems

* Chapters I-V have been written by J. G. Pike.

are of the same general age, the Upper pre-Cambrian, and differ only in rock composition and metamorphic grade.

The pre-Cambrian gneisses and schists have been extensively pene-planed in various cycles of erosion, and, owing to differential erosion between hard and soft formations, the harder intrusions of granite, syenite, gneisses, and other highly metamorphosed rocks are today physiographically prominent in the form of *inselberge* and the more ex-tensive highland areas rising above the peneplain surfaces of softer schists and gneisses. The intrusive elements of the pre-Cambrian were probably originally composed of basic intrusions into the meta-sedi-ments along zones of weakness, then, during the later stages of regional metamorphism, were altered to syenitic or granitic orthogneisses. These metamorphosed intrusives are common in the Shire Highlands where they form Michuru, Ndirande, and Soche mountains in the vicinity of Blantyre and Cholo mountain farther south. Elsewhere they make up the ring-structure of Chingale to the west of Zomba, the Mlindi ring-structure and the core of a north-trending, doubly-plunging closed syn-cline flanking the Shire River to the east near Matope that gives rise to the Little Michuru–Chipalanje hills. In central and northern Malawi they make up Dedza and Chongoni mountains, the isolated hills of Kasungu and Ngara, and underlie the extensive Nyika plateau.

The strike of the pre-Cambrian formations is invariably in a north–south direction with localized variations. In the Shire Highlands the strike varies from north-west along the Cholo escarpment to north-east in a northward direction. West of the Shire River the strike is generally north, but near Neno in the Kirk Range it becomes north-westerly. In the Central Province north-easterly strikes are predominant, and this is clearly demonstrated by the dominant north-easterly trend of the drainage pattern. In the upper Lifidzi valley, to the north of Dedza Mountain, the drainage pattern is classically developed in a trellis pattern between the more resistant bands of gneiss. In the Northern Province the strike varies from ENE. to WNW. Along the margins of main intrusive elements the strike is usually concordant, the intrusives forming these elements having been elongated along the strike of the schists and gneisses. Throughout the system there are areas where large scale isoclinal folding has taken place, and, as a result, harder bands of gneiss are often repeated on surface exposure.

The Karoo System

Occurring in scattered areas over a large part of Central and Southern Africa, the Karoo system is typically a horizontal formation. It is the youngest plateau system in the sub-continent and is now in the process of being removed by erosion from the sub-Karoo surface. The Karoo sediments were deposited from middle Carboniferous times to the Triassic, with a volcanic stage closing the period of deposition in some areas. The character of the sedimentation shows that the deposition probably took place in a continental basin under climatic conditions

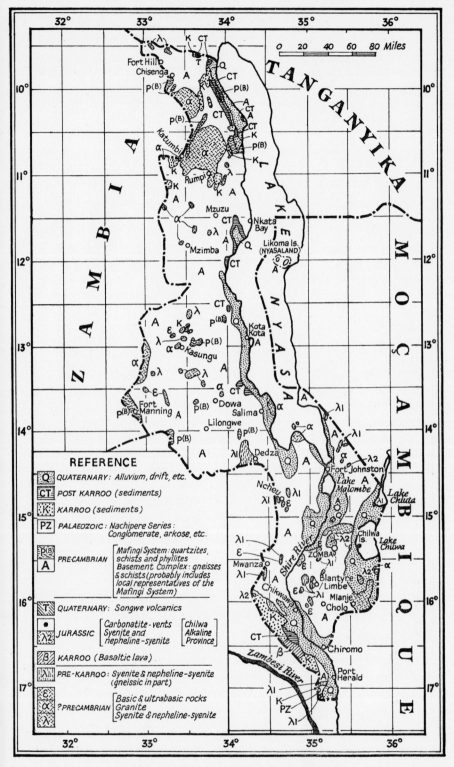

Fig. 1. Geological Map of Malawi
(Reproduced by permission of the Director, Geological Survey, Malawi.)

which began as glacial and changed to cool, warm, and finally arid. The system may be divided into a lower division (Permo-carboniferous) and an upper division (Triassic and lower Jurassic). In the lower

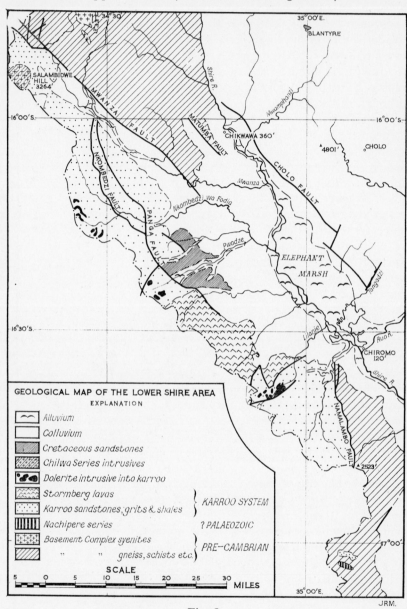

Fig. 2.

division occur the Dwyka and Ecca series, in the upper the Beaufort and Stormberg series. In Malawi there are two main areas of Karoo rocks that appear to have been preserved from erosion by down-faulting into the pre-Cambrian, since these rocks are found in wide *graben* or depressions below the 4,000 feet Miocene peneplain, though occasionally in or above it.

The Karoo beds of Malawi occur in two main areas; in the Lake Nyasa basin on the north-western shores of the lake and in the Zambezi–Shire basin of southern Malawi. In the north these sediments are derived from the local pre-Cambrian quartzites, micaeous schists, and phylites of the Mafingi system, whereas those of southern Malawi are mainly derived from the Moçambique system of gneisses and schists. Stratigraphically the beds in both areas are very similar, although the Stormberg lavas found in the Zambezi area do not occur in the northern areas.

In north Nyasa, Karoo beds outcrop as isolated remnants in some seven different localities, the most important block of sediments occurring in the Livingstonia area, where they cover an area of 100 square miles at the foot of the Nyika plateau overlooking Lake Nyasa. Numerous coal seams occur in the Ecca series, and have been systematically explored over the past decade in this area. To the south of this occurrence these beds outcrop in the North Rumpi and Henga valleys and in the former locality have been much dissected by the swift-flowing North Rumpi and Kaziwiziwi Rivers. On the Songwe River, northwest of Karonga near Nkana, a smaller area of these sediments covering some 25 square miles occurs as a down-faulted segment within the gneisses and schists. Coal seams have been examined in this area also. Further sediments of this system are to be found in the North Rukuru and upper Lufira valleys covering comparatively large areas in sheltered locations.

In the lower Shire–Zambezi area these sediments outcrop over an area of some 850 square miles within Malawi and are situated on the south-western border of the country. To the south-east they are bounded by a major fault that forms the western edge of the Port Herald hills and to the north by the upthrown Mwanza fault (see Fig. 1). In the Nkombedzi area the Stormberg basaltic lavas outcrop over an area of some 150 square miles and weather to fertile black 'cotton' soils (*makande*). The dip of these formations is to the north-east and an area of low ridges and a generally subdued topography may be observed. Coal seams in the Ecca series, too, have been explored here, but large scale faulting has done much to break up the continuity of these seams.

The close of the Karoo period was marked by the extrusion of basaltic lavas through fissures now occupied by dolerite dykes. Sills in the Karoo sediments and dykes cutting the pre-Cambrian formations are commonly found in the southern part of Malawi. Since the dolerite is generally harder than the majority of these rocks, linear ridges formed by these dykes are conspicuous as high, narrow crests between the deeply dissected valleys, particularly along the Cholo escarpment. The weathering of these dolerite dykes in the Cholo area has produced a red loam soil rich in minerals, now extensively cultivated and under tea plantations. These dyke swarms appear to be confined to the southern

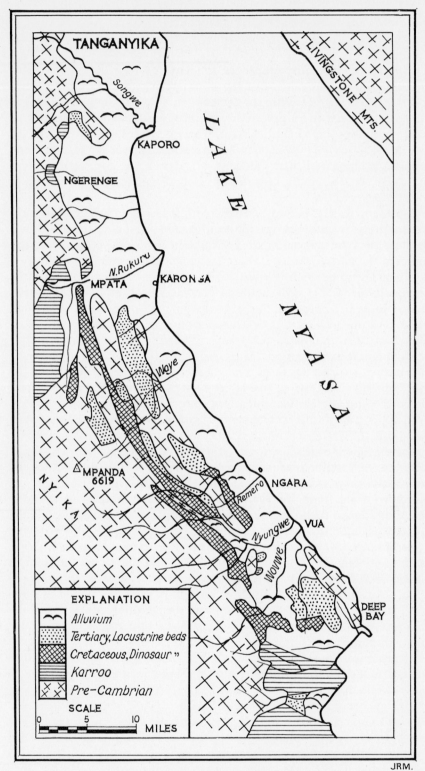

Fig. 3. Geological map of the Karonga Lake-shore area.
(After F. Dixey, 1927.)

part of Malawi, their occurrence being rare north of about 15° South latitude.

Of perhaps little importance to the general physiography of the country but of interest in tracing geomorphological history, is the occurrence of a small remnant of sediments on the Tuchila shelf of Mlanje Mountain at an elevation of 6,100 feet. These sediments have been thermally altered by the Mlanje syenite and are believed to be a remnant of a series of sediments that covered a considerable area of southern Malawi in Karoo times.

The Chilwa Intrusive Series

In the post-Karoo period, probably late Jurassic, a considerable part of Malawi is believed to have been covered by Karoo sediments, and into these formations came the intrusion, mainly through circular vents or ring-structures, of syenites, nepheline-syenites, breccia, and carbonatites; these were followed later by alkaline and dolerite dykes. There appear to be two chains of carbonatite vents and associated rocks, trending approximately north-east to south-west, extending over some 2,500 miles of Africa from Kenya to South Africa, and their association with the main structural features of this region is evident.

Although these intrusions were originally buried beneath a great thickness of sediments, the raising of the East African swell has succeeded in stripping the sediments in a series of erosion cycles, so that today the intrusions of syenite and carbonatite are present in the striking mountain features of southern Malawi. The syenites form the massifs of Mlanje, Zomba, Michesa, Nachema, Nasolo, Mpyupyu and the nepheline-syenites occur in the form of the four striking ring-intrusions of Chindusi, Mongolowe, Chaone, and Chikala covering an area of 80 square miles north of Zomba. The carbonatite vents are less conspicuous and form the isolated hills of Chilwa Island, Namangali and Tundulu on the Palombe-Chilwa plain, and Kangagunde hill to the west of the Shire River.

Geographically, the Chilwa intrusives are of importance to Malawi as it was during the period of their occurrence that the mountain massifs of Mlanje, Zomba, and lesser hills were emplaced. Although of importance in the physiographic picture, the presence of numerous rare earth minerals associated with the carbonatites may make them, in addition, important economically. Among the minerals found may be mentioned pyrochlore, monazite, strontianite, barite, and other rare earth minerals. On the various plateaux of Mlanje considerable deposits of bauxite occur as a result of the weathering of syenite.

The Post-Karoo Formations

In the eroded pre-Karoo valleys of northern and southern Malawi, and in isolated remnants along the course of the rift valley, occur pale to grey shales, sandstones, and conglomerates of late Jurassic or early Cretaceous age. These sediments occur in two main areas; along the north-western shores of Lake Nyasa over a distance of some 80 miles, and in the Zambezi–Shire area where they overlay the Karoo sediments to the west of the Shire River. These two main groups of sediments are considered to be of the same general age, although known by different names; the northern group have yielded fossil dinosaur remains and are known as the Dinosaur Beds, whereas those of the south are known as the Lupata Sandstones.

In north-west Nyasa the Dinosaur Beds have been preserved within parallel minor rifts in the pre-Cambrian or Karoo rocks and are, in places, overlain by later Tertiary deposits. In the Shire Valley the Lupata Sandstones overlay the Karoo beds and at one time were probably of much greater extent over this area, being confined now, however, to a small area between the Pwadze and Nkombedzi Rivers in the Chikwawa district. Along the course of the rift valley, water-worn pebbles occur in sheets and mounds up to a level of 800 feet above the lake, and are considered to be weathered residuals of the Cretaceous infilling of the Nyasa trough. Elsewhere, along the margins of the lake, remnant *in situ* deposits occur in sheltered locations, notably as bench terraces fringing the Limpasa dambo in the Nkata Bay area, a former arm of Lake Nyasa.

Along the Karonga lake littoral, in a belt extending from Deep Bay to Karonga, the Tertiary Lacustrine Series outcrop and, together with the Dinosaur Beds of Cretaceous age, upon which they lie uncomformably, give rise to topographical conditions of particular interest. The friable nature of most of these sediments, combined with the variations in lake level and the progressive recession of the north-western shore line since pre-Pleistocene times, has led to their rapid sub-aerial erosion over a considerable period. This has brought about the 'bad land' topography forming the boundary between the Nyika highlands and the lake shore plain.

Dr. F. Dixey has divided the Lacustrine Series into five groups:

5.	Recent Deposits.	Recent.
4.	Songwe Volcanic Tuffs.	
3.	The Chitimbwe Beds.	Pleistocene.
2.	The Chiwondo Beds.	
1.	The Sungwa Beds.	Pliocene (?)

Apart from the more southerly lake shore areas covered by Recent deposits, these beds are confined to the north-western shore of Lake Nyasa, where they cover an elongated area of some 500 square miles in a number of down-faulted strips in the pre-Cambrian and Karoo rocks. These formations are made up of grits, calcareous marls, silts, shelly limestones, red gravels and conglomerates, their most outstanding feature being their friable nature. The more resistant ferruginous conglomerates form battlemented scarps.

The Songwe Volcanics are a series of tuffs and lavas that appear to have been laid down under water and are derived from the Pleistocene

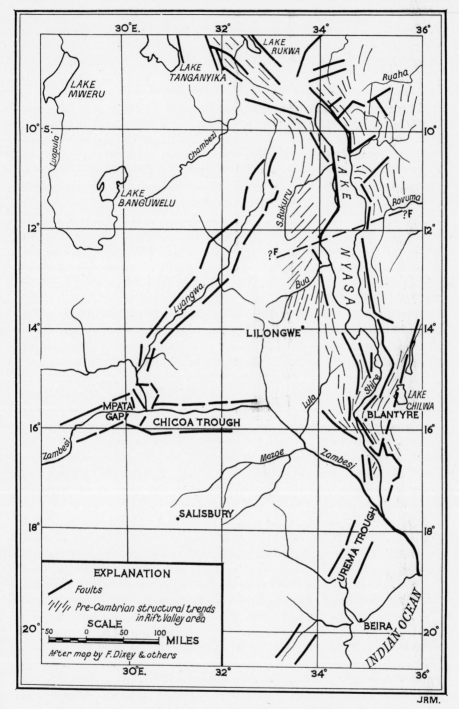

Fig. 4.   Structural map of the Nyasa–Zambezi–Luangwa area.

volcanic activity of the north Nyasa region that caused the large infilling
of the main rift valley, and which today form the high mountain ranges
of the Poroto in Tanganyika. These lavas and tuffs are of limited distribution in Malawi, but give rise to very fertile soil in Tanganyika
where they occur on a more extensive scale.

THE RIFT VALLEY IN MALAWI

The most outstanding geographical feature of Malawi is that part
of the great rift valley that traverses the country from north to south,
structually linked to the Rukwa rift in Tanganyika and the Urema
trough to the south in Moçambique. Malawi may be considered to
be wholly a rift territory as it occupies a position astride the Shire rift in
the south and the western catchment of the Nyasa rift to the north. The
trough occupied by Lake Nyasa and the Shire River with its flanking
plateaux, form two distinct physical divisions. For convenience, the rift
valley may also be considered in two separate, but related, sections; an
upper rift occupied by Lake Nyasa and a lower rift occupied by the
Shire River, which drains the lake.

The Lake Nyasa Rift

The Lake Nyasa rift valley, which averages 50 miles in width,
assumes the form of a great trough that runs almost due north over a
distance of some 400 miles. It intersects various plateaux of high average
altitude ranging from 7,000 to 8,000 feet in the north and from 3,000 to
5,000 feet in the south. The Nyasa basin is as a whole asymmetric; the
eastern side has been downthrown by one main fault or series of faults
whereas the western part of the downthrown block has been dropped in
a series of eastward sloping steps by parallel faults. Frequently subsidiary
rifts have developed on the western shore at various elevations which
are today separated from the lake shore by low crystalline ridges, often
up to 30 miles in length. There are, however, variations in this general
easterly asymmetrical shape, and near the Malawi shore between
Deep Bay and Nkata Bay the tilt is the reverse of the general direction,
the lake here attaining its greatest depth of 2,310 feet (760 feet below
sea level). This reverse tilt was brought about by the large north–south
Ruarwe fault, which is probably of Pleistocene origin. In longitudinal
section the floor of the Nyasa rift is of an average depth of some
1,200 feet in the north, deepening to over 2,000 feet towards the centre
and thereafter becoming rapidly shallower to an average of some 500 to
700 feet in the southern section, which is made up of a series of step
faults tilted towards the east, giving the impression of a synclinal depression rather than a rift trough. Although the trend of the rift as a
whole is north–south, the walls themselves have assumed a zigzag
course as a result of the intersection of two sets of faults that run NNE.
and NNW.; furthermore, these faults sometimes terminate against, and
are therefore older than, additional faults that run on a northerly
course.

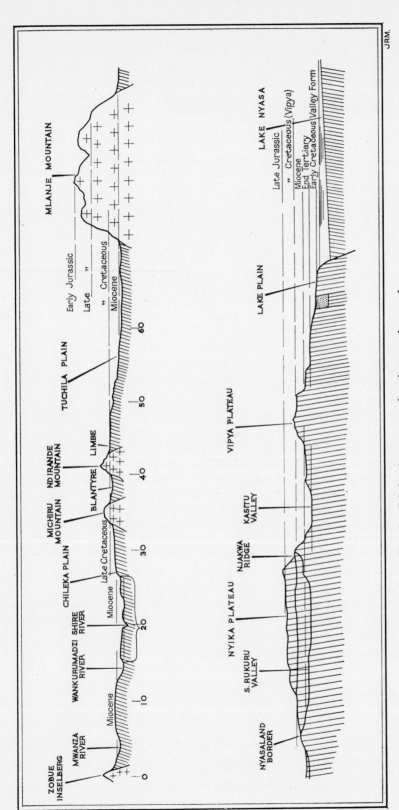

Fig. 5.　Malawi transects showing erosion cycles.

The greater part of the floor of the main rift is occupied by Lake Nyasa, around which extends a lake littoral of varying width. This littoral is at its widest in the northern and southern parts of the western coast. The slope of the plain lying along the north-western shores of the lake is continued for many miles below lake level, almost to the sub-lacustrine foot of the Livingstone mountains, which are bounded by a spectacular scarp rising sheer from the lake to heights nearing 9,000 feet above sea level.

The Shire Rift

The Shire section of the Malawi part of the rift valley comprises two main series of fractures that run SSW. and SSE. The Shire rift follows these two directions in turn and may be regarded as:

(a) The Upper Shire rift, running SSW., extending from the southern limit of Lake Nyasa to the Murchison cataracts, and

(b) the Lower Shire rift, running SSE. extending from the Murchison cataracts to Chiromo and thence southwards to Port Herald, bounded to the north-east by the Cholo scarp and to the south-west by the subdued Karoo formations.

Lying parallel to the Upper Shire rift is the long depression that includes Lake Chilwa and the adjacent low-lying country that extends from the Chilwa plain through the western edge of Mlanje to the Ruo valley. This depression extends northwards through Lake Chiuta and the Lujenda valley in Moçambique, and in a southerly direction may be traced across the Zambezi into the Urema trough that lies to the west of the Sheringoma plateau in Moçambique. Lying parallel to the Lower Shire rift is the broken depression that extends north-westwards from Lake Chilwa to Lake Nyasa, and includes Lake Malombe, and the level plain north of Chikala Hill. Lakes Chilwa and Malombe thus occupy depressions at the intersection of a SSE. rift and two SSW. rifts.

The Murchison cataracts are situated in the broken country at the angle of intersection between the Upper and Lower Shire rifts. This pattern of intersecting rifts has given rise to the roughly diamond-shaped Shire Highlands plateau bounded on all four sides by branches of the rift system, that has, however, been obscured by warping and later rifting to the north and east. As the result of this later warping the Shire Highlands slope towards the Chilwa–Lujenda depression at a uniform rate with no discernible rift margin.

THE ORIGIN OF THE RIFT VALLEYS

More than a century ago the Rhine rift valley was compared with the fallen key-stone of an arch; thus arose the traditional tensional theory, according to which a wedge-shaped block, tapering downwards, sank between two normal boundary faults as the compression on the sides was released. This tension hypothesis was accepted in principle by Professor J. W. Gregory in his well-known account of the rift valleys of East

Africa but this hypothesis is not without its difficulties, the most serious being that a rift block could not sink unless its weight displaced molten material at depth. Vulcanism would then occur along the boundaries and it has long been known that in several areas of the rift volcanic activity ceased altogether while the rift movements were in progress. Gregory based his conclusions mainly on work in Kenya and Tanganyika where the surface features of the rift appear to date from the late Cretaceous or early Tertiary and where tensional features are exhibited on the surface.

An alternate hypothesis, proposed by E. J. Wayland for the Lake Albert and Ruwenzori sections and by Bailey Willis for the Dead Sea section, postulated that the rift valleys were produced by deep-seated compression. The boundary faults are then regarded as steep upthrusts and the rift blocks as wedges (widening in depth) held down by pressure from the upriding sides. As the plateau blocks rode up the high angle of the thrust plane, their forward edges were left unsupported, strips of the overhanging sides slumped down, and the present walls thus appear to be normal faults. Such a rift block would be held down by compression, sealing the boundaries, and explaining the lack of contemporaneous vulcanism in certain areas of the rift. Further geophysical work by E. C. Bullard tended to support this hypothesis.

Over the past thirty-five years Dr. F. Dixey has studied the rift valleys of East Africa and in particular the Malawi section. His findings have been published in more than a dozen papers on the subject and it was in 1926 that he first drew attention to evidence in Malawi suggesting that the rift valley was probably much older than previously thought. In the post-war years a large amount of geological field work has been carried out in East and Central Africa and much new light has been thrown on the geomorphology of this feature.

The rift system has been found to be a complex structure that may be traced to crustal weaknesses in ancient or primordial times, and which cannot readily be explained in comparatively simple tensional or compression terms. In the Kenya rift, and in the Urema trough in Moçambique, only later post-Tertiary phases are exhibited, whereas in the Shire trough the Jurassic phase is exhibited, and in the Lake Nyasa–Rukwa troughs the pre-Cambrian, Jurassic, and post-Tertiary phases are all well-developed. Similarly, both tensional and compression phenomena are exhibited in various areas. Thus the early description of the post-Tertiary rifting in Kenya had long given rise to the erroneous impression that the rift system as a whole was essentially a late-Tertiary and post-Tertiary phenomenon.

Dr. F. Dixey has summarized the recent geological evidence from East Africa and he sees the Rift Valley as part of the much larger problem of the great intermittently-rising East African swell, which itself is complementary to the intermittently-sinking East African coast and the Moçambique Channel geosyncline. These in turn are but part of the great basin and swell structure of Africa as a whole, which are considered to be related to the pattern of a cooling and shrinking earth, a pattern initiated in primordial times. He further suggests that the rifts formed along the margins of major subsiding basins; with the rising of the margins of the main blocks or basins, due to greater subsidence in the centre, smaller detached blocks would tend to form along the ancient fractures and to lag behind during the upward movement of the main blocks and thus form lag zones or rifts. Along such marginal areas, plastic and magmatic flow would tend to be at a maximum, leading to the adjustment of the blocks and to local volcanic activity.

The rift valleys are thus envisaged by Dixey as being a north–south extension of the Moçambique Channel, known to have been sinking since Permian times, and are seen essentially as branches of this geosyncline, that have formed along ancient fractures and failed to keep pace with the rising East Africa and Madagascar swells, having undergone successive phases of deposition, rejuvenation, and erosion. By this process, which is described as 'a rise to the rift', the present day features of the Nyasa–Shire rift appear to have evolved, and lend weight to this hypothesis. In the lower Shire area the valley is bounded to the north-east by the Cholo fault but to the south-west there is no discernible escarpment. A similar 'one-sided' rift occurs in the north Nyasa area where the rift is bounded to the north-east by the spectacular Livingstone Mountains and to the south-west by a number of smaller scarps that have been developed by parallel minor rifting.

The age of the Rift System is suggested by Dixey to date from pre-Cambrian times. While there is much evidence to demonstrate the coincidence of pre-Cambrian structural lines and more recent faulting, not all geologists working in Africa agree with Dixey's theory in its entirety. One of the most fundamental implications of Dixey's emphasis on the antiquity of the Rift System, and particularly the Moçambique Channel, is that it points to the permanence of the major structures of the continent, and discourages belief in the hypothesis of continental drift.

THE DEVELOPMENT OF THE NYASA–SHIRE RIFT VALLEY

It is believed that during early Jurassic times a large part of the African continent was covered to a considerable depth by sediments and lavas of Karoo age, the surface of which had, at that time, been peneplaned to a remarkably smooth surface. In Malawi the main basins of Karoo deposition appear to have been the north Nyasa and lower Shire areas, and possibly some parts of central Malawi as well. Round about mid-Jurassic times, fractures along the present line of the rift valleys were initiated, which were however influenced by older fractures.

Further peneplanation took place before the beginning of Cretaceous times, followed by uplifting, fracturing, and tilting. It is in the latter tectonic movements that the origins of the main Cholo and Livingstone faults may be sought. To the north-east of these two faults there was a concomitant rise, bringing the deep-seated pre-Cambrian rocks nearer to the surface. Following upon cycles of uplift and erosion came further fracturing and down-warping, and it is thought that the intervening part of the rift between the northern and southern sections occurred at about this time. Simultaneously, the Karoo sediments let down into the rifted valleys were being rapidly eroded. Over a considerable area these were completely stripped to expose the pre-Cambrian rocks within the valleys. In isolated, down-faulted areas, such as the northern and southern sections, some of the Karoo sediments were preserved and their remnants may be observed in these areas today.

During the Cretaceous period occurred a prolonged and gradual depression under arid to semi-arid conditions allowing the early Cretaceous sea to encroach upon the eastern and south-eastern coasts of Africa; the inland Karoo valleys became filled with coarse sediments. The Dinosaur Beds of north Nyasa and the Lupata Sandstones were laid down at this time. Infilling of these inland valleys continued throughout the Cretaceous and possibly into the Eocene period. More stable conditions prevailed during the early Miocene leading to widespread peneplanation. The softer rocks were base levelled and remnants of the late Jurassic and late Cretaceous peneplains were preserved on areas underlain by resistant rocks, such as the harder syenitic and granitic intrusions and the harder quartzites and gneisses. These remnants of the Jurassic and Cretaceous peneplains include the Nyika Plateau and associated highlands, the Vipya Plateau and Zomba and Mlanje Mountains.

The Miocene uplift, of some 3,000 to 4,000 feet, led to the erosion of the greater part of the Cretaceous sediments from the inland valleys and coastal plains. This infilling of the Nyasa trough was probably removed by the ancient Shire river that had by this time established itself within the main valley and probably flowed southwards via the Chilwa Plain and the Ruo Valley, the middle Shire faulting not yet having taken place. This uplift, like that of the late Jurassic, was accompanied or followed by intermittent fracturing and tilting of the old surface, generally following older lines of weakness, but less striking in their effects. To these and later movements, rather than to those of the early Cretaceous, are tentatively ascribed the subsidence in stages of part of the floor of the Nyasa rift from a level of the north-west lake littoral (1,550 to 1,700 feet) to a maximum of about 700 feet below sea level, thus forming the basin now occupied by Lake Nyasa. Together with the subsidence of the Lake Nyasa floor, contemporary movements were taking place in the southern area where the upper Shire rift floor was lowered by some 300 feet along the Makongwa scarp, with local down-warping to form Lake Malombe. This movement, together with the depression of a few hundred feet along the foot of the Cholo scarp southwards to form the elongated lower Shire Valley, probably caused the diversion of the Shire River from its ancient course to the west. The down-warping

C

of the Shire Highlands Miocene peneplain which probably occurred at this time led to the formation of Lake Chilwa, which overlies a considerable thickness of drift material.

Along the north-western shores of Lake Nyasa the cycle of deposition and erosion was several times repeated in late Tertiary and Quaternary times and minor parallel rifts developed with intermittent subsidence and tilting of the rift floor towards the east. The main tilt was probably initiated when the Ruarwe fault became fully developed during the Pleistocene. The Nyasa–Shire rift valley dates from the late Jurassic or early Cretaceous, with renewed movements in the late Tertiary and post-Tertiary that led to the expansion of Lake Nyasa from a small lake in the north to its present limits. Thus, while the Nyasa rift valley is seen to date from the Mesozoic, Lake Nyasa was not fully developed until the middle and upper Pleistocene. The continued concentration of these movements over a long period along pre-Karoo lines of weakness has been responsible for the striking topography of the present day, one which gives rise to the great variations in climate, vegetation, and soils.

EROSION SURFACES

The great plateau of central and southern Africa is generally recognized as being due essentially to the erosion of an extensive peneplain that has undergone cycles of intermittent uplift and fracturing, and these various surfaces may be recognized in present day topography throughout the sub-continent. The slopes separating two cycles are often steep and sufficiently pronounced to be easily recognizable. In certain areas where the underlying rocks are of low resistance and the second cycle is sufficiently prolonged, the slope may be gently merged with the upper and lower surfaces and may not at first be apparent. Dr. Dixey has described these various cycles together with their relationship to other parts of central and southern Africa, and recognizes six main surfaces in Malawi, in the following sequence of age:

1. The sub-Karoo surface.
2. The late Jurassic peneplain (7,000 to 7,500 feet) (Gondwana Surface).
3. The early Cretaceous 'valley form' cycle.
4. The early Tertiary or late Cretaceous 'Vipya' peneplain (5,500 to 6,000 feet).
5. The mid-Tertiary or Miocene peneplain (4,000 to 4,500 feet) (African).
6. The end-Tertiary cycle. (3,000 to 4,000 feet).

The sub-Karoo surface underlies the Beaufort division of the Karoo in northern Malawi and in other places coincides with the later Miocene peneplain to a greater or lesser extent.

The late Jurassic peneplain is represented on the various high plateaux of Malawi on a far greater scale, in proportion to the size of the country, than in any other part of the sub-continent. This surface may

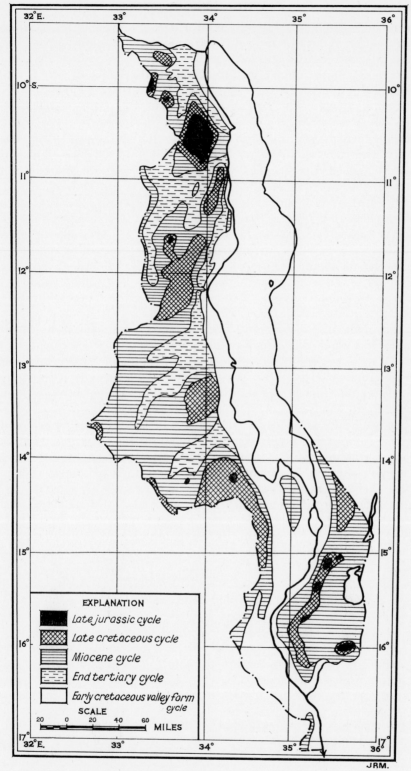

Fig. 6.   Generalized map showing erosion surfaces in **Malawi**.

be recognized on the Mafingi summit ridge, the Nyika plateau surface, the higher peaks of the Vipya, Dedza mountain, Zomba and Mlanje, and has been correlated with the Basuto highlands and the Zwarte-bergen in South Africa and the Khomas Mountains of South West Africa.

Following upon the late Jurassic peneplanation and subsequent up-lift, came the early Cretaceous cycle, one that Dixey terms a 'valley form' peneplanation, whereby the softer formations filling the rift valley were eroded to expose the pre-Karoo solid floor of the Nyasa–Shire rift valley. This floor is well exposed in the middle Shire valley and on low bevels along the lake shore at about 500 feet above lake level. In spite of being limited on one or both sides by high scarps of crystalline rocks, this peneplain is very well graded over areas of the Karoo sediments in the Shire–Zambezi area and elsewhere over the adjacent softer gneisses, so that its even surface is interrupted only by relic hills consisting of igneous and metamorphic rocks of exceptional resistance. It is thought that this surface corresponds with the valley floors of the Luangwa, Zambezi, Sabi, Limpopo, and also to the deep valleys in the Cape Ranges of South Africa.

Throughout the early and mid-Cretaceous the older late Jurassic peneplain was steadily being reduced and this cycle was terminated by late Cretaceous uplift. This cycle formed an extensive surface below the older Jurassic surface and is now recognizable as a bevel at about 5,000 feet around the flanks of the Nyika plateau, the Misuku uplands and, to the south-east, the extensive upland area of the Vipya plateau that extends southwards over a distance of 160 miles to a point some 40 miles south of Mzimba. To this plateau surface an early Tertiary or late Cretaceous age has been assigned and is generally known as the 'Vipya peneplain' in Malawi. Farther south, the even plateau surface near Dowa which stands at an elevation of between 4,500 and 5,000 feet, the surface surrounding Dedza mountain and the Mchinji hills near Fort Manning, are all considered to be of the same cycle. In the Shire Highlands this late Cretaceous surface is represented as a distinct plat-form along the Cholo–Limbe–Zomba crest, at Zomba, around Mlanje mountain, on the Chikala hills and in the well bevelled surface of Chilwa Island.[1]

Following uplift and further erosion the late Cretaceous surface was modified to form a lower peneplain lying at an elevation of between 3,500 and 4,000 feet, and this surface now constitutes the largest pene-planed surface in Malawi. This surface is considered to be of mid-Tertiary or Miocene age and in the central and northern areas of the country is well developed where it extends into the country from Northern Rhodesia. This Miocene surface is represented in Malawi

[1] Elsewhere this surface is well represented as residuals such as Gorongoza in Moçambique, the Chimanimani in Southern Rhodesia, the Zoutpansberg, Waterberg, Majuba, and Nieuweveld in South Africa. To the west the Mossamedes and Huambo plateaus in Angola and the Mpika–Abercorn ridge in Northern Rhodesia are also considered to be of the same age.

by the Fort Hill plains surrounding the Mafingi mountains, the broad divide forming the Lake Nyasa–Luangwa watershed, the Mzimba plain, the broad valley crests of the Central Province, and part of the Kirk Range. Flanking the Shire highlands to the north-west is the Chileka plain that lies at an average elevation of 2,200 feet, and to the south-east lies the Tuchila plain to both of which mid-Tertiary or Miocene age is ascribed. The same features are recognizable in the Port Herald hills.

In east and central Africa the end-Tertiary or Pliocene erosion surface takes the form of broad valleys, usually eroded below the level of the Miocene peneplain, and normally separated by flat slopes. This end-Tertiary surface is conspicuous in the Northern Province on either side of the Vipya plateau; to the west lies the deeply eroded Kasitu valley that merges with the Henga valley, and to the east, overlooking Lake Nyasa, there is a more or less continuous bevelled surface at an elevation of about 3,500 feet extending from Kasengadzi to Chikwina. Dixey considers this 'Kasengadzi' surface to be of end-Tertiary age and to be the inner margin remnant of a surface that extended across the Lake Nyasa trough on the Cretaceous deposits prior to their erosion by the ancient Shire River and by the later rift movements of the Pleistocene period. Elsewhere in Malawi this surface is perceptible only as a broad valley floor cycle that usually merges with the Miocene surface and is typically developed along the valleys of the South Rukuru, Dwangwa, Bua, and Lilongwe Rivers. On the Shire Highlands this surface has been subjected to post-Tertiary down-warping to form the Lake Chilwa basin on the eastern side of these highlands.

BIBLIOGRAPHY

K. Bloomfield, 'The Geology of the Port Herald Area', *Geol. Surv. Bull.*, No. 9, Nyasaland (1958).

E. C. Bullard, 'Gravity Measurements in East Africa', *Phil. Trans. Roy. Soc. of London* (A), Vol. CCXXXV (1936).

W. G. G. Cooper, 'The Geology and Mineral Resources of Nyasaland', *Geol. Surv. Bull.*, No. 6, Nyasaland (1957).

F. Dixey, W. Campbell-Smith, and C. B. Bisset, 'The Chilwa Series of Southern Nyasaland', *Geol. Surv. Bull.*, No. 5 (Revised) (1955).

F. Dixey, 'The East African Rift System', *Col. Geol. & Min. Res. Bull.*, Supp. No. 1, H.M.S.O. (1956).

——, 'The Dinosaur Beds of Lake Nyasa', *Trans. Roy. Soc. of S.A.*, Vol. XVI, pt. 1 (1927).

——, 'The Nyasa Rift Valley', *S.A. Geog. Jour.*, Vol. XXIII (April 1941).

——, 'The Tertiary and Post-Tertiary Lacustrine Sediments of the Nyasa Rift Valley', *Quarterly Journal of the Geological Society*, London, Vol. LXXXIII, pt. 3 (1927).

——, 'The Nyasaland Section of the Great Rift Valley', *Geog. Jour.*, Vol. LXVIII (1926).

——, 'Some Observations on the Physiographical Development of Central and Southern Africa', *Trans. G.S. of S.A.*, Vol. 41 (1938).

——, 'Erosion Cycles in Central and Southern Africa', *Trans. G.S. of S.A.*, Vol. 45 (1942).

F. Dixey, 'Some Aspects of the Geomorphology of Central and Southern Africa'
    Trans. G.S. of S.A., Annex. Vol. 58 (1955).

M. S. Garson, 'Chilwa Island', *Geol. Surv. Memoir*, No. 1, Nyasaland (1958).

J. W. Gregory, *The Rift Valleys and Geology of East Africa*, Seeley, Service & Co.,
    London, 1921.

A. Holmes, 'Sequence of Pre-Cambrian Orogenic Belts in South and Central Africa'
    C.R. XVIIIth Inter. Geol. Congr., Gt. Britain, 1948, pt. XIV.

A. M. MacGregor, 'Pre-Cambrian Formations of Tropical Southern Africa', *XIXth
    Inter. Geol. Congr.*, Algiers (1952–53).

J. E. S. Moore, *The Tanganyika Problem*, London (1903).

J. W. Pallister, Review in *Geog. Jour.*, Vol. CXXIII (1957).

F. E. Studt, 'The Geology of Katanga and Rhodesia', *Proc. R.S. of S.A.* (1913).

E. O. Theile, and R. C. Wilson, 'Portuguese East Africa between the Zambezi River
    and the Sabi River', *Geog. Jour.*, Vol. 45, No. 1 (1889).

A. L. du Toit, 'The Climatic Setting of the Vertebrate Fauna of the Karoo System and
    its Significance', *R.S. of S.A. spec. publication, Robert Brown Commemorative Vol.* (1958).

E. J. Wayland, 'Some Account of the Geology of the Lake Albert Rift Valley',
    Geog. Jour., Vol. 88 (1921).

Bailey Willis, *East African Plateaux and Rift Valley*, Carnegie Inst., Washington, Pub.
    No. 470 (1936).

CHAPTER II

PHYSIOGRAPHY

THE plateau in Malawi has been interrupted by rift movements of considerable magnitude that have formed the rift troughs of Lake Nyasa and the Shire River. As a result of these movements the country has been divided into two main physical divisions that bear the same geographical comparisons made by Professor J. H. Wellington in respect of South Africa. Modification of the plateau surface by rift faulting has given Malawi a remarkably diverse physiography. In altitude it ranges from a few hundred feet in the Shire valley to 7,000 or 8,000 feet on the higher plateaux. This has in turn produced a wide range of climatic, vegetational, and environmental conditions within a comparatively small area, and, while perhaps greatly adding to its scenic beauty, accounts for many problems involving development and communications.

The dominant feature of the Nyasa landscape is the Lake Nyasa trough and its flanking high plateaux, which, together with the Shire Valley trough south of Lake Nyasa, traverses the country from north to south. The physiographical development of Malawi is closely bound up with the evolution of this trough and to a large extent the presence of this great geographical feature has influenced the history and human geography of this part of Africa. It divided the streams of early Bantu migration and formed a natural boundary to British, German, and Portuguese spheres of influence in the latter half of the last century, and together with the Shire River connecting it with the Zambezi and the Indian Ocean, provided an access into Africa for explorers and missionaries.

High plateaux dominate the landscape to east and west of the rift valley. The plateau margins to the west of the Lake are composed of a series of stepped platforms or sheer fault scarps that rise to elevations of between 4,000 and 7,000 feet to form the highland areas of the Nyika, Vipya, and Central Province highlands. From these bordering highlands the country slopes away to the west where it either merges with or is stepped down to the Miocene and end-Tertiary peneplains at a level of 3,500 to 4,500 feet, that continue into Northern Rhodesia. To the east of Lake Nyasa the scarp is generally much bolder and reaches its maximum development in the Livingstone scarp bordering the north-eastern shore.[1]

South of the lake the Shire valley is flanked to the east by the Mangoche and Shire Highlands, and to the west by the Kirk Range, over part of the distance. The Shire Highlands, a gently warped surface that

[1] This shore is divided politically between Tanganyika, Moçambique, and Malawi, with only a small proportion in the south lying in Malawi.

ranges in elevation from 2,000 to 4,000 feet, is surmounted by the higher isolated massifs of Mlanje and Zomba which attain elevations of nearly 10,000 and 6,500 feet respectively.

The walls of the rift valley are by no means a series of continuous scarps and may be divided into three characteristic sections; the strongly faulted northern section giving rise to bold scarps; more gently warped stepped scarps in the central area and further strongly faulted scarps, somewhat disjointed by later faulting, in the Shire Valley. Filling the rift valley at the northern extremity of Lake Nyasa are the Pleistocene volcanic lavas and tuffs which form the high ranges of the Poroto mountains in Tanganyika that run transversely across the valley, limiting the Lake Nyasa basin. These mountains have an important influence on the rainfall of this area and consequently on the hydrology of Lake Nyasa.

Malawi may be considered to be composed of three main characteristic physiographic regions:

1. The Shire Valley and the Lake Nyasa littoral ranging in elevation from 120 to 2,000 feet.
2. The medium plateau areas of the Shire Highlands, Central Province, and the Mzimba district of the Northern Province.
3. The highland areas of the Nyika, Vipya, Misuku, Mafingi, Dowa, Dedza, Kirk, Zomba, and Mlanje, the latter two being of limited extent.

These main regions may be further sub-divided into sub-regions on the basis of altitude and surface form, with rainfall and vegetation as secondary considerations. Fig. 7 shows Malawi divided into twelve such separate physiographic sub-regions, which have been delineated so as to give each area as much physical homogeneity as possible.

THE SHIRE VALLEY

The Shire Valley extends from the southern limit of Lake Nyasa to where the Shire River leaves the Protectorate south of Port Herald, a distance of some 250 miles. In the section of the valley between Chiromo and Port Herald, only the western part of the valley lies within Malawi, the international border running along the course of the Shire River. The valley may be considered in three separate divisions: The upper Shire Valley from the southern limit of Lake Nyasa to the head of the Murchison Cataracts at Matope; the middle Shire Valley extending along the course of the river where it plunges through the cataracts over a distance of 50 miles, and the lower Shire Valley that extends from the base of the final cataract at Hamilton Falls to where the Shire River leaves the Protectorate.

1(a)—*The Upper Shire Valley*

The upper Shire Valley is a wide, flat valley extending from the southern limit of Lake Nyasa along the course of the Shire River as far

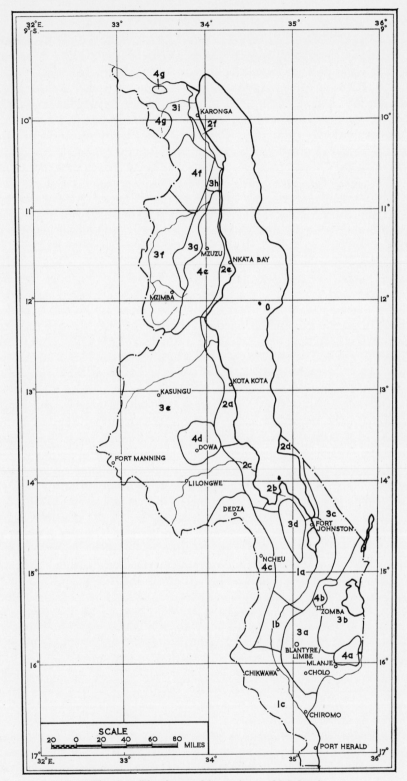

Fig. 7.   Physiographic regions of Malawi.

as Matope at the head of the Murchison Cataracts. At the northern end, a few miles south of the outlet from Lake Nyasa, the valley floor has been downwarped to form a basin now occupied by Lake Malombe. This northern part of the valley, probably as far south as Liwonde, formed the bed of Lake Nyasa during late Pleistocene or early Recent times and much of the valley floor is covered with recent alluvium and gravelly colluvium. The underlying floor is made up of pre-Cambrian gneisses and probably represents the early Cretaceous valley floor surface.

To the east the upper valley is flanked by the scarp of the Mangoche or Namwera highlands that trend to the south-west, this scarp being truncated by the Makongwa scarp, some 800 to 1,000 feet high, at a point 15 miles east of Lake Malombe. This scarp extends southwards to the Chikala–Mongolowe hills of the Kasupe area where the flat floor of the valley is considerably narrowed by these hills. South of Kasupe the valley margin is represented by the high western scarp of Zomba mountain and from here continues to the Chingale plain and then swings towards Matope at the head of the cataracts. To the west the valley is overlooked in the northern section by the Chiripa plateau scarp, which gradually diminishes in a southward direction until, near Liwonde, the valley broadens out to include the lower Rivi Rivi valley. This valley is actually a minor rifted segment, that runs from the region of Mpimbi on the Shire river in a NNW. direction towards the south-west arm of Lake Nyasa, thus isolating the Chiripa plateau as a block residual within the southern lake and upper Shire area. The Blantyre–Salima railway takes advantage of this valley to reach Lake Nyasa from Blantyre.

The gradient of the valley from Fort Johnston to Matope is very flat, the fall of the Shire river over this distance of 82 miles being but 23 feet or about 3 inches per mile. The section from Fort Johnston to Liwonde, in which is situated Lake Malombe, is even flatter, the gradient along the river being only about 2 inches per mile over 22 miles. During a period of low lake level this upper section of the Shire River became completely blocked by sand bars and vegetation, thus causing a reversal of flow northwards from Lake Malombe to Lake Nyasa.

1(b)—*The Middle Shire Valley*

This section is that part of the Shire rift that extends along the course of the Shire River from Matope to the Hamilton Falls over a distance of some 50 miles, through which the Shire river falls some 1,260 feet in a series of falls and cataracts known collectively as the Murchison Cataracts. This area should therefore be considered as a transitional zone between the two main sections of the valley, although possessing its own peculiar characteristics.

The course of the Shire river is controlled by two dominant directions of faulting and jointing, which follow the strike of the gneissic rocks of the pre-Cambrian formations and swing from the south-west in the northern section of the valley to SSE. in the southern half. This faulting has produced a series of fault scarps overlooking the valley and is also responsible for the cataracts. The bounding scarps of the valley rise to elevations of 2,000 to 2,500 feet which, however, die out to the north on the eastern bank. The valley floor is an early Cretaceous pene-plain modified by faulting, and represents a landscape resurrected by the erosion of Cretaceous sediments from the valley by the early Shire River which has now etched itself into the early Cretaceous floor. The Shire tributaries of this section are actively cutting down into their beds and have been successively rejuvenated at times of uplift, giving rise to rapids and falls at various points. This surface is well graded with harder intrusives forming isolated hills, such as Chisantwalu, Namphero, Mchena, Mpatachalo, and Mpatamanga through which the Shire river has cut a gorge by superimposition. In general, the topography of this part of the Shire Valley is rough, composed of broken, eroded hilly country along the margins of the valley, which in places is less than a mile wide. In these areas the soils are thin, stony, and infertile and, coupled with a prevailing low rainfall, present, during the dry season, a semi-arid inhospitable appearance.

1(c)—*The Lower Shire Valley*

This area, generally known as 'the Lower River', is composed of the low-lying valley of the Shire River extending from where it emerges from the cataracts of the middle Shire at Hamilton Falls, north of Chikwawa, to its exit from the country south of Port Herald. The altitude of the valley floor falls from 350 feet north of Chikwawa to 120 feet south of Port Herald over a distance of 110 miles. This region is actually a narrow extension of the Moçambique coastal plain into Malawi, and is the only area in the country lying wholly below 500 feet in altitude. The width of the valley varies from about 5 miles at Chikwawa to about 15 miles in the neighbourhood of the Elephant Marsh, the latter being some 9 miles wide. The boundaries of the valley are well defined only to the north-east by the Cholo scarp that rises as a wall-like mass of pre-Cambrian rocks, transversely dissected by numerous consequent streams, and to the south-west by the Port Herald hills that extend southwards from Namalambo Hill on the south-western bank opposite Chiromo. A major north–south fault to the north-west of the Port Herald hills faults out the pre-Cambrian rocks of these hills and brings in the younger Karoo formations of sandstones and shales extending along the south-western border until they are faulted out by the Mwanza fault that strikes WNW.–ESE. As a consequence, this down-faulted segment of weaker Karoo rocks has been eroded down to a subdued relief of low hills which form the broad water-shed between the Zambezi and Shire Rivers. Near the Nkombedzi River the Karoo rocks have been eroded out and infilled with Cretaceous sandstones which spread southward to Ngabu and eastward towards the Shire River where they pass under the superficial deposits.

The Shire River flows south-eastward for some 56 miles through the valley from north of Chikwawa to Chiromo, where it is joined by the Ruo River, which drains the southern part of the NNE. section of the rift valley branching out through Lake Chilwa and the Lujenda valley and forming the eastern limit of the Shire Highlands. The Ruo River has thrown up a narrow levee at its confluence with the Shire River, upon which Chiromo is situated and which has afforded a crossing of the Shire River for the Beira–Blantyre railway in an otherwise marshy area. From Chiromo and the Ruo confluence, the Shire River flows southwards towards the Zambezi on the western side of a broad valley overlooked from the Malawi side by the Port Herald Hills.

The main feature of the landscape of the valley floor is the Elephant Marsh, an area of semi-permanent marsh of approximately 170 square miles, about 40 miles long and about 10 miles in width at its broadest point. The marsh is contiguous with the Shire River, which maintains a channel close to the western margin of the marsh. On the eastern side there is evidence of an older channel known in parts as the Namichimba. This channel is to a large extent obstructed by vegetation and silt and is composed of a multiple system of smaller channels and lagoons.

Downstream from Port Herald on the western bank there is a further area of marsh some 10 square miles in extent within Malawi known as the Ndindi Marsh. Periodical flooding of these marshes has probably been in progress for a considerable time, dependent on the level of Lake Nyasa and the discharge of the Shire and Ruo Rivers. From 1915 until 1936, during which time the discharge of the Shire River was very much diminished owing to a low lake level and obstructions in the upper Shire area, large areas of the marsh were dried out and were intensively cultivated under cotton and food crops. Since 1936, however, the marsh has once again come under water from a higher discharge in the Shire River and the majority of this fertile flood plain has been lost.

Flanking the Shire River to the west between Chiromo and the southern border are the Port Herald hills which form the main watershed between the Shire and Zambezi Rivers in this area. These hills extend into Portuguese territory to the south and west and are an isolated hilly area within the broad Shire–Zambezi coastal plain and, from a regional point of view, should be separated from the Lower River region. These hills form a continuous range over a distance of 38 miles from Nyanthana on the Tangadzi stream in the north, to the southern border of Malawi. The southern part of the range is higher, with hills rising to a general elevation of 2,500 feet, with a number of higher hills rising above this general level, prominent of which are Malawi Mountain at 3,190 feet in the central part of the range and Lulwe at 2,588 feet in the southern part. In the southern area there is no well defined scarp between these hills and the Shire plain at its eastern foot, but the scarp takes the form of a series of low foothills gradually decreasing in height. Farther north, however, truncated spurs on the hills may be observed and a true fault scarp runs for a distance of 7 miles between the Malindi and Nyamadzere streams. Most of the streams of these hills flow east or south-east directly to the Shire River and appear to be little affected by the structure.

There is little evidence of peneplanation in these hills, but it is thought that the surface is a dissected remnant of the Miocene surface. L. C. King has deduced that the present physiography of the Port Herald Hills was determined during the first of three riverine erosion cycles which have penetrated up the larger African rivers.

THE LAKE LITTORAL

The littoral of Lake Nyasa, estimated to be some 3,000 square miles in extent or 8 per cent. of the total land area of the country, exhibits two main characteristic features along its southern and western shores. First, there are the wider lake-shore plains varying in width from 5 to 15 miles, comprised mainly of colluvial deposits with recent alluvia flanking the river estuaries, which have been built up by a receding lake since the Pleistocene. These plains are characterized by swamps and lagoons along the shore, and flat open plains rising in a series of low terraces towards the main foothill boundaries. These terraces probably represent old shore lines of Lake Nyasa during past pluvial cycles and as the result of a lowering lake level due to tectonic activity. In this normally flat, low-lying plain there frequently occur residual hills composed of harder rocks, and in the southern lake littoral such features are common.

At the other extreme, the coast is characterized by a drowned topography or by fault scarps with truncated spurs, and along shore lines such as these there is virtually little littoral. The most spectacular example of this type of coast is along the north-eastern shores in Tanganyika where the Livingstone mountains rise precipitously from the lake. There are, of course, gradations between these two extremes but generally changes are abrupt.

2(a)—*The South-Eastern Lake-Shore*

This region is that part of the eastern shore of Lake Nyasa that lies within Malawi and stretches for a distance of some 75 miles from Fort Maguire to the outlet of Lake Nyasa near Fort Johnston. The lacustrine plain is, in places, up to five miles in width and is backed by the foothills of the main rift escarpment. The plain is made up of lacustrine sediments and along the shore these deposits are fringed by an almost continuous belt of reeds and swamp. Only in the vicinity of Chikulo and Malindi are there uninterrupted stretches of clear beach.

The main escarpment of the south-eastern wall of the Nyasa trough forms the eastern boundary to this region, its most prominent physiographic features being formed by the Namizumu fault, the main rift fault of this area. Below this main escarpment lies a backward-tilted fault block which forms a range of foothills emerging from beneath a cover of lake-shore alluvium some eight miles north of Malindi. Not only does this fault block show an easterly tilt away from the lake, so that an accumulation of colluvial material occurs overlying the Basement rocks of which it is formed in the re-entrant angle between it and the main fault, but it also shows a southerly tilt so that from where it emerges from beneath the alluvial cover the ground rises steadily northwards. Evidence that a similarly tilted fault block is further repeated westwards is provided by a tilted outlier of Basement rocks north of the Lingwena river. Some of the larger rivers draining the high plateau beyond the escarpment have cut across the tilted block below the escarpment, but the general drainage pattern reflects the easterly and southerly tilt, and the majority of streams escape to the lake by flowing parallel to the lake-shore before they emerge on to the lacustrine plain.

2(b)—The Southern Lake-Shore

The southern limit of Lake Nyasa is divided into two separate arms or bays by a broad rocky peninsula, an extension of the Chiripa plateau. The head of the peninsula is composed of a pre-Cambrian granite intrusion and this gives rise to a broken topography of rounded hills in the Monkey Bay–Cape Maclear area. The western shore of the south-east arm near Fort Johnston has a littoral plain some 5 to 6 miles wide built up by a receding lake level. About 20 miles north of Fort Johnston this open plain gives way to numerous rocky hills along the foreshore and the coast-line is characterized by small bays, inlets, and islands. While this form of coastline is suggestive of having been drowned, the existence of a series of raised beaches up to 150 feet above the present lake level would suggest the contrary. It is considered that this type of coastline has been formed mainly as a result of the peculiar nature of this intrusion that has formed a series of boss-like hills separated by areas of softer rocks that have been eroded out by the action of the lake.

The south-west arm of Lake Nyasa is bounded to the west by a high scarp and littoral of the Kirk Range and to the east by the western flank of the Chiripa plateau. The southern shore of this re-entrant is a low-lying swampy area that represents the termination of the Rivi Rivi–Bwanje valley referred to earlier. Like the Malombe–Liwonde area of the upper Shire, this valley was probably also covered by the waters of Lake Nyasa in recent times and is now made up of residual swamps, derived from the lake and from the imperfect drainage of the Bwanje and Gubidira Rivers that drain this valley.

These comparatively narrow lake-shore areas flanking the southern peninsula are characterized by seasonal swamps with a vegetational community of mixed savannah, palms and grassland, interspersed with narrow alluvial fans of fertile soil on the fluvial margins.

2(c)—The South West Lake-Shore

The classification of this sub-region is based mainly on climate and vegetation which is of the drier mixed savannah type associated with the Shire Valley and which, at the northern limits of the sub-region, gives way to moister climatic conditions and a change in vegetation. The coastline may be divided into two separate sections; a flat swampy southern section and a rocky, well defined northern section near Salima.

This sub-region extends along the south-western shore of Lake Nyasa from the vicinity of Ntakataka to the north of Salima where the shoreline turns westwards to Domira Bay. The littoral varies in width from 5 to 15 miles and is bounded on the inland side by the high scarp of the northern Kirk Range rising to over 4,000 feet, but losing height in a northward direction as it approaches the Linthipe valley. This scarp is well developed immediately inland from Ntakataka showing a spectacular scenery of waterfalls, deep valleys, and heavily-wooded ravines. The rivers draining the high scarp, the Livulezi, Namikokwe, Nadzipulu, and Nadzipokwe, have all built up considerable deltas within the Ntakataka area, which, when coupled with a high lake level, have caused the flooding of valuable alluvial land. From Chipoka to Domira Bay the coastline becomes better defined by rocky promontories, offshore islands and low hills fringing the shore, the most prominent being Senga Hill that rises to over 1,200 feet above lake level. Inland from this coastal ridge of resistant rocks the ground falls away to a broad valley some ten miles across, terminating against the low platform of foothills of the plateau area. This inland depression is composed of open woodland and *dambo*,[1] the most extensive being the Mpatsanjoka *dambo* between Salima station and the airfield near Senga Hill. The Blantyre–Salima railway is routed along this lake-shore plain after it leaves the Rivi Rivi–Bwanje valley, and after Chipoka it follows this inland valley to Salima.

2(d)—*The Kota Kota Lake-Shore*

This more or less continuous lake-shore plain extends from Domira Bay to Kazando near the Dwambadzi river over a distance of some 110 miles. The littoral is invariably wide, ranging from five to fifteen miles in width, and consists of a considerable thickness of sands and clays, through which protrude crystalline platforms dipping gently under the lake. This sub-region is similar in many respects to the southwest lake-shore. Along the inland margin of the plain there is a low eroded platform at an elevation of about 2,000 feet, composed mainly of schists and gneisses. This platform has been recognized to be part of the early Cretaceous valley floor surface and is well exposed along the inner margin of the plain between Chitala and Benga. The bordering scarp is variable along this section of the littoral, varying from a series of low steps to more well-defined scarps that reach their maximum development inland from Benga, along the edge of the Dowa–Mwera Hill–Visanza late Cretaceous highland surface.

Except in the Kota Kota area, the lake-shore is characterized by flat,

[1] *Dambos* have recently been described as 'shallow swale-like depressions . . .' by M. M. Cole, 'The Rhodesian Economy in Transition' *Geography*, Vol. XLVII (1962), p. 19.

swampy areas immediately behind a raised sand storm beach and in the vicinity of the mouths of the Bua, Kaombe, and Dwangwa rivers. In the Kota Kota area, the presence of a low crystalline ridge extending for approximately 26 miles along the shore has given rise to an area of impeded drainage of particular interest. This ridge, closely following the lake-shore, has been faulted on the inland side so as to form a minor inland rifted valley, and as the consequent drainage has been unable to keep pace with the faulting, large swamps and a number of minor lakes have been formed behind this ridge. The most extensive of these lakes is Lake Chia, which has, however, been able to erode a narrow passage into Lake Nyasa. Farther north the smaller seasonal lakes of Chimi-kombe, Mdila, and Chikukuta are additional manifestations of impeded drainage. At Sani, some five miles south of Kota Kota, this rocky ridge is well developed and the shore is composed of rocky promontories with sandy beach inlets. Kota Kota, in the past one of the major slave ports of Lake Nyasa, is situated on the dip slope of this ridge overlooking a good harbour formed by a long north–south sand spit opening out to the north. North of Kota Kota this ridge continues to Katimbira, gradually decreasing in height, causing the Bua River to describe a large loop around its northern end. From the Bua River to Bana and Kazando, the plain is more or less homogeneous in character, composed of flat, terraced plains frequently traversed by minor streams with large areas of *dambo*. To the north of the Dwangwa river the prevailing south-east wind of the lake has caused considerable sand accumulations from the Dwangwa river mouth to form the reed covered sand spits and lagoons of Bana.

2(e)—*The West Nyasa or Vipya Lake-Shore*

Covering a stretch of 110 miles of coastline from Kazando to Florence Bay this sub-region is unlike any other part of the western Lake Nyasa shore, there being little or no littoral. The coastline has been formed as a result of two main faults or sets of faults; in the southern section faulting has produced a series of step faults with minor inland rift troughs trending NNE. and to the north of Nkata Bay this line of faulting has been truncated by the considerably later Ruarwe fault of middle Pleistocene times. This later fault runs from near Nkata Bay to Florence Bay and north of Usisiya follows a remarkably rectilinear course almost due north–south in direction. Over a large part of this distance of 65 miles, the scarp of the high level Vipya plateau descends steeply to the water's edge and continues for hundreds of feet below, the 300 fathom line running close inshore under this scarp. This sub-region will be considered in two sections; the Kazando–Nkata Bay section and the Ruarwe fault section.

Just north of the Dwambadzi river, on the border of the Kota Kota sub-region, Kiwiriri hill, a south-easterly trending spur of the Vipya, overlooks Lake Nyasa by nearly 2,000 feet and the wide littoral of the Kota Kota lake-shore is much narrower at this point. To the north of this ridge, however, the plain widens once again, rising in a series of low steps towards a well defined end-Tertiary erosion surface that stands at 3,300 feet in the vicinity of Kasengadzi. This hummocky plain, traversed by innumerable small streams, extending northward to the vicinity of Bandawe over a distance of 20 miles, is considered to be part of the early Cretaceous valley floor peneplain. In many areas it is overlain with pebbles, which are probably residual deposits resulting from the disintegration of the friable pebbly Dinosaur beds.

Near Bandawe the plain gives way to a narrow crystalline ridge on the coastline and gradually gains height to the north, culminating in the Kandoli ridge north of Nkata Bay. In the Bandawe area this ridge is some 200 feet above lake level and overlooks a broad, inland rifted valley which is, in some respects, similar to the low inland troughs of the Kota Kota area. In this area, however, the two main rivers, the Kawiya and Luweya, have managed to maintain their courses across this ridge through wide valleys to the lake. Nevertheless, drainage has been impeded on the inland side, the valley being made up almost entirely of the large permanent swamps of Limpasa, Majinene, and Kawiya. This trough is continued up the Limpasa valley until it meets the end-Tertiary surface in the vicinity of Chikwina, at an elevation of 3,300 feet.

From near Nkata Bay to Florence Bay the coastline has been formed by the subsidence of the rift floor along the Ruarwe fault, the coastline exhibiting faceted spurs rising out of the lake with little to no beach. Over a considerable length of coastline micaeous schists and gneisses have slumped down into the lake, and the length so affected presents a typical landslide topography. The rectilinear nature of the Ruarwe fault, which trends firstly north-west and then almost due north, is interrupted only by the indentation of Usisiya Bay, some ten miles across, which appears to be an older feature than the main fault; around this bay a narrow littoral has been preserved and supports a relatively dense population. From the north end of Usisiya Bay the coastline resumes its rectilinear course with high faceted spurs and no littoral. At Mlowe, however, the South Rukuru River enters the lake, having breached the high plateau through a series of deep gorges following block-fault lines and the contact between the Karoo sediments and the pre-Cambrian rocks of the Vipya. It has built up an alluvial fan that provides a flat, low plain some six square miles in extent. From Mlowe northwards the evidence of the Ruarwe fault becomes less pronounced on the block of Karoo sediments lying between Mlowe and Mount Waller. Here numerous indentations have been carved out of the softer rocks to form small bays.

2(f)—*The Karonga Lake-Shore*

From Mount Waller and the Livingstonia escarpment at Florence Bay, the main wall of the rift changes its general direction to the north-west to form the edge of the high Nyika plateau. From the Tertiary

D

period this escarpment has formed the main coast of Lake Nyasa at varying levels. A series of lacustrine sediments has been laid down within the basin. Together with a receding lake level this has led to the development of a littoral some five to seven miles wide extending from Mount Waller to the Songwe River over a distance of 80 miles. This plain continues across the Songwe River into Tanganyika to form the broad fertile littoral at the northern end of Lake Nyasa.

In the area between Deep Bay and the North Rukuru river the plain is traversed by a number of crystalline fault ridges lying parallel with the shore line. Between these ridges narrow strips of Cretaceous, Tertiary, and post-Tertiary deposits are preserved. By the end of the period of deposition, the crystalline ridges were buried beneath these sediments. Thereafter, as the waters of the lake receded, streams draining towards the lake cut their way down to the buried ridges, and the incised deep, narrow gorges through them; at the same time subsequent streams opened up wide transverse valleys in the softer sediments lying between the ridges. Consequently, the numerous rivers of this lake plain run directly across the grain of the country in their progress from the foot of the western scarp to the lake-shore through a series of deeply eroded gorges. Some of the weaker streams have been captured by headward erosion along the subsequent streams and a number of small wind gaps occur on the harder crystalline ridges.

The Deep Bay hills and peninsula are derived from a similar crystalline ridge that lies on the lake-shore, with the result that the shore line from Deep Bay to Vua is rocky and steep. From Vua to Karonga the plain varies from one to three miles in width and is bordered on the inland side by these low crystalline and sedimentary ridges which have been greatly dissected by the erosion of the softer rocks. North of the North Rukuru River the plain widens to a maximum width of some eight miles, having been built up by the three major rivers that reach the lake across the plain in this area.

THE PLATEAUX

Three quarters of the total land area of Malawi is made up of plateaux lying between 2,500 and 4,500 feet in elevation, which, in the southern and central parts of the country, are the main centres of population. On these plateaux surfaces two main erosion surfaces are generally recognizable; the upper Miocene surface grading gently into the end-Tertiary surface that is typically developed below the former as a broad valley form feature along the major rivers of the plateaux. Surmounting these plateaux are the higher residual, late Cretaceous and late Jurassic surfaces of the highland elements and in most areas a three or four cycle topography may be observed. The Miocene and end-Tertiary surfaces are typically developed in the Central Province and are part of a continuous surface that extends from the Luangwa valley margin in Zambia to the scarp of the rift valley in Malawi. These two surfaces, generally well graded into each other, are characterized by flat, gently undulating country, the monotony being broken only occasionally by residual *inselberge* of more resistant rocks.

3(a)—*The Shire Highlands*

The Shire Highlands surface, some 2,800 square miles in extent, bounded on the west by the Shire valley and on the south-east by the Ruo valley, is tilted away from the Shire Rift, and the eastern limits of this surface merge, either by a series of low steps or by gradual slopes,

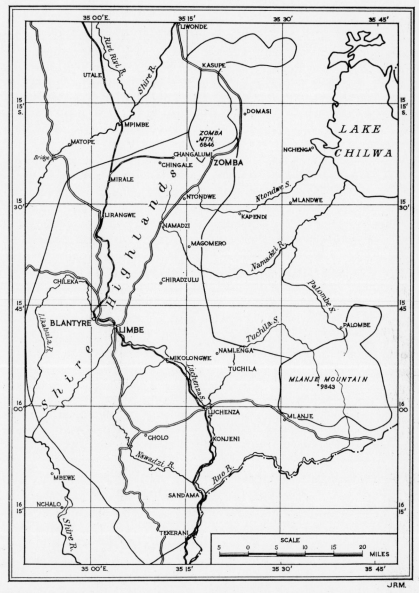

Fig. 8.   Sub-Regions 3(a), 4(a), and 4(b)—The Shire Highlands, Mlanje, and Zomba Mountains.

into the Lake Chilwa–Palombe plain. This plateau ranges in elevation from 2,000 to 3,600 feet and is surmounted by the massifs of Mlanje and Zomba and a number of lesser residual mountains. The present day surface of the Shire Highlands comprises a narrow, probably late Cretaceous, remnant at about 3,500 feet along the western edge, and a very well planed lower surface, ascribed to the Miocene, at about 2,000 to 2,500 feet forming the widespread plain surrounding Mlanje mountain; this lower surface is also well developed to the north-west of Blantyre in the Chileka area where it forms a step from the Shire River up to the late Cretaceous ridge.

The late Cretaceous ridge may be recognized in the form of distinct platform remnants at about 3,200 to 3,500 feet that extend along the Zomba–Limbe–Cholo crest, surmounted by a number of higher residuals of the Jurassic and intermediate cycles, of which Chiradzulu (5,820 feet), Ndirandi (5,293 feet), and Cholo (5,670 feet) are the most prominent. On the eastern edge of this late-Cretaceous ridge the step between this surface and the lower Miocene surface is well developed on an arc from Chiradzulu to Mikolongwe through Bangwe hill and is marked by a large number of small flat-topped or rounded hills on the edge of the lower surface. When viewed from the Cholo crest, these hills, backed by the distant Chiradzulu, present a very hummocky and rugged appearance, and is a scene that has been described by Professor F. Debenham as a 'lunar landscape'. The Miocene surface of the Mlanje–Lake Chilwa plain is well graded, with local development of laterite.

The main Shire Highlands ridge is the ancient watershed, as in the present day, between streams draining west towards the Shire Valley and east towards Moçambique, or what used to be the ancient Shire River valley when it followed the Lake Nyasa–Chilwa–Ruo rift. These eastward draining streams flow either into the Ruo or into Lake Chilwa. Along the south-western edge of the plateau the Likabula, Mwamphanzi, Maperera, and Tangadzi rivers have been rejuvenated in cycles of uplift along the main Cholo fault and, as a result, have incised deep valleys into the plateau surface, being controlled by the north-east trending dolerite dyke swarms of late-Karoo age. These form sharp, crested ridges between the softer pre-Cambrian gneisses and schists of the valleys.

3(b)—*The Lake Chilwa–Palombe Plain*

This elongated sub-region, lying between the Shire Highlands to the west and the Moçambique border to the east, is one of low relief, over half the area being occupied by Lakes Chilwa and Chiuta and their associated swamps. This surface is contiguous with the Shire Highlands Miocene surface but has been down-warped into a shallow depression extending from Mlanje mountain in a NNE. direction to the Lujenda valley in Moçambique and filled to a great depth by sediments. Dominating the scene to the south-east and the north-west are the high massifs of Mlanje and Zomba and, when viewed from these heights, the plain is seen to be remarkably flat and uniform, the monotony broken only by a number of hill features formed of intrusive syenites, nepheline syenites, and carbonatites of the Chilwa Series. They include Chilwa Island, Mpyupyu Hill, and the low range of hills that extend in a NNE. direction from the north-eastern corner of Mlanje mountain into Moçambique to the east of Lake Chilwa.

In spite of its apparent evenness, closer study of the plain reveals that there are at least five terrace levels indicating five drops in lake level during recent times. The highest of these fossil shores lies at a level of 110 feet above the present lake level but the most pronounced are those found at the 80 feet and 55 feet levels, the latter level corresponding to wave-cut platforms on islands in the lake. These shores may be traced, except where they have been obscured by recent erosion or deposits of colluvium, over the greater part of the western, southern, and eastern areas of the plain. The lacustrine deposits which occupy the greater part of the Lake Chilwa area indicate that this lake once extended over a much greater area, and was continuous with Lake Chiuta, from which it is now separated by a 50 feet high barrier of recent wind-blown sand known as Kwituto. The southernmost extension of Lake Chilwa was near the foot of Mlanje mountain and it was possible that at various times the lake was provided with alternate outlets; by way of the Ruo river or the Lujenda river.

3(c)—*The Mangoche or Namwera Hills*

Lying to the east of the south-east arm of Lake Nyasa is the plateau surface known either as the Mangoche Highlands or Namweras, more commonly the latter. This surface lies at a general elevation of 3,000 feet to 3,500 feet, is surmounted by higher hills rising to over 5,000 feet, and is a southerly extension of the widespread plateau lying to the east of Lake Nyasa in the Niassa Province of Moçambique. This plateau is bounded to the west by a main rift fault scarp (Namizumu Fault) trending in a south-easterly direction which is truncated by the Makongwa fault to the east of Lake Malombe. To the east this surface is bounded by the northerly extension of the Ruo–Chilwa rift and may be envisaged as a highland peninsula gradually decreasing in both height and width in a southerly direction and overlooking the Shire rift to the south-west and the Chilwa–Lujenda depression to the south and east. The entire plateau surface is tilted to the south-east and loses height in this direction. The later Makongwa fault appears to have induced further tilting of the plateau block in the southern area. This is clearly demonstrated by the drainage pattern; in the northern area consequent rivers from Lake Nyasa have reached far back into the plateau surface whereas in the south the tributaries of the Shire river have been beheaded by this fault and their upper reaches captured by streams draining to the Lujenda or Lakes Chilwa and Chiuta.

This south-easterly tilting has led to a partial rejuvenation of the

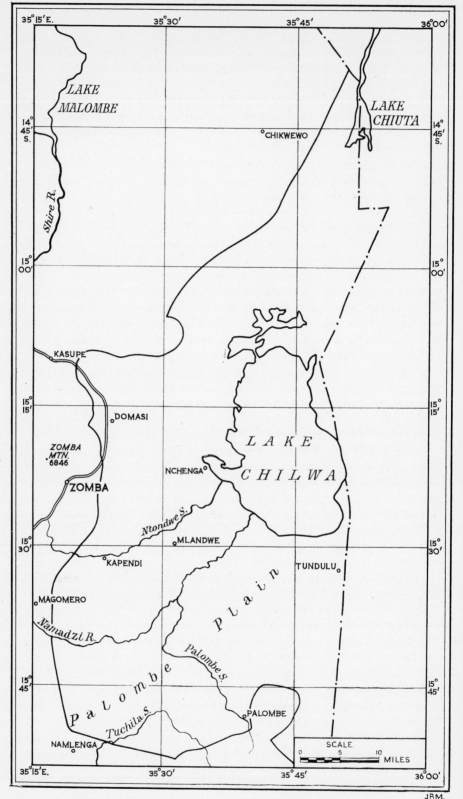

Fig. 9. Sub-Region 3(b)—Lake Chilwa and Palombe Plain.

plateau landscape to the north-west, while in the central and south-eastern areas more resistant rocks crop out from beneath the colluvial cover of the plateau, the most prominent being those of the Matemangwe–Ilindi Range and the syenite mass of Mangoche mountain, which rises to over 5,000 feet. In the northern area there are a number of prominent peaks, mostly resistant masses of syenite resulting from the preferential erosion of the surrounding gneisses. Although there is a rough accordance of summit levels of these peaks, indicating a possible earlier erosion surface, most of them assume a conical or slightly convex form without levelling and are excellent examples of *inselberge*.

3(d)—*The Chiripa Plateau*

This residual plateau is situated at the head of the Shire Valley and its northward declining surface forms part of the peninsula that divides the southern part of Lake Nyasa into two arms. This outlier lies wholly within the rift valley and is probably bounded to the east and west by subsidiary rift faults. Its general elevation is between 2,500 and 3,000 feet but resistant masses of syenite rise above this level to elevations of 4,500 feet or more, the most conspicuous being the high tor of Pirilongwe at 5,098 feet. The surface of this plateau has been dissected by a radial drainage pattern although the watershed areas show an accordance at approximately 3,000 feet. This surface may be correlated to the peneplain of the central Namwera plateau to the east, and the 3,000 feet 'step' flanking the Kirk Range to the west, and probably formed part of a greater Miocene peneplain which existed in this area prior to the diversion of the Shire River to its modern valley by the middle Shire faulting during the post-Miocene era.

3(e)—*The Central Province Plateau*

This plateau, covering some 9,000 square miles, is the largest continuous plateau surface in Malawi and extends from the margin of the rift valley into Northern Rhodesia on the western border. To the north it is bounded by the line of the Chimaliro hills, which merge into the Vipya plateau; to the south by the northern extension of the Kirk Range and by the Dzalanyama Range. On the eastern limits the Dowa highland element overlooks the plateau to the west and the rift valley to the east. This area is treated as a separate sub-region later.

The topography exhibits multi-cycle features, but in the main is composed of a gently undulating Miocene surface traversed by the succeeding end-Tertiary cycle in the form of broad valleys along the main river courses. Rising above this plain are a number of *inselberg* residuals of intrusive rocks and on the eastern and southern limits more extensive residuals of the late Cretaceous and late Jurassic surfaces. There is a remarkable summit level concordance of the majority of these *inselberge* (4,700 to 5,000 feet) over the central and western areas of the plateau, which might well represent the older late Cretaceous surface.

The Miocene surface, standing between 3,800 and 4,100 feet, is exposed principally along the Luangwa–Nyasa watershed, in the Nam-buma–Mponela–Lumbadzi area, and to the south of the Lilongwe val-ley in the upper Diampwe catchment and in many other isolated areas along the broad crests of the watersheds between the main rivers. There is considerable local development of laterite on this surface but no special surface deposits have as yet been recognized. Along the eastern margin of the plateau overlooking Lake Nyasa a well marked but dissected plat-form at an elevation of 3,000 to 3,200 feet is recognizable inclined east-wards. This surface has been assigned an end-Tertiary age and may be correlated with the Kasengadzi surface of the Chinteche area. It has de-veloped rapidly up the major river valleys and has outflanked the high-land Dowa area. The Lilongwe, Bua, and Dwangwa Rivers, which rise on the western watershed, are all graded to this surface and leave it in their descent to the lake shore through gorges eroded into these broad valley plains during a later cycle.[1] The main drainage of the plateau runs in an ENE. direction. The well graded profiles and numerous ox-bows and meanders reveal a pattern of great antiquity. The main tributaries of these rivers usually take the form of wide flat *dambos* in an advanced stage of maturity; free running streams are rare.

3(f)—*The Mzimba Plain*

This sub-region covers an area of some 2,500 square miles lying at an elevation of between 3,500 and 4,500 feet, situated to the west of the Vipya Highlands and to the south of the Nyika Plateau, this surface be-ing part of the continuous peneplain that extends westwards to the Luangwa valley in Northern Rhodesia. The western border of this re-gion is the low, broad Luangwa–Nyasa watershed and to the east it is bounded by the Vipya Highlands into which it merges upwards by a series of steep stepped slopes or fingers. The plain is traversed from south to north by the South Rukuru river; rising on the western or inland slopes of the Vipya, south of Mzimba, this river flows first westward, then describes a sharp turn to the north, gradually turning north-east-wards to the Njakwa gorge through which it flows to enter the Henga Valley prior to its final descent to the lake.

The Mzimba plain exhibits a three cycle peneplain topography of flat undulating country interspersed with broad *dambos* and, rising above it, the occasional *inselberg* of resistant syenite or composite gneiss. To the east the plain is overlooked by the late Cretaceous Vipya surface that is either stepped down or graded to a lower Miocene surface some 800 to 900 feet below. Into this Miocene surface the end-Tertiary cycle has ex-tended up the main South Rukuru valley as a broad valley form feature which gradually merges into the higher surface in a southward direc-tion. This higher Miocene surface is well exposed at Mzimba, along the north road near Hora mountain (an *inselberg* rising nearly 1,000 feet above the plain), over a considerable part of the Chinde and Mperembe

---

[1] These have been compared with the gorges of the Upper Zambezi tributaries above Victoria Falls, by F. Dixey.

chiefdoms to the north-west, and along the Mzimba–Lundazi road near Loudon Mission. The end-Tertiary surface is well developed in the Lake Kazuni area some 400 feet below the Miocene surface and extends up the main valley and into the tributaries. The Mzimba river is part of this later cycle and at Mzimba stands about 50 feet below the Miocene surface. Farther south this surface merges almost imperceptibly into the higher Miocene surface.

3(g)—*The Henga and Kasitu Valley*

This sub-region is a broad valley between five and ten miles wide and extending along the courses of the lower South Rukuru and the Kasitu rivers that lie immediately to the west of the Vipya Highlands. It is separated from the Mzimba surface by a low ridge extending from Mtangatanga near Mzimba to Njakwa. The northern part of the valley, occupied by the South Rukuru River, is bounded to the west by the Nyika Plateau and to the east by the northern extension of the Vipya Highlands.

The surface of the Henga valley is part of the end-Tertiary surface developed at 3,500 feet on the lakeward side of the Vipya (Kasengadzi surface). It also extends farther south along the rift valley escarpment and up the major rivers of the Central Province, which were described in the preceding paragraphs. This cycle has also spread from the Henga valley up the South Rukuru to the main tributaries of the Mzimba plain (see above). This north–south valley was an area of Karoo deposition and the Henga surface was able to attain its present extensive development owing to these weaker formations; the preceding Miocene cycle and the end-Tertiary cycle have stripped off the Karoo sediments and exposed the old floor. Along the margins of the valley the Miocene surface is exposed in bench remnants on the valley sides and at Njakwa it stands fully 500 feet above the end-Tertiary surface. Farther south, this height is lessened to 200 feet near Ekwendeni and in the upper reaches of the Kasitu valley the two surfaces tend to merge. Thus the valley is characterized by a broad, flat floor, with residual hills rising from it in parts, and by considerable areas of flat open country on colluvial and alluvial soils. In the Kasitu valley, slopes tend to be steeper and these areas are seriously eroded. This has been brought about in the short space of fifty years by over-grazing of large numbers of cattle, burning, and the primitive cultivation methods of the Ngoni pastoralists.

3(h)—*The Nchenachena–Livingstonia Hills*

Overlooking the Henga valley from the north and situated between the main wall of the Nyika plateau and Lake Nyasa lies a vigorously dissected surface standing at an elevation of between 3,500 and 4,500 feet. Let down into the pre-Cambrian formations, this area comprises a block of Karoo sediments, some 140 square miles in extent, that has undergone rapid erosion since Miocene times to form an area of rugged topography with youthful valleys traversed by fast-flowing mountain streams from the Nyika. The remnants of the Miocene surface may be observed on the many bevelled summits of the hills within the area, the most conspicuous of these being Mount Waller, Khondowe, Tunda, Kamori, and Ntunguja opposite Nchenachena. All these summit levels show a concordance of level at about 4,500 feet and may be correlated with the bevel of this elevation on the margins of the Henga valley to the south. Livingstonia Mission is situated on the flat-topped summit of Khondowe at 4,500 feet and commands a spectacular view across Lake Nyasa. The end-Tertiary surface is recognizable on the flat valley between Khondowe and Mount Waller and along the Junju and Kambwia valleys near Nchenachena. The main river draining this sub-region is the North Rumpi which rises on the Nyika Plateau. This river is graded to the margins of the end-Tertiary surface at an elevation of 3,500 feet. Thereafter it has eroded a series of deep canyons along major block fault lines in the Karoo sediments. These spectacular deep gorges and canyons, some 200 to 1,000 feet deep, are representative of the post-Tertiary erosion cycles that are developing along the Nyasa rift.

3(i)—*The Fort Hill–Lufira Plateau*

This sub-region covers an area to the north-west of the Nyika Plateau and to the north and east of the Mafingi Mountains in the extreme north-western part of the country. The western margin forms the Luangwa–Nyasa watershed, the plateau surface being continuous with that of the upper Luangwa valley. To the east and south this rugged surface has been dissected to a considerable degree by the North Rukuru and Lufira Rivers, the ruggedness increasing towards Lake Nyasa in the east.

The area is underlain by a series of micaceous and quartzitic schists, foliated intrusive gneisses, and plutonic intrusions of granitic gneisses of the Mafingi system of pre-Cambrian rocks, the more resistant quartzites, gneisses, and granites making up the more striking elements of the topography. In the valleys of the North Rukuru and Lufira there are down-faulted blocks of Karoo sediments which form areas of rugged low relief traversed by numerous streams. Surmounting this plateau surface are the high quartzite ridges of the Mafingi Mountains that rise to nearly 8,000 feet, the intrusive gneissic ridges of the Misuku highlands rising to over 6,500 feet and the granites forming a complex of hills to the south. The whole area exhibits a multi-cycle topography; the Nyika Plateau and Mafingi Mountains being relicts of the late Jurassic peneplain; the Misuku, Msissi-Kayuni hills being remnants of the late Cretaceous surface; the 4,500 feet peneplain upon which Fort Hill stands being ascribed to the Miocene period and the broader valleys of the Lufira and North Rukuru at about 3,500 to 4,000 feet representing the end-Tertiary cycle. At a lower elevation to the east, the post-Tertiary cycles are represented by the gorges of Mwankenja and Ngerenge on the two main rivers.

THE HIGHLANDS

The highland areas of Malawi constitute isolated remnants of the late Jurassic and late Cretaceous erosion surfaces, standing at elevations of between 4,500 and 8,000 feet, and of rolling down-like montane grasslands with patchy remnants of montane forests in sheltered locations. These highland elements are best developed in the northern areas of the country where they are represented by the Nyika, Vipya, Misuku, and Mafingi. The Nyika Plateau is the highest continuous plateau surface in Malawi, covering some 900 square miles and standing at an elevation of between 7,000 and 8,000 feet, with higher peaks rising out of the undulating grasslands up to 8,500 feet. Farther south, the only other extensive highland areas are the Dowa and the Dedza–Kirk Range Highlands, neither of which approach the proportions of the Nyika or Vipya. Above the Shire Highlands plateau surface the highlands are represented only by the isolated massifs of Mlanje and Zomba.

4(a)—*Mlanje Mountains*

The Mlanje Mountains rise abruptly from the south-eastern corner of the Shire Highlands, where they constitute an almost rectangular mass of syenite dominating the landscape. Precipices showing well-marked exfoliation features form the lower slopes, rising to more than 6,000 feet, and marking the outer edge of a number of bench plateaux above them. These benches are situated on the periphery of the main central mass of peaks and ridges, the main peak of which, Sapitwa, is nearly 10,000 feet in height. Other prominent peaks are Chinzama (8,391 feet), Manene (8,695 feet) on the south-eastern flank, and Chambe (8,385 feet) on the north-western bastion.

Originally an intrusion of the Chilwa Series into the overlying Karoo sediments, the massif is essentially an erosional feature that has undergone intermittent uplift. Since late Jurassic times the Karoo sediments have been eroded away to expose the pre-Cambrian floor of schists and gneisses which has itself been subjected to further cycles of erosion. These cycles are today represented by remnant bevels at varying elevations around the mountains; the uppermost bevelled surface is the line of peaks that show an accordance of level around 9,000 feet, which is followed by a lower surface at about 8,000 feet, notable around the Chambe, Litchenya, and Linje plateaus. At 6,000 to 6,500 feet there is a distinct platform forming the Linje, Litchenya, Tuchila, and Mlosa plateaux. On the Tuchila plateau the surface is made up of sediments of Karoo age that have undergone thermal alteration from the syenite and is the only evidence that these mountains were at one time covered by rocks of Karoo age. At a lower level, between 3,200 and 3,500 feet on the edges of the precipices, a narrow bevel is recognizable. This may be correlated with the late Cretaceous surface of the Shire Highlands some 25 miles to the east. The higher bevels of Mlanje are considered to be of late Jurassic and early Cretaceous age.

To the north-east and north-west there are situated the two main out-liers to the Mlanje massif of Mchesa and Chambe. Both these outliers are ring structures, the ring pattern being classically developed on Chambe, where the central plug has been eroded down below the bounding ring of harder rock to form a large circular amphitheatre at an elevation of 6,000 feet. The Chambe ring structure is connected to the main massif by the narrow ridge that forms the watershed between the Likabula and the western arm of the Tuchila rivers. The Mchesa ring structure is a much more eroded feature than Chambe and is separated from Mlanje by a broad high valley known as the Fort Lister Gap. This pass, underlain by pre-Cambrian schists and gneisses, has been eroded down by the Palombe and Sombani rivers.

Erosion is at present proceeding around the flanks of the massif at a very considerable rate, and is greatly assisted by exfoliation and by the systems of vertical joints in the rocks. Headward erosion along joints running at right angles to the scarps has given rise to deep narrow clefts that run far back into the mountain. Where these clefts meet another joint running transversely or parallel to the face of the scarp, there is a tendency for deep cauldron-like hollows to develop. The best example of this is the deep cauldron known as 'The Crater' on the southern flank of the mountain; this spectacular erosional feature having given rise to the belief, held by early travellers, that the mountains were of volcanic origin. An important effect of the rapid retrogression of the main scarps is the diversion of the rivers of the upland valleys into new channels run-ning directly down the mountainside. The modern scarps bear little re-lation to the upland valleys; they may run parallel with them or trun-cate them at any angle. In many cases the lateral erosion of the scarp has exceeded the vertical erosion of the upland valley and the valley wall is breached, thus diverting the river to the main scarp. These features are well exemplified at a point where the Mlosa river suddenly departs from its valley and plunges down the eastern flank of the mountain, having previously flowed in a north-eastward direction into the Sombani.

4(b)—*Zomba Mountain*

Zomba Mountain, like Mlanje, is a tabular syenitic massif rising out of the Shire Highlands plain to a maximum elevation of 6,846 feet and is more than 50 square miles in extent. The massif is situated on the north-western margin of the Shire Highlands; its western edge over-looks the upper Shire valley and to the south-east it looks out across the broad Lake Chilwa depression and the Tuchila–Palombe Plain to Mlanje, some forty miles away. At the south-eastern foot lies Zomba, the capital of Malawi.

The relatively flat plateaux making up the tabular surface of the massif lie at an elevation of 6,000 feet, although various peaks stand out above this general surface, notably Chiradzulu or Zomba peak (6,846 feet), Norimbe, and Chagwa. To the east and south, the massif is bounded by a sheer scarp of 2,500 feet, while to the west it is bounded by one of the main rift valley faults with a drop of some 4,000 feet to the floor of the Shire Rift valley. The plateau as a whole is divided into two separate sections by the Domasi river that has eroded a deep valley transversely across the plateau from west to east. The southern part is known as Zomba plateau and the northern part as the Mlosa Plateau. The massif is made up of two annular bodies of syenite surrounding a central plug of perthosite and is described by K. Bloomfield as '. . . like Chambe, another example of a ring dyke complex'. In the Mlungusi valley of the plateau there is a large inclusion of pre-Cambrian gneiss which is considered to be either a roof pendant or screen between the outer and inner rings of syenite. The ring structure of the massif is not considered to have been upfaulted along its margins and the present high scarps bounding the mountain result from prolonged differential erosion. The surface of the plateau is considered to be a remnant of the late Jurassic or early Cretaceous peneplain and the bevelled ridge standing at some 3,500 feet at the foot of the mountain to be of late Cretaceous age. This latter bevel is correlated with the main Shire Highlands ridge extending to the south of the mountain.

It has been suggested that, from present-day features, the Domasi river, dividing the two sections of the plateau, previously crossed the main plateau, commencing on land to the west which at that time stood at a considerably higher altitude relative to it. Following the initial development of Zomba mountain as an upstanding massif as a result of erosion, the Domasi was for a time able to maintain a superimposing course across it. With the faulting of the western scarp during the late Cretaceous or early Tertiary period the Domasi river was beheaded, losing those parts of its catchment which lay to the west of the scarp. The level of the ancient Domasi valley at the time of the rift faulting is shown by the deep wind gap in the present ridge leading from Zomba plateau to Mlosa plateau.

Since the emplacement of the Zomba ring structure, regional uplifts have occurred with associated fracturing, faulting, and tilting. One major fault, trending in an ESE.–WNW. direction, follows a line to the north side of the lower Mlungusi valley on Zomba plateau, intersecting the course of the Mlungusi stream where it changes direction abruptly from south to south-east. This fault is considered to be a hinge fault and rotational movement of the block south of this fault has taken place, while the northern block has remained stable. This is evident from the general tilted nature of the southern block, which has caused the main peak at the western edge of the plateau to be 1,000 feet above the general plateau surface and the Mlungusi stream near a point where it disgorges from the plateau to be 1,200 feet below it. This fault also gave a steeper gradient to the Mlungusi and the resultant rejuvenation extended up the lateral tributaries, one of these probably capturing the upper reaches of a tributary of the Domasi river that flowed northeastwards. This caused the capture of the western headwaters and the reversal of drainage of a part of this stream to the east. This reversed drainage area, having been earlier deprived of water, was reduced to a belt of marsh and today forms the headwaters of the modern Mlungusi Stream.

4(c)—*The Dedza–Kirk Range Highlands*

Flanking the southern Nyasa and northern Shire rift to the west is the highland area of the Dedza–Kirk Range. This surface falls gradually in a north–south direction from an elevation of 5,500 feet near Dedza to 1,400 feet in the south where it gives way to the Lower Shire–Zambezi lowlands. The underlying formations are mainly westerly dipping pre-Cambrian gneisses and amphibolites with intrusions of pyroxenites, norites, and syenites.

The range may be divided into two separate peneplaned surfaces; from Dedza to the headwaters of the Mwendangombe River, over a distance of 70 miles, the plateau surface stands at an elevation of between 4,500 and 5,200 feet, and is probably a late Cretaceous residual surface; at the Mwendangombe river the high plateau is terminated by a minor east–west scarp and to the south of this river the surface stands at an average elevation of 3,500 feet and gradually declines southward. Mwanza stands at 2,200 feet on this lower surface where the Blantyre–Salisbury road crosses the range. To this lower surface has been ascribed a Miocene age and it has been correlated with the Chileka surface lying to the east on the opposite side of the Shire Valley. Above these two plateau surfaces stand the residuals of a former erosion surface and on the lower surface in the Mwanza area there is a pronounced *inselberg* topography exemplified by the biotite gneiss of Zobue mountain near Mwanza. On the higher plateau of the Kirk Range these residuals surmounting the plateau surface become progressively higher in a northward direction culminating in Dedza mountain at an elevation of 7,120 feet. Other high mountains surmounting the plateau are Chirobwe (6,638 feet), Mvai (6,184 feet), and Nkokwe (5,284 feet).

The drainage of the entire Kirk Range has been strongly controlled by the strike of the isoclinally folded pre-Cambrian rocks as well as by major rift faulting. In the southern area of the range both the Mwanza and Wankurumadzi rivers follow fault valleys across the strike of the formations but in the northern section the main rivers have followed the softer bands of gneiss and to the north-west of Dedza mountain a trellis drainage pattern is well developed.

4(d)—*The Dowa Highlands*

The Dowa or Chitembwe-Mwera Highlands form a rectangular area of some 360 square miles standing at an elevation of between 4,500 and 5,000 feet, and overlooking the rift valley to the east and the Miocene and end-Tertiary surfaces of the Central Province to the west. This plateau consists of rolling hills surmounted by higher ridges and hills, the most outstanding being Dowa (5,570 feet) and Nchisi (5,430 feet), and

is underlain mainly by resistant gneisses and graphitic schists representing a remnant of the late Cretaceous erosion surface. On all sides this
highland element is limited by comparatively steep slopes. To the east
the slopes are generally steep and long, forming the main western wall
of the rift valley in this area. To the north and south it overlooks the
Bua and Lilongwe valleys respectively which are both graded to the
much lower end-Tertiary surface. To the west this surface is terminated
abruptly by a line of resistant gneissic hills overlooking the Miocene
peneplain extending westwards from this point along the Lilongwe–Bua
watershed.

The drainage pattern of this plateau is a radial one; the streams to the
south, west, and north flow either north or south to the Lilongwe or Bua
rivers, and to the east by short, steep rivers that flow directly to Lake
Nyasa. Owing to a lack of vegetal cover and the steep nature of these latter
rivers, floods of considerable magnitude have coursed down them and in
1957 caused considerable damage to bridges on the Chitala–Benga road.

4(e)—*The Vipya Highlands*

On entering the Northern Province from the south there is a marked
change from the gently undulating surface of the Central Province to
the much more hilly area near Chimaliro. Thereafter, and extending
over a distance of 130 miles in a NNE. direction to form a long backbone
to the whole region, lie the Vipya highlands which stand at an elevation
of between 5,000 and 6,000 feet. The northern end of the range near
Uzumara is terminated by the Livingstonia block of Karoo sediments,
along the margin of which the South Rukuru river has eroded a deep
gorge from the Henga valley to the Lake.

The plateau surface, which is markedly undulating or even much dissected giving the area a down-like appearance covered with grass and
patches of forest, is underlain by a series of schists and gneisses together
with intrusions of syenite and granite which, by injection and impregna-
tion, have given rise to zones of composite gneiss. Such complexes, as
well as the intrusions themselves, frequently form residual hills rising
above the plateau surface, besides having formed the plateau itself above
the lower surface of the Mzimba plain to the west. These residual hills
rising above the plateau surface are well represented in the central Vipya
by the *inselberg* of Nkalapia (6,960 feet), Luandika, and Kandindi which
flank the main Mzimba–Mzuzu road north of Chikangawa.

The Vipya surface has been shown to be of late Cretaceous age. It
probably attains its maximum surviving element in these highlands. To
the west it overlooks the Miocene and end-Tertiary surfaces of the
Mzimba plain and to the east the Lake Nyasa rift.

The Vipya may be envisaged as being composed of two main blocks
divided by a broad saddle some 15 miles in width standing at an elevation of 4,000 feet and situated between Likulu and Choma hills. The
town of Mzuzu is situated in this saddle and the main access road from
Nkata Bay to the inland plateau areas passes through this gap. Ignoring

this saddle for the moment and considering the Vipya highlands as a complete block, the plateau surface rises gently eastwards towards the edge of the Nyasa trough, being 200 to 300 feet higher on the east, and at the same time it rises northwards, being about 800 feet above the Miocene surface in the south and 1,300 feet in the north. On the lakeward side a number of parallel rift faults have let down portions of the plateau to form north–south valleys that are particularly well exemplified by the Mazamba valley. The topography on the eastern side is rugged and much dissected, although the remnants of lower erosion surfaces occur as platforms, particularly near Kasengadzi and Chikwina. To the west the plateau is either stepped down by steep scarps or long, low ridges to the Miocene surface that are well developed in the Mtangatanga and Perekezi areas. The morphology of the northern block of the Vipya that extends from Choma to Uzumara is complex, having been deeply dissected on both sides by the lakeward and South Rukuru tributaries. North-east of Choma, from above Ruarwe, the surface rises to overlook Lake Nyasa by fully 5,000 feet, the lower surfaces being recognizable only as very narrow platforms at levels of 4,800 and 3,400 feet respectively.

The main rivers of the Vipya plateau are the sources of the Luweya and Limpasa rivers that flow eastwards directly to the lake and the Kasitu and Lunyangwa that flow firstly to the west, then north to join the South Rukuru river, which, in turn, eventually outflanks the plateau to the north to reach the lake. The eastern rivers have, to a large extent, been controlled by the regional NNE. strike of the formations as well as by a number of minor parallel rift valleys and, as a result, have had to cut their way through resistant ridges of gneiss to reach the lake. To the west the Kasitu river has followed an ancient *graben* of Karoo deposition that runs parallel to the Vipya highlands to join the South Rukuru in the Henga valley.

4(f)—*The Nyika Plateau*

Covering some 900 square miles, and standing at an elevation of between 6,500 and 8,000 feet, the Nyika plateau is the highest and most extensive high plateau surface, not only in Malawi but also within the Central African region. The plateau is bounded on all sides by steep scarps and to the north-east forms the main wall to the rift valley. The position of the plateau, lying astride the northern part of the country, has necessitated the routing of the main north road out of Malawi in this area, and also makes overland communication with Karonga difficult as the road has to traverse the broken foothill country that lies between the eastern Nyika scarp and the lake-shore in the Livingstonia area. From this plateau surface, with its higher rainfall, emanate the majority of the perennial rivers of the northern part of Malawi and indeed 'nyika' is the vernacular word given for 'from whence the water comes'.

The plateau may be considered to be a tilted block with its eastern

edge lying at 8,000 feet and its western edge at 7,000 feet, with its surface dissected by numerous rivers rising in the central and eastern regions. The surface has been ascribed a late Jurassic age for it is bounded

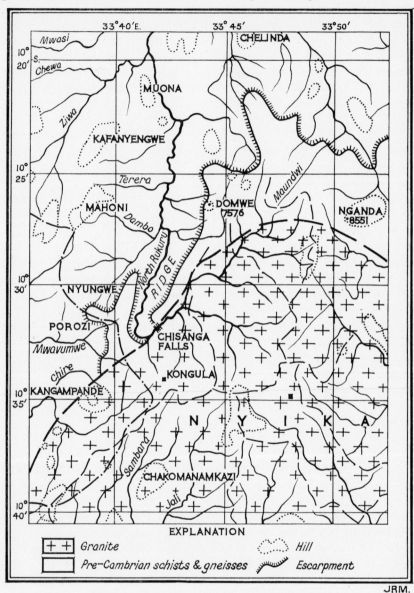

Fig. 10.   The North-western Nyika Plateau.

by the major Karoo boundary faults of this region, which are probably
not later than the lower Jurassic. At a lower level, at about 5,500 feet,
there is a distinct bevelled surface that can be traced around the plateau,
and this surface has been correlated with the Vipya–late Cretaceous
surface lying to the east of the Henga valley. This latter surface may

E

also be recognized on the crest of the spur that extends southwards from Njakwa gorge to Emanyeleni.

The underlying rocks of the Nyika are made up of a group of metamorphosed sediments of the Mafingi series together with a large granitic intrusion or series of intrusions that make up the resistant southern and central areas of the plateau. Rising out of the undulating and down-like surface are a number of low rounded peaks and ridges, the most prominent of which are Nganda (8,851 feet) and Chejara (8,200 feet). On the lower late Cretaceous bevelled surface the peaks are more prominent, of which the most outstanding is Fingira Rock, a high *inselberg* of intrusive granite in the southern part of the plateau.

The main rivers of the plateau find their sources in the wide, flat *dambos* which, in many respects, resemble the peat bogs of temperate regions. These rivers, the North Rumpi, Chelinda, Runyina, and North Rukuru have all eroded deep valleys back into the plateau, principally in the weaker rocks surrounding the central granitic core. Where these formations are particularly weak, headwater erosion has been rapid and, in some cases, has resulted in river capture. This is particularly noticeable in the headwaters of the North Rukuru River. This river commences its course by flowing south-westwards along the north-western contact between a zone of metamorphosed sediments, that form a low ridge to the north-west, and the granite intrusion. In former times it is apparent that this reach formed the headwaters of the Chire River that flows south-westwards to the Luangwa River. Subsequent headward erosion of the North Rukuru River southwards into the softer rocks has succeeded in breaching this north-westerly bounding ridge and diverting the headwater of the Chire northwards. The point of capture is today represented by the Chisanga Falls where the North Rukuru River falls from the edge of the granite intrusion and changes course abruptly to the north.

4(g)—*The Mafingi Mountains*

The Mafingi Mountains situated in the north-western part of Malawi and west of the Nyika Plateau may be considered to be composed of three separate units; the Namitawa or Mafingi ridge on the western watershed lying at a general elevation of about 7,000 feet; the Pirewombe Hills that are situated to the east of the Mafingi in the upper Lufira catchment; the Kayuni–Msissi hills, with their outstanding twin peaks situated on the North-Rukuru–Lufira watershed to the east of the Mafingi ridge. These three components are probably remnants of a much larger, high plateau that has now been dissected by the Mbalise, Lufira, and North Rukuru rivers.

The upland elements of these mountains are made up principally of quartzites, phyllites, and felspathic sandstones of the Mafingi Series that pass into more schistose, and therefore weaker, formations in the valley areas. These mountains are not formed by the intrusion of igneous formations into the pre-Cambrian as is the case in the majority of uplands in

Malawi, but represent the more highly metamorphosed elements of the pre-Cambrian formations. The structure of these mountain remnants is almost identical; the grey, craggy crests are composed of a thick band of vertical or steeply dipping quartzite graduating to quartz-schist. In most cases the flanks are composed of weathered schistose sandstones that give rise to steep, grassy slopes seamed by innumerable deep gullies. The Mafingi or Namitawa ridge comprises a flat ridge 7 miles long rising to about 7,500 feet and is formed by a close syncline that can be clearly seen from the Chisenga–Fort Hill road.

4(h)—*The Misuku Highlands*

The Misuku Highlands are made up of four parallel high ridges of intrusive gneiss and cover an area of some 65 square miles at an elevation of between 5,500 and 6,200 feet. These hills and ridges lie to the north-east of the Mafingi mountains and to the north they overlook the deeply incised Songwe River that forms the northern border of Malawi. From the north the Musanga stream has eroded a shallow bowl within the central upland area, and this basin is overlooked on all sides by the higher ridges of Mugesse, Wilindi, and Matipa.

The topography is composed of ridges and undulating hills bounded on all sides by moderate to steep scarps. The strike of the gneisses is consistently in a north-west–south-east direction which has firmly controlled the drainage of the north-western and south-eastern sections of the mountains. The numerous streams follow almost straight courses along the softer bands of gneiss in these directions towards the lower areas. The surface of the Misuku is probably a remnant of the late Cretaceous surface which has survived by virtue of its more resistant rocks.

BIBLIOGRAPHY

K. Bloomfield, 'An Outline of the Geology of Zomba Mountain', *Geol. Surv. Bull.* (1957).

——, 'The Geology of the Port Herald Area', *Geol. Surv. Bull.*, No. 9, Nyasaland (1958).

K. Bloomfield, and A. Young, 'The Geology and Geomorphology of Zomba Mountain', *Nyasa. Jour.*, Vol. XIV (1961).

F. Debenham, *The Way to Ilala: Dr. Livingstone's Pilgrimage*, Longmans (1955).

F. Dixey, 'Some Aspects of the Geomorphology of Central and Southern Africa', *Trans. G.S. of S.A.*, Annex. Vol. 58 (1955).

——, 'The Nyasa Rift Valley', *S.A. Geog. Jour.*, Vol. XXIII (1941).

——, 'The Geomorphic Development of the Shire Valley, Nyasaland', *Jour. of Geomorphology*, Vol. IV (1942).

——, 'The Mafingi Series of Northern Nyasaland', *Annual Report, Geol. Surv.*, Nyasaland (1928).

——, 'The Mlanje Mountains of Nyasaland', *Geog. Review*, Vol. XVII (1927).

——, 'Erosion Cycles in Central and Southern Africa', *Trans. G.S. of S.A.*, Vol. 45 (1942).

M. S. Garson, 'The Geology of the Lake Chilwa Area', *Geol. Surv. Bull.*, No. 12, Nyasaland (1960).

D. N. Holt, 'The Geology of the Fort Johnston District East of Lake Nyasa', *Records of Geol. Surv.*, Nyasaland, Vol. I (1959).

L. C. King, *South African Scenery*, Edinburgh (1951).

S. Morel, 'The Geology of the Middle Shire Area', *Geol. Surv. Bull.*, No. 10, Nyasaland (1958).

J. G. Pike, 'The Upper Pleistocene Raised Beach of the Karonga Area', *Nyasa. Jour.*, Vol. XI (1958).

K. V. Stringer, D. N. Holt, and A. W. Groves, 'The Chambe Plateau Ring Complex of Nyasaland', *Col. Geol. Min. Res.*, Vol. 6 (1956).

J. H. Wellington, *Southern Africa*, Vol. I, Cambridge Univ. Press (1955).

CHAPTER III

CLIMATE AND WEATHER

THE climate of the regions from the southern districts of the Congo Basin to the Tropic of Capricorn has been described as a 'modified Sudan type', a climatic type associated with the two zones to the north and south of equatorial latitudes. These two zones represent a climatic and vegetational transition from equatorial conditions of heat and humidity to drier conditions in the northern and southern deserts. However, the southern region is narrow from east to west when compared with North Africa and, moreover, its poleward coast opens to a wide ocean. Therefore, while the North African Sudan type climate is more continental in character, giving great extremes of temperature, the climate of the southern sub-continent is greatly modified by oceanic influences serving to reduce temperatures and to introduce moisture-bearing winds into the interior. By comparing sea-level summer temperatures it will be seen that those of Southern Africa are more than 10° F lower than those of the Sahara, despite the fact that the southern summer occurs in perihelion. The narrowness of the southern sub-continent would appear to be sufficient reason for this difference. A further modifying factor is the high plateau altitude of the southern area when compared to its northern counterpart.

Owing to its proximity to the east coast, Malawi, with its lake, high plateaux, and accentuated relief, has a distinctive climate that bears only general relationships with the Central African modified Sudan type climate. While the plateau areas are cool with a good to moderate rainfall, parts of the low-lying rift valley are excessively hot and, in places, semi-arid. During the summer months the country lies in an inter-tropical zone and comes under the influence of the rain-bearing Equatorial Low Pressure Zone and the North-East Monsoon, while during the winter months the South-East Trade Winds blowing inland from the Indian Ocean often bring bring with them considerable moisture. The climate of Malawi may therefore be considered as belonging to a maritime zone of the modified Sudan climatic area.

PRESSURE AND WIND SYSTEMS

As Malawi lies within an inter-tropical zone, its weather is dominated by the interaction of the pressure systems and winds of the tropics and the high pressure zones of the 'horse latitudes' that lie between 25° and 35° South. During the months of June, July, and August the high pressure zone is well developed across Southern Africa, while the Equatorial Low Pressure Zone prevails over North Africa and Asia. During this period the South-East Trades, that emanate from these high pressure zones, blow towards the low pressure zone, extending beyond the equator as a South-West Monsoon. During these months the weather conditions over Malawi come under the dominating influence of the South African continental high or anti-cyclone. Easterly winds associated with this anti-cyclone are dry, and weather is characterized by warm days with clear skies and brilliant sunshine, cold nights and rapid terrestrial radiation. These typical dry season conditions are, however, often broken up by the invasion of light rain and mist over high ground

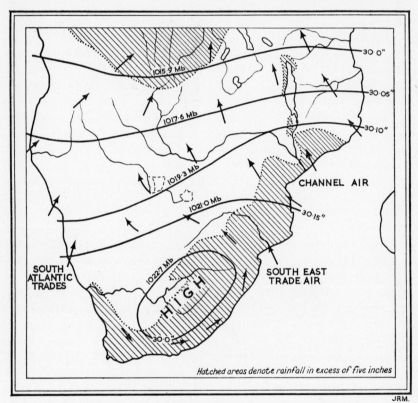

Fig. 11.   Synoptic Chart for Southern Africa (June).

facing south-east. These invasions of moist air, known as *chiperone* in Malawi and *guti* in Southern Rhodesia, are caused by a shift of the South African anti-cyclone to the east coast. Under this condition the winds in front of the anti-cyclone now blow northwards over the warm waters of the Moçambique Channel, and when they reach the east coast they are moist, warm, and unstable. As this high moves up the South African coast these winds are forced inland over the escarpment areas of Rhodesia and Malawi, condensation taking place as the air currents rise over the plateau slopes.

During September, October, and November, the Equatorial Low or Inter-Tropical Convergence Zone in the northern hemisphere is moving south in the wake of the sun and at the same time, owing to intense heating, a low develops over the Kalahari Desert in the sub-continental interior. The continental anti-cyclone then becomes established to the north-east and the wind over Malawi backs to the east and north-east. With a corresponding increase in temperature these easterly winds bring in moist oceanic air that eventually leads to the development of thunderstorms during the month of November. Usually the air is too dry for the widespread development of thunderstorms during October, but once the air over the interior has become humid subsequent to the

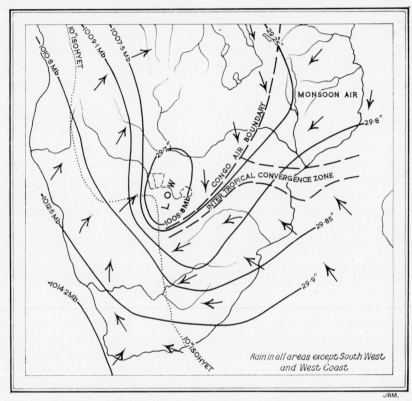

Fig. 12.   Synoptic Chart for Southern Africa (December).

main indraughts from the east and north, the distribution of humidity is effected partly by the process of convection and the movement of heat thunderstorms. These thunderstorms of November are normally confined to high ground in the south-eastern part of the country where the orographic influence is considerable in causing turbulence and convection. The more inland areas of the Central and Northern Provinces receive little of this rain, the moisture having already been taken up by the thunderstorms over the more southerly highland areas. Thus it is popularly said that the 'rains arrive earlier in the south'.

During the latter part of December, Malawi comes under the influence of the Inter-Tropical Convergence Zone which, moving south, enters Malawi from the north, causing widespread rain from thick layer cloud with thunder activity confined to the boundary of the zone. The main Convergence Zone reaches far down the African continent and draws with it moist air from the north-west and north-east, known as Congo Air and Monsoon Air respectively. Congo Air is caused by the recurvature of the mild South Atlantic Trades blowing over the humid Congo Basin and where this airstream meets the north-easterly wet monsoon air a further front is formed, known as the Congo Air Boundary or the Central African–East African Monsoon Front. Fig. 12 shows the position of the main fronts and airstreams typically developed during the rainy season. When the Congo Air Boundary is associated with the Convergence Zone over Malawi heavy widespread rain occurs.

Thus during the period December to March the weather over Malawi is dominated by the passage of the Equatorial Low in its southward movement in December and January to its southern limit over Southern Rhodesia, and its northward movement in February and March, this whole period constituting what is known as the 'main rains'. The movement of this front is not by any means a regular southward and northward movement over the country, but may oscillate over one area, become diffuse at times and retreat northward in the face of the South African coastal high that often forms during the months of January and February. This outbreak of southerly air causes a forward surge of the south-easterly winds causing widespread heavy rain ahead of the advancing boundary, and is, in effect, a combination of dry season and wet season conditions. The average pattern, however, is a southward movement during December and January and a northward movement in late February and March. The effects of this movement may be noted in the northern part of Malawi where a short, dry spell of some two weeks occurs between the passage of this front.

Following the sun at the end of March the inter-tropical convergence zone moves northward out of Malawi and the South-East Trades advance once again and bring about orographic type rain to the south-easterly windward slopes and to the highland and lake shore areas of the Northern Province. This type of rainfall continues throughout April and May and, in some areas in the extreme north, into June. However, with decreasing temperatures the rain mechanism of this airstream gradually weakens to occasional outbreaks of light rain and mist and typical dry season conditions now set in. Areas that lie to the west of the escarpment and montane areas receive little of this late rain and by the end of March nearly all rainfall has ceased in these areas. This is particularly noticeable in the Central Province plain and over the Mzimba area which lies in the shadow of the Vipya plateau.

Cyclones

Associated with the movement of the Equatorial Low are the tropical cyclones of the Indian Ocean which sometimes travel inland over Malawi and may cause considerable flooding and damage from the high winds and heavy rain normally associated with this type of disturbance.

An Indian Ocean Cyclone[1] has as its origin an intense low pressure system with air spiralling in a clockwise direction into a central vortex that usually originates in the doldrum belt over the Indian Ocean during the main rainy season. At this time—December to April—the

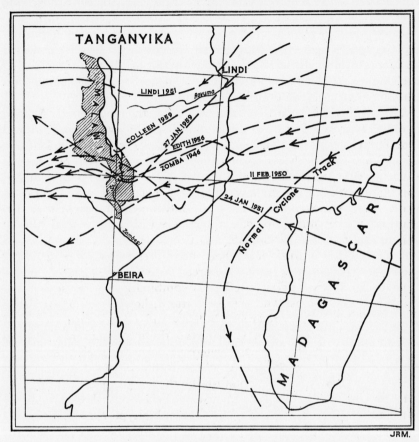

Fig. 13. Tracks of cyclones entering Malawi 1946–59.

surface of the sea has reached its maximum temperature (27°–30° C) and the doldrum belt has moved so far south of the equator that the increased centrifugal force of the earth's rotation sets into action the whirling motion of a cyclone. A cyclone is therefore formed by intense heating of a large mass of warm sea air which is drawn upwards to meet cooler air, thus forming clouds and raindrops. This liberates more heat which increases the rate of ascent and this heat in turn becomes its motive power. Meanwhile, at lower levels, cooler air is replacing the ascending warm air and is set spiralling by the earth's rotation. As the speed of this ascent increases, the spiralling increases and the cyclone takes on an increasingly forward movement towards the west.

[1] The same phenomenon known as a Typhoon in the Pacific or a Willy-Willy off the north-eastern coast of Australia.

Normally a cyclone's track will be in a westerly direction towards Madagascar, where it tends to curve away to the south and south-east. On occasion, however, there is a tendency for the presence of a high pressure zone lying in the Moçambique Channel to block this southerly course. If the Inter-Tropical Convergence Zone is, at the same time, lying over Malawi, a cyclone will cross the coast and enter the country to merge gradually with this low pressure zone. On the other hand, if a cyclone moves into the Moçambique Channel and is then deflected away southwards, the weather over the interior will become much drier. This comes about as the inland areas lie in the area of descending air, where there is a rise in pressure inhibiting rain.

During the past sixty years twelve cyclones have entered Malawi, although considerably more have crossed the Moçambique coast and have either moved out to sea again or into Southern Rhodesia. Of these twelve cyclones, two have been severe; the first known as the Zomba Cyclone, which passed near this town in December 1946 and caused considerable damage when some 28 inches of rain fell within thirty-six hours, and, more recently, Cyclone 'Edith' which passed over the Southern Province in April 1956, causing heavy flooding in the Chiromo area of the lower Shire.

ATMOSPHERIC TEMPERATURE, INSOLATION AND HUMIDITY

Insolation and radiation from the earth's surface are the controlling factors in ground and atmospheric temperature and are of importance in controlling certain forms of land utilization and human environment. In common with the greater part of the sub-continent, the air temperature near the ground in Malawi is strongly affected by altitude, and the effects of increasing altitude often outweigh those of decreasing latitude, as the following table shows.

TABLE I

Altitude and Temperature

Station	Latitude	Longitude	Altitude, ft.	Mean Temperatures, ° F		
				Jan.	July	Annual
Port Herald	16° 58′ S	35° 17′ E	190	81	68	77
Kota Kota	12° 50′ S	34° 20′ E	1,600	76	68	75
Livingstonia	10° 35′ S	34° 10′ E	4,498	68	61	66
Fort Hill	9° 42′ S	33° 14′ E	4,193	69	62	68

Atmospheric Temperature

Fig. 14 shows the mean annual temperature over Malawi, and it will be noted that the coolest areas are those of the highest parts of Malawi. During November the areas of highest mean temperature, that is over 80° F, are the Shire Valley and the Lake Nyasa basin, that of the

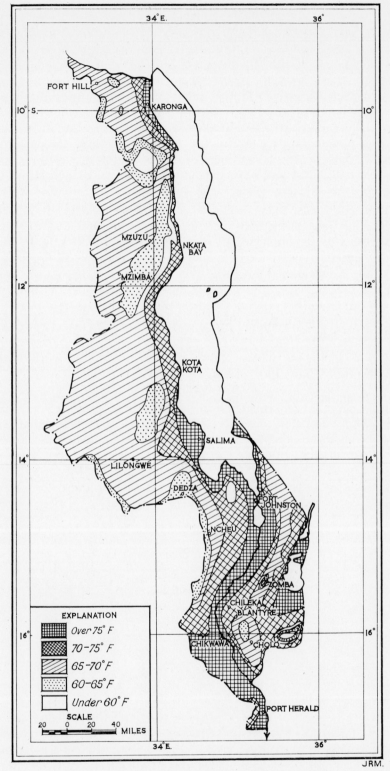

EXPLANATION

Over 75° F

70-75° F

65-70° F

60-65° F

Under 60° F

SCALE
20   0   20   40
MILES

Fig. 14.   Mean annual temperatures in Malawi.

former being a few degrees higher. At the onset of the rains the mean temperature drops and the relative humidity rises and life in the lower areas becomes uncomfortable. By the end of March the medium high plateau areas are much cooler, the relative positions of hot and cool areas having remained unchanged. By May, winter conditions are becoming established to the south of Malawi and by July, radiation gains on insolation in the higher areas and a mean monthly temperature of less than 60° F is now found over most of the medium and high plateau areas. On the Nyika, Vipya, Kirk Range, and Mlanje, frost occurs at this time in sheltered valleys and snow has been reported on occasion from the Mlanje peaks. By September insolation has gained on radiation and the plateau areas begin to warm up, but nevertheless temperatures are still lower than those of March.

Considering the year as a whole, three definite thermal regions may be recognized:

(1) The Shire Valley and the Lake Nyasa rift valley with a mean temperature of between 74° F and 78° F.

(2) The medium plateau areas at elevations of between 3,000 and 4,500 feet with an annual mean temperature of between 66° F and 74° F.

(3) The higher smaller plateau and mountain areas with an annual mean temperature of between 58° F and 64° F.

In more detail Table II shows the annual mean temperature and range at various stations in Malawi.

TABLE II

Mean Temperature and Range at Selected Stations

Station	Altitude, ft.	Mean 24-hourly temp., ° F	Mean max. temp., ° F	Mean min. temp., ° F	Abs. max. temp., ° F	Abs. min. temp., ° F	Mean annual range ° F	Mean extreme range ° F
Port Herald	190	77·1	89·1	67·6	111	41	13·6	21·5
Chikwawa	500	78·0	89·8	66·1	113	35	15·7	23·7
Fort Johnston	1,589	74·6	86·1	65·1	104	41	13·9	21·0
Kota Kota	1,641	74·2	83·0	66·5	98	49	12·8	16·5
Karonga	1,590	75·2	85·0	66·6	99	51	11·6	18·4
Mlanje	2,000	69·9	82·0	59·6	101	36	13·3	22·4
Zomba	3,140	69·0	78·7	61·6	97	45	13·0	17·1
Ncheu	4,200	66·3	75·5	59·4	92	43	12·2	16·1
Lilongwe	3,722	67·2	80·2	55·5	97	26	15·0	24·7
Mwera Hill	4,960	64·7	73·3	56·1	89	35	12·3	17·2
Mzimba	4,430	66·2	77·1	57·8	92	33	13·0	19·3
Mzuzu	4,125	65·5	74·7	56·3	89	31	13·8	18·4
Fort Hill	4,193	68·3	79·3	60·7	94	38	12·7	18·6

A thermal factor of significance in human health and land utilization is the seasonal range of temperature and Fig. 15 shows the annual extreme range of temperature. From this figure and the table above an indication is given of areas of greatest and least thermal fluctuation. That Lake Nyasa serves as a moderating effect is apparent as the Lake shore and eastward flanks of the plateaux show the least annual range, with a general increase in a westward direction. The Shire Valley shows the highest range where the very high November day temperatures contrast most strongly with cool July nights when radiation of heat from the ground is the main thermal factor. The sheltered position in relation to the main winds would also tend to increase this range and the comparatively high extreme range of 24° F occurring on the south-western border, is an extension of conditions prevailing in the middle Zambezi valley.

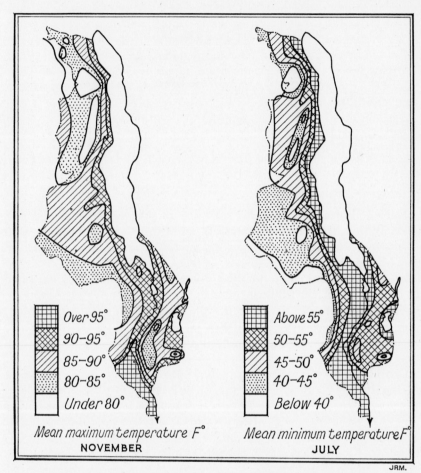

Over 95°
90–95°
85–90°
80–85°
Under 80°

Mean maximum temperature F°
NOVEMBER

Above 55°
50–55°
45–50°
40–45°
Below 40°

Mean minimum temperature F°
JULY

JRM.

Fig. 15. Mean maximum and minimum temperatures.

With regard to absolute minimum temperatures, very rarely do they drop below 32° F on the medium plateau areas, but on the Vipya, Nyika, Kirk Range, and Mlanje, early morning frosts and ice sometimes occur in the valleys during the cold months of June and July.

Insolation

Closely related to atmospheric temperature from an environmental aspect, is the heating of the ground by the direct rays of the sun, or insolation, exercising an important influence on all forms of human, animal, and plant life. The duration of sunshine is an essential factor in insolation and should therefore receive our attention.

With well-defined wet and .dry seasons, Malawi enjoys abundant sunshine throughout the dry season, and this is at a maximum in the rain shadow areas of the Shire Valley, southern lake shore, and over the western plateau areas. Table III shows the mean monthly duration of sunshine hours from selected stations in Malawi.

TABLE III

Duration of Sunshine—Malawi
(Hours)

Station	Jan.	Feb.	Mar.	Apr.	May	Jun.	Jul.	Aug.	Sep.	Oct.	Nov.	Dec.	Mean
Makanga	6·4	6·6	8·2	8·6	8·4	6·9	7·7	7·8	7·9	8·8	8·3	7·0	7·7
Bvumbwe	5·5	5·7	6·7	7·4	7·9	6·3	7·4	7·6	7·8	8·4	7·5	4·9	7·0
Chileka	6·0	6·0	6·1	7·7	8·0	7·1	7·3	7·9	8·2	8·6	7·3	6·2	7·2
Monkey Bay	5·4	5·9	7·5	8·9	9·3	8·7	8·2	9·2	9·3	9·8	9·5	7·9	8·3
Lilongwe	4·6	4·9	6·1	8·0	8·4	7·7	8·3	8·3	8·5	9·9	7·9	5·4	7·3
Mzimba	4·1	4·0	5·3	7·4	8·5	8·6	9·0	9·4	9·7	10·3	8·5	5·4	7·5
Fort Hill	5·0	3·9	4·7	7·4	9·5	9·2	9·3	8·7	9·9	9·1	7·5	4·6	7·4

During the rainy season the duration of sunshine in most areas is normally less than half the possible number of sunshine hours, and during some months of the dry season, certain areas in the south-eastern part of the country are similarly affected. At Bvumbwe, the average number of sunshine hours for June is less than that normally recorded at the height of the rainy season in the Shire Valley. In contrast, Mzimba, lying to the west and in the rain shadow of the Vipya highlands, experiences a high duration of sunshine throughout the dry season, reaching a maximum of 10·3 hours per day for the month of October.

During the past few years attention has been given to the heat-producing effects of sunshine in Malawi in relation to plant growth and evaporation. Since 1959 the amount of insolation has been measured at Chitedze, Bvumbwe, and Makanga by means of Gunn–Bellani radiation integrators that were previously calibrated against a solarimeter. Although these observations cover a comparatively short period, the annual cycle is clearly shown. Fig 16[1] shows the mean monthly amounts of radiation in gram calories per square centimetre throughout the year at these three stations. The apparent passage of the sun southwards in October and early November and northwards in February is clearly shown by the peaks in all three records at these times. The plateau areas of the Central Province receive the greatest amount of radiation throughout the dry season but the drier Lower Shire area receives the highest during the rainy season. Bvumbwe, in the Shire Highlands, shows a reduced level for a greater part of the year and this may be attributed to the greater cloudiness and humidity in this area.

Of great importance to human health and comfort in Africa is the

[1] Data supplied by Department of Agriculture, Nyasaland.

reaction of the human body to insolation, air temperature, and humidity. This reaction is difficult to measure as there are widely differing reactions associated with constitutional and racial differences. In recent years, attempts have been made to measure the influence of temperature and insolation on the human body by means of an instrument known as the cooling-ball. Physiological strain can be approximately

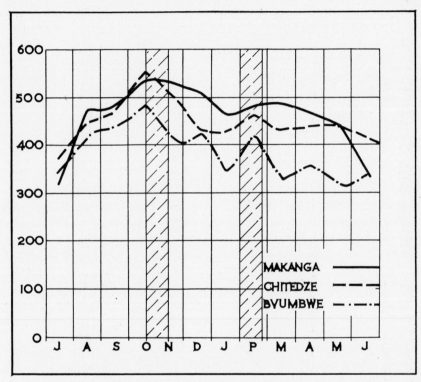

Fig. 16. Monthly means of radiation in gm. cal./cm²., Malawi.
(Shaded areas represent passage of sun.)

indicated under varying conditions of insolation and exposure to air, the least strain being where these conditions combine to produce a cooling-ball temperature near that of the human body. While these measurements are of value in connexion with the effects of solar radiation and temperature, they do not indicate the important effects of humidity, and, as we know for most people, 'it isn't the heat, it's the humidity' that counts. In this respect methods to measure human comfort in terms of atmospheric temperature and humidity have been devised, but these, on the other hand, do not measure the effect of direct radiation on the body. As an indication of the effect of climate on humans in Malawi, however, we may apply Sir David Brunt's conditions of temperature and humidity which the human body can tolerate without risk of heat stroke. His conclusions are based on experimental tests in which the degrees of physical exertion, clothing worn and the rate of air movement were varied.

In Fig. 17 these limits are given, the line CC referring to a lightly-clothed man resting in sunshine and EE to a lightly-clothed man walking at a normal rate in sunshine. If a point specifying the conditions of temperature and humidity of the air at a particular time lies to the right

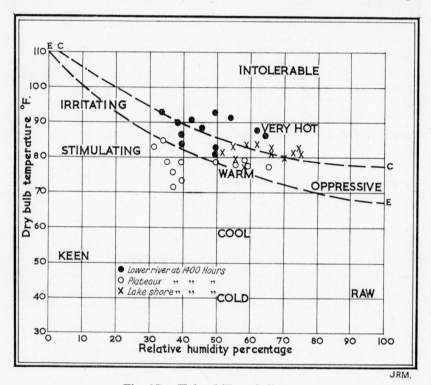

JRM.

Fig. 17.   Tolerability of climate.

of these lines, then to the man so occupied for any length of time there is some risk of heat-stroke. Brunt further suggests that where the mean monthly temperature exceeds 76° F there are likely to be periods of three to four hours per day when the actual temperature and humidity are above tolerable limits. Such conditions are found for eight months of the year in the Lower Shire Valley and for six months of the year on the lake-shore. The points plotted on Fig. 17 are from various stations in Malawi at 1400 hours and it will be seen that outside activity at this time of day can be carried out in comfort for about seven months of the year in the higher areas only. Throughout the year mid-day conditions in the Shire Valley and lake-shore show that there is some risk of heat-stroke and during four months of the year risk is great even when resting in the sun. Early morning conditions throughout the year in the plateau areas are comfortable, but in the lower areas are inclined to be oppressive, particularly during the wet season.

Humidity

The distribution of humidity over Malawi is influenced largely by the position of the various physiographical regions in their relation to the main moisture-bearing airstreams and Lake Nyasa. Mean monthly percentage humidity for selected stations in the country is given in Table IV.

TABLE IV

Relative Humidity at Selected Stations—Malawi (%)

Station	Jan.	Feb.	Mar.	Apr.	May	Jun.	Jul.	Aug.	Sep.	Oct.	Nov.	Dec.	Mean
Makanga	77	81	78	79	78	76	76	65	61	69	76	77	72
Bvumbwe	83	88	86	85	80	80	70	69	65	62	69	84	77
Chileka	79	80	80	75	70	69	63	57	52	50	60	74	67
Zomba	82	82	86	80	77	76	70	60	61	52	64	82	73
Lilongwe	83	86	82	77	72	67	61	58	54	50	62	77	69
Mzimba	82	83	82	80	74	72	68	65	60	52	64	76	71
Fort Hill	80	83	82	80	74	70	64	61	52	47	54	74	68

During the dry season months of April to October the south-easterly winds are normally well established over Malawi and at times bring with them considerable amounts of moisture. A large percentage of this moisture is precipitated over high ground to the south-east and a rain shadow is caused over the Upper Shire Valley and over the southern part of Lake Nyasa. After losing much of its moisture over the Shire Highlands this wind is partially funnelled into the Lake Nyasa trough and on its passage northward it undergoes a moisture recharge from the lake that is subsequently precipitated over the mountains of the northern and north-western parts of the lake basin when sufficiently saturated and cooled. This recharge of moisture to the south-easterly air stream is evident when we consider the mean dew point temperature for the period April to October at stations sited on an approximate line from the Shire Highlands to Karonga northward along the lake-shore.

TABLE V

Increase in Humidity due to Lake Nyasa.
(April–October)

	Mlanje	Ft. Johnston	Kota Kota	Nkata Bay	Karonga
Dew Point	60·1°	59·0°	60·4°	62·3°	63·4°

The driest parts of Malawi, as indicated by relative humidity data, are the Upper Shire Valley, the Salima lake-shore, the Fort Hill and Mzimba areas, and during October this percentage drops below 50 per cent. This comparatively low percentage is however greater than that experienced over the greater part of Southern Rhodesia and Zambia

F

during the same period. In the Lake Nyasa and lower Shire areas the relative humidity does not drop below a mean of 57 per cent. in any one month and during the rains it remains in the region of 80 per cent. with a mean temperature of about 80° F. Over the plateau areas the mean relative humidity is also about 80 per cent. throughout the rains but the mean temperature is much reduced by altitude. It is evident therefore that during this period the rift valley areas of the Lower Shire and Lake Nyasa present a trying climatic environment to both human and animal life, conditions that are somewhat alleviated with ascent to the plateau areas.

RAINFALL

The seasons in Malawi are popularly divided into two—the 'dry' and the 'wet'. The Meteorological Department classes the period from November to March as the 'wet season' and the remainder of the year as the 'dry season'. While this division may apply to Southern Rhodesian conditions, upon which it is based, it does not strictly apply to all areas of Malawi, where the wet season may continue well into April and in some cases into May. The meteorological year in Malawi may be divided into three characteristic periods; the main rains that coincide with the *official* period of November to March; the late rains during the months of April and May; and the dry season from June to October with occasional outbreaks of light rain in favourable localities at the beginning of this period.

Rainfall over the country is derived from three main sets of conditions, being (a) the early rains of October and November, which con-

TABLE VI

Rainfall Characteristics in Malawi

Rainfall district	Average rainfall (in.)			Driest year %	Wet-test year %	Coefficient of variation			Season rainfall in % of mean of district			
	Wet	Dry	Ann.			Wet	Dry	Ann.	N–M	A–M	J–A	S–O
Mlanje	73·2	11·0	85·2	60	146	0·21	·045	0·20	75	12	8	5
Cholo Highlands	48·7	6·1	54·8	59	144	0·27	0·39	0·22	79	10	7	4
Shire Highlands	46·1	3·2	49·3	53	154	0·23	0·48	0·23	88	7	3	2
Palombe	37·0	0·9	37·9	50	164	0·31	—	0·31	92	5	1	2
Lower Shire	30·1	3·0	33·1	42	167	0·29	0·46	0·30	85	8	5	2
Upper Shire	29·4	1·1	30·5	55	150	0·24	—	0·24	91	6	1	2
Port Herald Hills	53·0	10·1	63·1	47	154	0·27	0·44	0·28	77	10	10	3
Namweras	39·4	1·0	40·4	51	165	0·23	—	0·23	92	5	1	3
Kirk Range	39·1	2·1	41·2	53	150	0·24	0·35	0·21	90	6	2	2
S.W. Lake	44·5	1·2	45·7	58	184	0·26	—	0·25	90	8	0	2
Central Province	34·9	0·7	35·6	58	144	0·21	—	0·21	94	5	0	1
Mzimba	33·5	0·5	34·0	64	142	0·17	—	0·15	94	5	0	1
Vipya	38·6	20·4	59·0	60	166	0·23	0·65	0·24	73	25	1	1
West Nyas	67·4	4·2	71·6	60	165	0·25	0·75	0·26	66	28	5	1
Nyika	49·6	3·6	53·2	66	157	0·24	0·55	0·25	74	21	4	1
North Nya a	38·9	1·9	40·8	62	161	0·20	0·56	0·20	90	8	1	1
Fort Hill	33·6	2·9	36·5	60	158	0·19	—	0·19	98	1	0	1

Notes:
1. The percentages for the driest and wettest year are 'percentage of the average'.
2. The seasonal distribution of rainfall is divided into four characteristic periods; November to March, April and May, June to August, and September and October.
3. Data from *Water Development Department Professional Paper No. 1, 1959*; 'Rainfall Characteristics in Nyasaland', 1959 (Tetley and Pike).

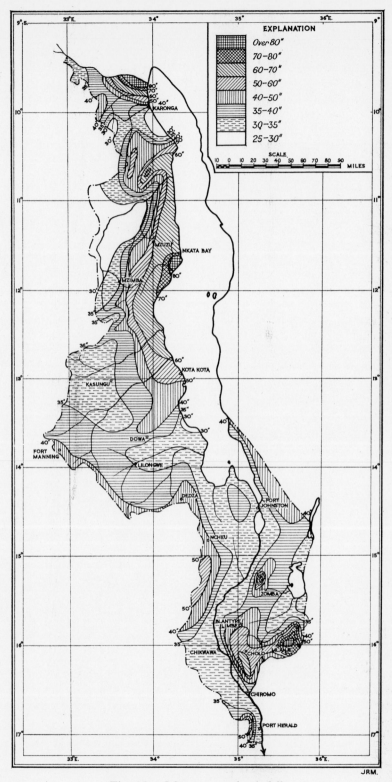

Fig. 18. Mean annual rainfall.

sist mainly of heat thunderstorms over high ground and the escarpment areas, and are derived mainly from the south-easterly and easterly in-draughts of moist air; (b) the Inter-Tropical Convergence Zone and the eastward encroachment of the Congo Air boundary which either singly or together bring widespread rain and unstable conditions with thunder-storms confined to the margins of these zones. This type of rain, charac-terized by widespread falls of medium to heavy rain, occurs mainly during the period December to March; (c) in April and May the south-easterly wind becomes re-established and brings with it rain over high ground and the south-eastern facing scarps. As the dry season pro-gresses these indraughts become less frequent and by the end of June the dry season is normally well established in most areas. Mention should be made of the increased rainfall that often occurs in September that cannot be classified with any of the above groups. Low cloud, high winds, and cold weather with occasional heavy falls of rain may persist for a few days or more during this month and it is thought to be the result of the favourable phasing of an upper level cold wave travelling from west to east with an influx of moist channel air at a lower level from the south-east.

During the periods when convergence zone rainfall is absent from Malawi and the rainfall is characterized by convectional type thun-derstorms, the effect of Lake Nyasa is apparent. At night the cool air from the surrounding land blows towards the lake where, the water being warmer, it rises and forms towering cumulo-nimbus, and thunder and downpours of rain occur during the night, continuing until about 9 a.m. the following morning. These storms may drift slowly in either a north-westerly or south-westerly direction with the prevailing wind at that time, and give rise to early morning rain along the western shores of Lake Nyasa. During the day, the circulation is reversed and the shallow lake breeze, charged with vapour, sets steadily on to the shores, the lake now being a focus for descending air. By the afternoon masses of cloud may form over the lake-shore and, other factors being equal, may result in further rain during the late afternoon.

Fifteen rainfall 'districts' based on homogeneity of phase and ampli-tude, have been recognized in Malawi. These rainfall districts closely follow the main physiographic regions of the country and the import-ance of this factor is thus emphasized. A summary of these rainfall characteristics by districts is shown in Table VI, and with regard to seasonal distribution it will be seen that the Mlanje, Cholo, and Port Herald hill rainfall districts normally receive some rain all year round, the former two districts receiving from 21 to 25 per cent. of their mean annual total during the period April to October. The effect of the north-ward moving convergence zone in late March and April is reflected in the seasonal distribution of rainfall along the lake-shore escarpment areas of the western lake-shore and the Nyika, where 21 to 34 per cent. of the mean annual rainfall occurs in April and May. In the extreme north, at Mwangulukulu on the Songwe river and at nearby Kyela in

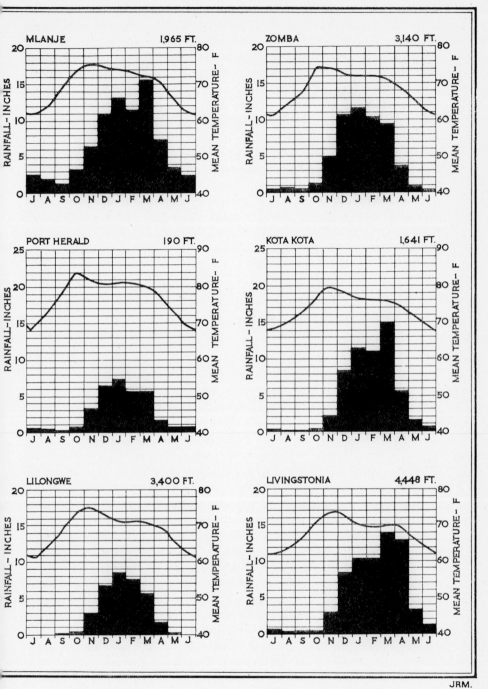

Fig. 19.   Rainfall and temperature graphs for selected stations.

Tanganyika, almost half the annual rainfall falls during these two months, derived mainly from the south-easterly air stream and caused by peculiar physiographic conditions that are discussed later. On the other hand, the areas lying in the rain shadows of the main plateaux and over the medium plateaux surfaces of the Central and Northern Provinces, receive very little of the south-easterly dry season rain, and the wet and dry seasons are sharply marked in these areas. For example, at Kasungu 97 per cent. of the annual total of 33 inches falls during the period November to March.

The seasonal distribution of rainfall over the country is a question of the greatest importance as it is one of the main controlling factors of land utilization. For instance, it has been shown that the 7-inch dry season isohyet limits the true tea growing areas of Malawi. These conditions are met in the Mlanje and Cholo areas and in combination with favourable soils, make them two of the most economically important areas of the country.

TABLE VII

Distribution of Rainfall over Malawi

Mean annual rainfall (inches per annum)	% of total area
Under 30	5·1
30– 40	61·6
40– 50	17·4
50– 60	12·0
60– 70	2·2
70– 80	0·4
80– 90	0·5
90–100	0·5
Over 100	0·3

Owing to the variable and broken topography of Malawi, large variations in average rainfall amounts occur within relatively short distances. These variable physiographical conditions lead to the development of areas of high precipitation over the south and south-eastern slopes of the highland areas and to the development of comparative rain shadows lying to the north and west of the escarpment or highland areas. Nevertheless, these rain shadow areas, in common with large areas of adjacent Zambia and Moçambique, do receive a normal 30 to 40 inches per annum derived mainly from the Inter-Tropical Convergence Zone. From the isohyetal map of mean annual rainfall, it will be seen that the Shire Valley, the south-west lake-shore, the Central Province plain, the Mzimba plain to the west of the Vipya and the areas lying to the north-west of the Nyika, all lie within partial rain shadows. The annual average rainfall on the south-eastern slopes of Mlanje Mountain and the Cholo Highlands varies from some 50 to 130 inches, whereas immediately to the west in the Shire Valley the annual average drops to some 30 inches. A repetition of this quantitative pattern may also be observed in the Kasungu and Mzimba areas.

The percentage area between various limits of mean annual rainfall is shown in Table VII. The mean annual rainfall for the country as a whole is approximately 45 inches with a recorded maximum of 130 inches and a minimum of 25 inches. It will be noticed that only 5 per cent. of the country has an average rainfall of below 30 inches, which is a limit that is generally considered to be the minimum for successful dry land farming. Comparatively speaking, Malawi may be considered to possess an adequate mean annual rainfall.

With regard to the areas of high rainfall, the highest annual averages of recorded rainfall are those of the comparatively limited area of the high plateau or shelves of Mlanje Mountain where an annual average of 130 inches is recorded from Litchenya plateau standing at 6,500 feet. In the Ruo valley above Lujeri Tea Estate the average rainfall is also about 130 inches, and it is possible that it might even be higher farther up this narrow valley towards the precipice, this area being a natural trap to the south-east wind. The other plateau shelves of Mlanje also show annual averages of above 100 inches although there is a sharp decrease to approximately 60 inches to the north of the main peaks. On the south-eastern slopes of Mlanje, at an elevation of between 2,000 and 2,800 feet, the orographic effect dominates the precipitation pattern and averages of between 80 and 130 inches are found in the tea growing areas situated here. The western and northern slopes of the massif experience a lower rainfall and in the Palombe area there is a well marked rain shadow where the mean annual rainfall is 38 inches. The isolated Zomba massif also has a higher rainfall than the surrounding lower country and records show an annual average difference of 24 per cent. between the foot of the mountain and the Mlungusi basin of the Zomba plateau at an elevation of between 5,000 and 6,000 feet.

Along the western lake-shore from Kota Kota to Livingstonia the lake is bordered by the high Vipya plateau and its eastern slopes present a barrier to the south-easterly moist air stream in April and May. Where the shore line changes direction to the north-east between Kiwiriri and Vizara in the Nkata Bay district, this orographic effect is accentuated and the annual average rainfall in this area increases to between 70 and 100 inches.

Of considerable importance to the hydrology of the Lake Nyasa basin is the high rainfall area situated at the northern limit of the lake, that feeds a number of large rivers draining into Lake Nyasa in this area. The Karonga lake-shore plain has a large variation of rainfall over short distances; in the Florence Bay area the rainfall (60 inches) is consistent with other lake-shore stations with immediate orographic influence. However, in a northward direction along the lake-shore, rainfall amounts fall off rapidly as the influence of the Nyika escarpment moves away from the lake littoral and the average rainfall between Nyungwe and Lupembe is as low as 25 to 30 inches in an average year. At Karonga the annual average increases to 42 inches, at Mwenetete, some 12 miles north of Karonga, it is 65 inches, and at Mwangulukulu on the Songwe

River, the annual average is approximately 120 inches. On the lake-shore plain that continues across the Songwe River into Tanganyika this high rainfall is maintained and continued into the Poroto Mountains that rise to heights of between 7,000 and 8,000 feet. Tukuyu, known as

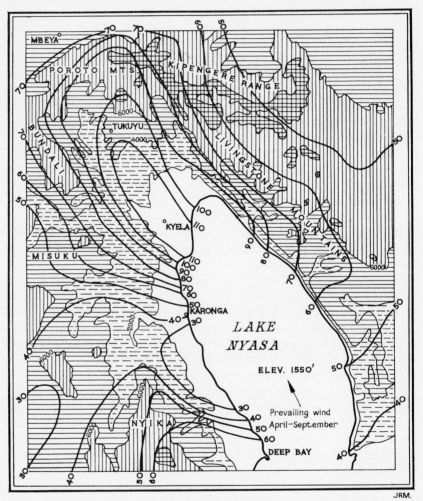

JRM.

Fig. 20.   Map of North Nyasa showing increase in rainfall.

New Langenberg in German days, situated on the southern flanks of the main Poroto–Rungwe range, has an average rainfall of 101 inches. This pocket of high rainfall is caused by high mountains on three sides with the southern side open to Lake Nyasa and the south-east wind, and has been described as a 'rainfall shute similar in many respects to the high rainfall "traps" of Cherrapunji and Shillong in the Khasi hills of Upper Assam, but, of course, on a much reduced scale'. The south-easterly air stream, moisture laden in April and May, proceeds unhindered over the still comparatively warm lake and is then suddenly funnelled into the Nyasa–Poroto–Livingstone shute with a consequent concentration, rapid ascent, and precipitation in that area. The record from Kyela shows that over 50 per cent. of the mean annual total rainfall of 116·5 inches falls during the two months of April and May—(April 38 inches, May 23 inches).

The lowest rainfall areas of the country are those that lie in double rain shadows, and three main areas are recognizable: the low-lying area bordering the western Shire Valley protected from the north, east, and south-east by higher ground; the Lupembe area of the Karonga lake littoral where the shore line of Lake Nyasa lies parallel to the main south-easterly airstream with the absence of immediate orographic influence, lying in the shadow of the Vipya to the south and the Nyika to the north-west; and the Lake Kazuni area lying to the south of the Nyika plateau and to the west of both the Vipya plateau and the Njakwa hills. The average rainfall in these areas is approximately 25 to 30 inches per annum, with a minimum as low as 13 inches in some years.

Precipitation Characteristics

From the foregoing we have seen that Malawi's rainfall is derived mainly from three different sets of conditions and similarly there are three main types of precipitation associated with these conditions. They are the convectional thunderstorms of the early rains, the heavy monsoon type rains of the tropical low pressure system, and the light rain and mist or *chiperone* of the dry season. In addition, the occasional passage of a tropical cyclone will precipitate large amounts of rain over high ground over a period of days.

The convectional thunderstorm is a common phenomenon in all parts of Malawi during the early period of the wet season as well as during the intervening period associated with the passage of the inter-tropical convergence zone. A 'heat thunderstorm cycle' can often be recognized which usually starts with clear, hot weather, the air having a high relative humidity due to the indraughts of maritime air from the coast. After the main winds have dropped, convection currents are set up and lead eventually to the development of the anvil-shaped cumulus cloud. In time the water-drops or hail overcome the updraughts that have now been weakened by the clouds shadow and the storm then breaks and the temperature drops steeply, bringing about a clearing of the sky, and, in terms of human comfort, a certain relief from tension; thus a new cycle starts again. Frequently, however, this cycle is not ideal and does not culminate, on account of a low atmospheric humidity. It would appear that in Malawi little or no rain results if the dew point is below 55° F, and these frustrated thunderstorm cycles are a common occurrence during the month of October prior to the main indraughts of moist air. The main characteristics of thunderstorms are their high intensity and their narrow path of movement that frequently drenches a limited area only.

The rainfall associated with the inter-tropical convergence zone is usually of the prolonged type from a heavy cover of stratus cloud. This zone may be as much as 100 miles wide, and although its circulation and rain mechanism are imperfectly known it is evidently a zone of strong convergence marked by the occurrence of heavy widespread rainfalls of up to 5 inches a day over a period of two or three days, often occurring when the convergence zone is particularly well developed over any one area.

After the convergence zone has moved northward in March or April, the South-East Trade Wind becomes established and orographic type of rain falls over the southern and northern lake-shore areas of the country. As temperatures decrease in May this type of rainfall becomes lighter in character and is associated with frequent mists over the highland areas of Mlanje, Cholo, the Vipya, and Nyika. The precipitation resembles warm front rain and is generally of moderate or low intensity, except where high mountain features force the wind to great heights and cause a marked increase in amount and intensity. This has already been described in the case of Mlanje and Zomba mountains.

Precipitation from a tropical cyclone is not a general occurrence over Malawi, but when a cyclone does pass over the country it gives rise to high winds, widespread heavy rain and, where the relief is pronounced, heavy orographic type of precipitation. The 'Zomba' cyclone of December 1946 passed over Malawi well to the north of Zomba, but the mountain presented the maximum orographic influence to the easterly winds in the south-east quadrant of the cyclone and, as a result, some 28 inches of rain fell in thirty-six hours on Zomba town at the foot of the mountain, and it is probable that considerably more fell over the plateau area.

Of considerable interest was the heavy storm that centred over Kota Kota on 20/21 February 1957, precipitating some 22 inches of rain in twenty-four hours, and subsequently moving south-westwards towards the Dowa highlands. This has been described by some meteorologists as a convectional type storm associated with a rare upper level cold pool. However, prior to the onset of this storm the synoptic chart showed the rapid development of a closed circulation similar in many respects to a tropical cyclonic disturbance and its subsequent south-easterly track inland towards Dowa has given rise to the suggestion by some observers that this disturbance was a small scale tropical cyclone that formed over Lake Nyasa. There is no record of a cyclonic disturbance originating over a large inland body of water, owing perhaps to the fact that most lakes elsewhere lie outside the latitude of tropical cyclones. Lake Nyasa, however, occupies a unique position in this respect inasmuch as it is sufficiently far from the equator for geotropic effects to be applied to an area of low pressure forming over a heated area of its surface when other conditions are favourable for this to take place. With these considerations in mind, however, it is considered that the area of Lake Nyasa is too limited for an oceanic type of cyclonic mechanism to form and the causes of this disturbance may possibly be found in a phenomenon known as a 'lee depression'. With a prevailing easterly wind a depression could form in the lee of the eastern scarp of Lake Nyasa in the same way that 'lee depressions' form under the scarp of the Drakensberg mountains in Natal, and with intensification over the lake and applied circulatory force such a depression could track westwards towards the Malawi shore and gradually fill up once over the land. This hypothesis is unfortunately based on a single storm of this nature and the process will become clearer when more data come to hand. That cyclones do intensify over Lake Nyasa was recently demonstrated when cyclone 'Colleen' did so over Lake Nyasa in December 1959.

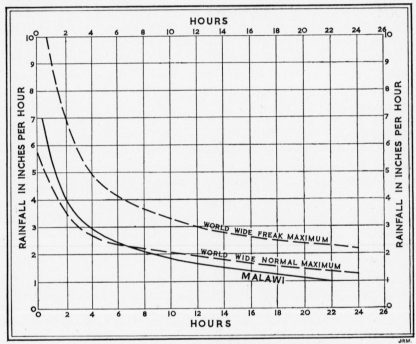

Fig. 21.   Provisional rainfall intensity graph.

Rainfall Intensity

One of the more important factors influencing soil conservation and run-off is the intensity of rainfall. Records of intensity in Malawi are scattered and of short duration, being measured at only twenty-one stations throughout the country. From the scanty data to hand and from records of intense storms that warranted noting in the past, a duration intensity curve has been compiled and is compared with world-wide intensities (Fig. 21).

Over Southern Africa high rainfall intensities are usually associated with convectional thunderstorms and, to a certain degree, this is also true for Malawi. However, the maximum intensities recorded over the country have been mainly derived from heavy orographic type rainfall from the south-easterly air stream or from the passage of a tropical cyclone. The highest intensity yet recorded occurred at Nkata Bay on 11 January 1957. This storm was of the 'early morning lake-shore' oro-graphic type in which 6 inches fell in fifty minutes during a total storm of 7·5 inches lasting ninety minutes. This intensity ranks close to the highest yet recorded from the sub-continent; that of Tjompani in Southern Rhodesia where, on 7 March 1926, 6 inches fell in forty minutes. It also ranks within world-wide maximum intensities although well below the phenomenal rainfall of parts of monsoon Asia. Although the Nkata Bay intensity is the maximum recorded in Malawi, Talbot-Edwards, writing on the 'Zomba' cyclone of December 1946, when 28 inches fell in thirty-six hours, mentions that the normal 5-inch rain gauge was emptied twice within one hour during the storm, and on the second occasion the gauge had already overflowed. This would give an intensity of over 10 inches per hour and would therefore constitute a record that is comparable with world-wide freak maximum values. The Kota Kota storm that occurred in February 1957 described previously, precipitated a total of 22·5 inches in twenty-four hours of which 15·2 inches fell in six hours, thirty-seven minutes. For longer periods both this and the 'Zomba' falls are above any intensities recorded elsewhere in Central or South Africa, the only long period storm approaching these values being the Eshowe, Zululand, storm of 4 and 5 March 1940, when 23·4 inches fell in thirty-six hours.

Within the sub-continent Malawi probably experiences the highest rainfall intensities as a result of its broken topography and its relation to the tropical cyclones of the Indian Ocean, and these rainfall intensities warrant the closest attention from the standpoint of soil conservation and flood control.

Rainfall Reliability

It is of considerable value when studying the rainfall of any particular area to have some measure by which one may obtain an idea of the variation of the annual rainfall in relation to the arithmetical mean. The coefficients of variation as derived from the standard deviation is a useful measure for ascertaining the degree of these variations as it takes into account not only the relationship between absolute maximum and minimum values, but also variations in all the years of record. Thus, a small coefficient of variation for the rainfall of any one area would mean that one may count on obtaining more nearly the normal rainfall each year in that area than in an area with a large coefficient.

The average coefficient of variation for the various rainfall districts of Malawi are shown in Table VI on page 66. From the data presented it is apparent that the most reliable rainfall areas in Malawi are the Cholo Highlands and the Central and Northern Province plains, with an increase in reliability in a westward direction away from the Lake Nyasa trough. The broken topography of this trough is thought to be responsible for the larger variations found in this area. While the wet season rainfall shows a high reliability, dry season rainfall is shown to be much less so, coefficients ranging from 0·35 to 0·75. The Cholo Highlands and the Kirk Range have the highest reliability of dry season rainfall, whereas the west Nyasa lake-shore along the slopes of the Vipya shows the lowest reliability. That variation of the dry season rainfall is controlled by physiography, is clearly illustrated in the case of Limbe and Blantyre. Limbe lies on the main Shire Highlands crest that is exposed to the south-east, while Blantyre is situated in a valley some 4 to 5 miles to the west of Limbe; the dry season coefficient of variation at Limbe is 0·38, whereas that of Blantyre is 0·49.

The average annual coefficient of variation for Malawi as a whole is approximately 0·23, ranging from 0·17 to 0·31. In the Republic of South Africa the coefficient of variation appears to be lower in the high rainfall areas of the eastern seaboard, whereas in Southern Rhodesia the converse is the case, the higher rainfall areas having a higher coefficient of variation, a pattern also found in Malawi. Professor J. H. Wellington has drawn attention to this difference in reliability patterns and considers that if more information were available on the reliability of the great escarpment area of South Africa, more conformity with Southern Rhodesia and Malawi might be observed. The 'normal' pattern of rainfall reliability found in other parts of the world has been shown to be generally less for the lower rainfall areas, but it is possible that along the escarpment areas of the southern sub-continent the dominant effect of physiography may well outweigh the pattern found elsewhere. The coefficient of variation of annual rainfall in Southern Rhodesia has been shown to be of an average value of 0·28, which is some 0·05 higher than that found in Malawi. This is probably due to the latter's geographical position being nearer the east coast, and also well within the intertropical zone, whereas Southern Rhodesia is situated close to the southernmost limits of this zone.

Secular Changes in Rainfall

Throughout Southern Africa the secular fluctuation of rainfall has received considerable attention owing to its bearing upon land utilization and soil conservation. There have been many assertions that parts of the sub-continent were rapidly becoming a desert owing to a decreasing rainfall, but a closer examination of rainfall trends shows that these assertions are not borne out by the facts. In many areas there has in fact been an increase in rainfall over the past fifty years or so. That there has probably been a decrease in rainfall effectiveness, however, owing to traditional methods of cultivation and the associated destruction of vegetation, is generally agreed; in parts of Malawi considerable erosion has taken place with a consequent drying up of many streams, and has given rise to the belief that there has been a decrease in rainfall. In the Kasitu valley of the Mzimba district, for instance, there has been widespread erosion and desiccation, but rainfall records show that there has been an increase in average totals over the past thirty years in that area.

Values of five year progressive averages of rainfall from a number of long term stations in the country are shown in Fig. 22. These show, for the higher rainfall areas of Mlanje and Chinteche, an increase in average rainfall, particularly over the past two decades. On the other hand the Zomba and Fort Johnston records show a more or less steady fluctuation about the mean, although a long-term trend may be detected showing a decrease over the period 1920–45. This, it will be noted, is owing largely to the well-marked fluctuations during this period that are also apparent

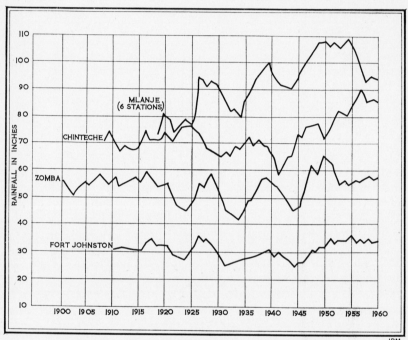

JRM.

Fig. 22.   Secular Change in Rainfall – Malawi
(5 Year Progressive Averages.)

in the record of the Mlanje stations. These periodicities appear to be confined to the years 1920–55 and are not discernible before or after this period. These fluctuations in average rainfall have received considerable attention in Malawi in relation to run-off and evaporation from Lake Nyasa and the consequent effect upon the hydrology of the Shire River. A relationship between lake level, inasmuch as it is affected by changes in rainfall, and sunspots, has been sought by a number of workers. Partial successes in these correlations have been confined to short periods but no marked relation has been proved to continue for a long period.[1]

While the causes of secular change in rainfall may be beyond complete understanding at the present time, what has occurred in Malawi over the past fifty years is of particular interest. The records from a great number of rainfall stations in the country show that the past

[1] For a discussion on the 'Lake level sunspot theory' see Chapter V, p.p. 115-6.

twenty-five years have been, on the average, wetter than the preceding twenty-five years. If this difference is but part of a longer periodicity we may perhaps expect rainfall to decrease within the next two decades, leading to drier conditions. When a possible decrease in rainfall amount is considered with the problem of a rising population on the land leading to a decrease in rainfall effectiveness, the need for the careful conservation of natural resources is vital if even the present rate of production is to be maintained.

Evapotranspiration and Rainfall Effectiveness

In a country where the greater part of the annual rainfall occurs over a period of five to six months, the effectiveness of rainfall, which is closely linked with evapotranspiration and surface run-off, is of the greatest importance to all forms of land utilization. The disposal of rainfall begins with its interception by vegetation, and when the interception capacity of the foliage is reached, further rain falls to the ground. The amount of interception, therefore, depends largely upon the type of vegetation and will vary according to such factors as rainfall intensity, leaf area, duration of fall, &c. Infiltration is the next stage in the process; the soil surface controls the rate of entry of the water into the soil, and this rate may be high if the surface is sandy, consists of humus or has a good crumb structure, whereas it will be low on hard, compacted surfaces. The rate of infiltration depends upon land utilization and it is at this stage that man usually exercises his influence. After the soil surface has been wetted, water moves through the soil profile by percolation, its rate dependent upon soil moisture, texture, and structure. The percolation rate may be greater than the infiltration rate but under good conditions it is usually less. If the rainfall intensity is equal to or less than the intake rate of the soil, then no surface run-off occurs. As water percolates through the soil profile, some is held in the soil particles and the maximum that can be held by any soil is known as the 'field capacity', and water in excess drains through the soil and replenishes the ground water reservoirs.

The water held in the soil is that which is made available to vegetation and ranges from field capacity, when the profile is saturated, to 'wilting point' where the available moisture is no longer able to supply water at a rate to sustain life. Research into the consumptive use of water by vegetation is at present being undertaken by the Agricultural Department and preliminary results of this work have been made available. This has shown marked variations under different crop rotation treatments and also the large amount of water removed by the indigenous vegetation when compared with that removed by crops. This may be directly related to the greater density and deeper root systems of indigenous vegetation and this can exert a harmful effect on the following season's crops if the rainfall happened to be poorly distributed during the season. This has been clearly demonstrated in semi-arid areas of Tanganyika where the rainfall distribution is erratic.

The soil moisture status under tea is an important factor in the need for conserving moisture during the protracted dry season, as drought conditions may often cause severe wilting or death of this plant. From soil moisture measurements carried out under tea plantations at Mlanje one of the most significant results to date has shown that by pruning tea early in the dry season, soon after the main rains, a considerable saving in moisture is effected. The normal practice was to prune in July and August when the least crop was available, and this led to delayed break-away and sunscorch of the unprotected framework of the bush during the latter part of the season. By early pruning recovery is facilitated and increased yields are obtained.

Over the past ten years the measurement of evaporation from open raised pans or tanks sited at a number of climatic stations has been undertaken, and at the end of 1961 there were thirty-three such stations in operation. The measured loss from these pans does not represent true evaporation from a free water surface and coefficients must be applied. Calculated potential open water surface evaporation rates for a number of stations in Malawi have been made by the Water Development Department. These estimates are based on the energy balance method devised by H. L. Penman, that successfully combines the meteorological factors of radiation, temperature, humidity, and wind. Besides providing more realistic estimates than those provided by pan readings alone, these have also served to determine coefficients for existing pans, which are found to vary from 0·6 to 1·2 during the course of the year, dependent upon season and location.

As is to be expected, the rain shadow areas of the country show the highest totals. The lowest values are found in the highlands in the southeast of the country or to the north-west of Lake Nyasa. The moderating influence of Lake Nyasa is apparent, there being a steady increase in evaporation to the west into Zambia as the climate becomes drier and more continental in character. Annual average potential evaporation totals range from about 50 inches on the higher mountains to over 80 inches in the hotter, drier areas of the rift valley and the rain shadow areas lying to the west of the main plateau.

Penman has shown that potential evapotranspiration, that is evaporation from the soil and transpiration through plants, is usually less than open water evaporation and may vary from 60 to 80 per cent. of the latter. This is caused mainly by the higher albedo of vegetation and the fact that vegetation does not transpire at night. Although this relationship is subject to some controversy, annual water loss from humid mountain catchments in Malawi, assumed to be equivalent to evapotranspiration, has been found to be approximately 80 per cent. of the calculated open water evaporation.

Climatic Regions

The general distribution, spatial and seasonal, of climatic factors will be apparent from the preceding discussion and four climatic regions are

recognizable. Thesefour divisions fall within Köppen's classification of
(a) Hot, dry steppe climate (*BShw*), (b) Warm, temperate climate
(*Cwah*), (c) Warm, moist, temperate climate (*Cwb*), and (d) Warm,
tropical, rain climate (*Aw*). A further classification of climate in Malawi
has been made applying the principles of C. W. Thornthwaite's
classification of climates. This is based upon a comparison of rainfall
with evapotranspiration estimates deduced from radiation, temperature, humidity, and wind records from individual stations, and therefore
takes all those factors affecting climate into account. This method requires the determination of a 'moisture index' and positive values are
shown for humid regions and negative values for arid regions, the index
zero separating the two. Climate classification on this basis confirms the
division of the country into four main regions and the following table
summarizes the characteristics of these four main regions.

TABLE VIII

Malawi Climatic Divisions

Köppen		Thornthwaite		Characteristics	Locality
Type	Classification	Moisture index	Type		
BShw	Hot, dry, steppe	− 30 to −60	Semi-arid to arid	Rainfall 25–32 inch Mean temp. over 70° F	Shire Valley, SW. Lake-shore Mzimba plain
Cwah	Warm, temperate	−15 to −30	Semi-arid to sub-humid	Rainfall 32–40 inch Mean temp. over 65° F	Medium plateau areas; Shire Highlands, Central and Northern Prov.
Cwb	Warm, temperate	Zero to +15	Sub-humid	Rainfall 40–60 inch Mean temp. over 60° F	Highland areas of Nyika, Vipya, Kirk Range, Dowa
Aw	Warm, tropical rain	Zero to +100	Humid	Rainfall over 60 inch Mean temp. over 70° F	Mlanje, Cholo and NW. Lake-shore

BIBLIOGRAPHY

Sir David Brunt, 'Climate and Human Comfort', *Proc. Roy. Inst. Gt. Britain*, Vol.
XXXIII, No. 151 (1950).

E. Frith, *Q.J. Roy. Met. Soc.*, Vol. LXVI, p. 363 (1940).

W. Fitzgerald, *Africa; A Regional Geography*, Methuen, London.

H. L. Penman, 'Natural Evaporation from Open Water, Bare Soil and Grass', *Proc.
Roy. Soc.*, London, A, 193 (1948).

H. C. Pereira, *et al.*, 'Water Conservation in Semi-Arid Tropical East Africa', *Emp.
Jour. Expt. Agric.*, 26 (1958).

——, *Annual Report. Water Development Dept.*, Nyasaland (1961).

J. G. Pike, 'Northern Nyasaland: A Regional Geographical Study with Special
Reference to Hydrography and Hydrology', Blantyre (1957).

——, 'Evaporation and Evapotranspiration in Nyasaland', *Prof. Paper No. 2, Water
Development Dept.*, Nyasaland (1962).

G. Riemerschmid, 'Climatic Strain in Human Beings as indicated by Cooling-Ball
Temperature Measurements in the Union of S.A.', *S.A. Med. Jour.*, 1941.

C. L. Robertson, 'Variability of Rhodesian Rainfall', *S.A. Jour. Sc.*, Vol. XXIV
(1927).

G

T. E. W. Schuman, and W. L. Hofmeyer, 'The Partition of a Region into Rainfall Districts', *Q.J. Roy. Met. Soc.*, Vol. LXIV (1938).

N. P. Sellick, 'Barometric Pressure and Weather in S. Rhodesia', *Rhod. and Nyasa. Met. Serv. Notes*, Series A, No. 1 (1953).

——, *Meteorological Report for S. Rhodesia, 1926*, G.P., Salisbury (1927).

J. Talbot-Edwards, 'The Zomba Cyclone', *Nyasa. Jour.*, Vol. 2 (1947).

A. E. Tetley, and J. G. Pike, 'Rainfall Characteristics in Nyasaland', *Prof. Paper No. 1, Water Development Dept.*, Nyasaland (1959).

C. W. Thornthwaite, 'An Approach toward a Rational Classification of Climate', *Geog. Review*, No. 38, pp. 55–94 (1948).

J. D. Torrance, 'A Review of Cyclones passing over, or near to, the South of Nyasaland', *Meteorological Notes No. A3, Fed. Met. Dept.*, Salisbury (1957).

J. H. Wellington, *Southern Africa*, Vol. I, p. 223, Cambridge (1955).

R. A. Wood, 'Determining Water Use of Vegetation in Nyasaland by Changes in Soil Moisture', *Nyasa. Far. & For.*, Vol. V, No. 1 (1959).

CHAPTER IV

SOILS AND VEGETATION

T HE soils of Malawi show a close resemblance to the nature
of the underlying parent rock, but the interactions of climate,
topography, age, soil drift, and location have all played their part
in the formation of the complex soil pattern of the country. The soils
may be divided into the following main groups:

(1) The red ferruginous soils or latosols of the plateau and montane
areas.
(2) The red, brown, yellow gritty clays.
(3) Brown soils.
(4) Colluvials.
(5) Alluvia.
(6) Kawinga grey sands.
(7) Hydromorphic soils.
(8) Black clays.
(9) Mopanosols.
(10) Dunes and Beaches.

The most commonly encountered soils fall into the red earth category, together with those soil types of different colour which are found
in catenary association. A catenary sequence is formed from the weathering of the rock on hills and watersheds, the soil being transported down
the slope to the valleys and deposited in bands of differing composition.
Thus the upper slopes of rocky hills are generally covered with soils of
recent formation, the older soils being washed downhill, the lighter particles being transported to the lowermost band of the catena. A familar
example of this may be seen on the edges of *dambos* where there is generally a zone of sand colonized by *napini* trees (*Terminalia sericea*). These
bands of soil or catena are repeated many times in a region giving rise
to a complex soil pattern.

Plateau Red and Yellow Red Soils (Latosols)

Found in catenary sequence over large areas of the plateau and most
commonly beneath those areas of continuous *Brachystegia–Julbernardia*
woodland are the red, yellow red, and grey soils. These soils are of
peneplain origin and, as a result, have become lighter in colour through
prolonged leaching, the indurated laterite in profile often being exposed on the surface wherever erosive forces have been particularly
active. These soils are mainly derived from the gneisses, schists, granulites, and syenites and coupled with their arrangement in catenae hetero-
geneous groups of soils occur in comparatively small areas resulting in

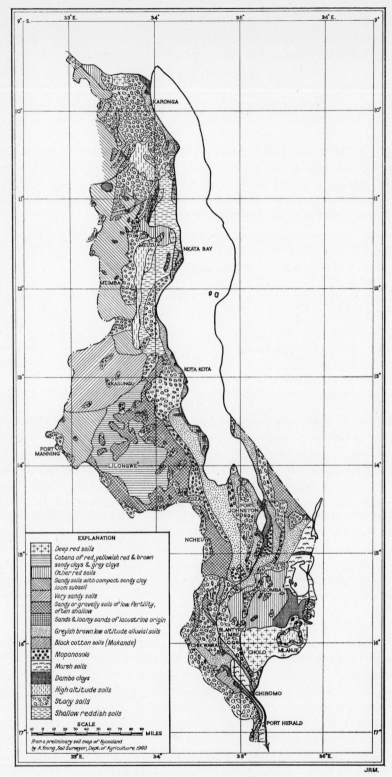

EXPLANATION

Deep red soils
Catena of red, yellowish red & brown sandy clays & grey clays
Other red soils
Sandy soils with compact sandy clay loam subsoil
Very sandy soils
Sandy or gravelly soils of low fertility, often shallow
Sands & loamy sands of lacustrine origin
Greyish brown low altitude alluvial soils
Black cotton soils (Makande)
Mopanosols
Marsh soils
Dambo clays
High altitude soils
Stony soils
Shallow reddish soils

SCALE
10 0 10 20 30 40 50 60 70 80 90
MILES

*From a preliminary soil map of Nyasaland
by A. Young, Soil Surveyor, Dept. of Agriculture 1960*

JRM.

Fig. 23.   The soils of Malawi.

necessarily patchy cultivation. Although these soils are generally poor plateau types they are cultivated on a comparatively large scale. Good groundnut production is possible from them but maize generally requires fertilizer and a high standard of cultivation. Where the underlying gneisses and granulites have been intruded by dolerite dyke swarms, the soils derived from the former are modified to a certain extent and are richer in minerals. The soils of the Cholo district of the Shire Highlands are an example of this type where there is evidence of a high phosphate and potash availability, these minerals being particularly important for the growth of tea, which is a high consumer of potash. In contrast are the latosols of the Vipya plateau near Mzuzu derived from the Basement rocks, with no dolerite dykes, where potassium and phosphate are appreciably lower.

Within the plateau areas, however, there are areas of fertile yellow to red sandy clay soils which are heavily cultivated and often distinguished by the presence of an *Acacia–Combretum–Piliostigma* vegetation. Soils of this type, probably derived from the graphitic schists and crystalline limestones of the Basement Complex, or where the topography has been rejuvenated, are found over a moderately large area to the north, east, and south of Lilongwe. Smaller areas are also found on the Chileka plain, on the Limbe–Zomba crest and to the north of Lake Chilwa. These soils produce a large proportion of the country's dark fired tobacco, maize, and groundnut crops.

Associated with these two main soil types of the plateau areas are two different catenary sequences. The following table sets out the two sequences as found in the two main vegetational areas:

TABLE IX

Catena Sequence of Soils—Plateau Areas

Brachystegia–Julbernardia Woodlands	*Acacia–Combretum–Piliostigma* Woodlands
1. Dark red or brown sandy clay loams	Red soils
2. Yellow red soils with a dark grey-brown sand clay loam surface	Yellow-red clay loams to sandy loams, massive in structure and well drained
3. Yellow-brown soils	Brown sandy clay loams marginal to semi-swamp and swamp soils, often associated with outcrops of indurated laterite
4. Grey sandy clays in *dambos*	Grey-black *dambo* soils

Of the *Brachystegia–Julbernardia* sequence the most commonly encountered are the yellow red soils which show a marked tendency to compaction on the surface to form crusts which interfere with water penetration and account for soils under natural vegetation being less moist after prolonged rain than those of adjacent cultivated lands. In the Kasungu area and in parts of the Fort Johnston district the yellow brown soils of this sequence are the most widespread and are dark, grey-ish brown loams over yellowish brown sandy clay with a distinct red mottling that increases with depth. On drying these soils lose their bright colour and become lighter, dusty, and more pastel in shade. This gives rise to the typical 'sand veldt' country of the Kasungu district. In the Acacia–Combretum–Piliostigma woodland the most commonly en-countered soils of this sequence are the yellow red clay loams to sandy loams, which are massive, well drained, and highly fertile.

The red soils of the Mlanje, Cholo, Dowa, Mzuzu, Misuku, Living-stonia, Ncheu, and Dedza highland areas have many features in common with the plateau red earths although in these montane red soils a dis-tinct structure consisting of pellet-like accretions in the soil has been de-tected. These soils carry a tall Brachystegia–Uapaca woodland, often with evergreen elements. The soils of the high montane areas tend to be paler in colour, more friable and leached. This is particularly so on the higher levels of the Nyika plateau where the soils are derived mainly from granites and are not suited to cultivation.

The Red-Brown and Yellow Gritty Clays

These soils are found throughout the country but are limited in ex-tent. There are good examples in the Bwanje Valley, Balaka area, and in the Nkamanga Plain area of the Northern Province. At the surface the soils are dark yellowish brown, coarse, sandy loams and in the sub-soil reddish-brown, gritty clay loams. The main feature of these soils is the tendency to erode easily and they often demonstrate 'bad-land' gullying in areas of appropriate topography. In catenary association with these soils there are more yellow brown to brown clays with a faint red mottle in the sub-soil.

Brown Soils

In a limited number of localities a very distinct soil type is en-countered with a uniform brown clay loam sub-soil and a dark greyish-brown clay loam surface. The profile is featureless but a close examina-tion by hand reveals soft, $\frac{1}{4}$-inch aggregates of soil in the profile. In catenary sequence with this type are soils with concretions at depth, which appear to be related to the soft concretions of the former type but are much more solid, distinct, and yellow-brown in colour.

Both these types have high phosphate reserves and are typical of the well cultivated Dedza highlands where they are deep, well drained, and of a good structure. Associated with these strong, brown soils are rela-tively shallow soils which overlie indurated laterite or have a loose pea-iron horizon. The laterite occurs at varying depths and the pea-iron horizon may represent a decomposing indurated horizon. The profiles are often mottled and there are indications that the indurated laterite in packed pea-iron reduces soil permeability.

Colluvials

In a country as hilly as Malawi, with a long history of earth movements, colluvial soils of various types are widespread. In the Shire Valley
and at the foot of the main escarpments of the country, soils of this type
are extensive. Textures vary greatly but the soils are generally related by
a common grey-brown to brown coloration. These soils are often very
deep and textures vary within the profile. Those found in the Bwanje
valley are very fertile and vary from sandy clay loams to sandy loams.
In the Fort Johnston area, however, they are of a sandy nature with
some clay, which tends to cement and become intractable. Vegetation
on these soils ranges from *Julbernardia–Burkea* woodland to thicket and
standard, this latter type of vegetation being most prevalent.

In the category of colluvial soils fall the *dambo*-head sands which occur
throughout the medium plateau areas at the head of *dambos*. These invariably deep sands are the result of erosion from the watersheds, the
coarse grains in suspension having been deposited at the head while the
finer grains have been carried farther downstream. These '*dambo*-head'
sands are pale in colour, either grey or light greyish-brown, often mottled
at depth, with angular irregular concretions where there is a tendency
to waterlogging. In certain areas, notably Kasungu, where lateritic
type soils predominate, the sand wash soils are also a feature of the
dambo margins as well as the heads. Also found in the plateau areas are
sands over clay that are characterized by a distinct break in texture in the
profile from loamy sand to sandy clay or clay. This phenomenon, caused
by drift and wash, gives rise to peculiar water conditions in these soils as
the heavy layers tend to resist water percolation and, as a result, the
sand becomes waterlogged early in the rainy season. This type of *dambo*
is most commonly found in the Central and Northern Provinces. Occasionally red soil drifts over black swamp clay giving rise to a red sandy
clay loam over black clay and this is usually found where red soils on
fairly steep slopes adjoin a much flatter valley bottom. There are good
examples of this double profile in the Ncheu district.

Alluvia

In parts of the lake littoral and the Shire Valley, the rivers draining
the plateau areas have laid down alluvia in narrow fluvial zones. Also
in certain parts of the plateau alluvium is found under similar conditions,
notably in the Nkamanga plain and Henga valley fringing the South
Rukuru river and along the course of the Bua river farther south. These
alluvial soils, usually characterized by the large *nsangu* tree (*Faidherbia
albida*), are highly fertile and, as a result, densely populated. In tone the
soils are grey-brown, the profiles showing marked stratification with a
variation in texture from pebbly sands to silty clays, often with a great
deal of apparent muscovite mica.

In addition to these areas of alluvia there are at present soils being
laid down around the margins of Lake Chilwa and in the Elephant

Marsh. These very young alluvial soils show very little profile development and are also highly fertile.

Kawinga Grey Sands

This name has been given for the soils of probable diluvial origin of the plain fringing the Lake Chilwa swamps, being typically developed in the area of Kawinga. They have also since been recognized in the Kota Kota and Salima lake littoral areas and are normally characterized by napini (*Terminalia sericea*) woodlands. The soils, although no longer seasonal swamp soils, retain the profile characteristics of such soils and, to a certain degree, do become waterlogged in the rains. In texture the soils are grey, loamy sands on the surface becoming heavier with a gradual development of mottle in depth. The colour variation appears as a strong brown fine mottle with a few black-centred spots; the brown mottles gradually become larger and the black nodules increase in size until the mottles fuse to give a pattern of strong brown and grey-pink.

Hydromorphic Soils

Into this category fall the soils of the *dambo* systems in the plateaux catenae. They are sands impregnated with clay, grey in colour with mottle developing at depth. The mottle is immediately apparent beneath the topsoil of humus stained sand as brown flecks in the grey. Pea-iron nodules and irregular concretions, sharp and angular, with black centres and distinct sand grains, are found at depth. There is a marked increase in clay content with depth in the above soil and with progress along the *dambo* towards the main river system there is an increase in soil heaviness until one has, in the *dambo* bottoms, a very dark clay overlying a grey clay with a distinct fine olive brown mottling and often with calcium carbonate accumulation at depth. In parts of the lake littoral where there are excessive amounts of sodium salts, the grey clays become very intractable and on drying crack into large angular shiny surfaced blocks. Often the cracks have sand washed or blown into them and this can be detected well below the surface.

Black Clays

Black clays occur in two main areas in Malawi; in the Chilwa–Tamanda plain and in the Ngabu area of the Chikwawa district. These soils are often referred to as 'black cotton soils' or margalitic clays (*makande*), similar in many respects to the *regur* of India. This type of clay forms under conditions of high alkalinity; in the Lake Chilwa area by the endoreic drainage system and in the Ngabu area from the underlying basaltic lavas (Stormberg lavas). Normally, therefore, these black clays are only found in *dambo* areas in the former locality but in the Ngabu area they are not so restricted. The common factor of these clays is their montmorillonite content which causes them to dry out and crack, resulting in the phenomenon of self-ploughing and self-mulching.

Into these cracks are swept or blown the clay crumbs of the surface which, on wetting, swell at the same time as the body of the soil, so causing a heaving action. This self-ploughing action will often give rise to a microtopography known as 'crab-holes' or *gilghais*. Unless tilled very soon after the onset of the rains these soils become extremely sticky and difficult to work. Such areas are usually extensively cultivated, principally under cotton, the Ngabu area producing the greater part of the country's crop.

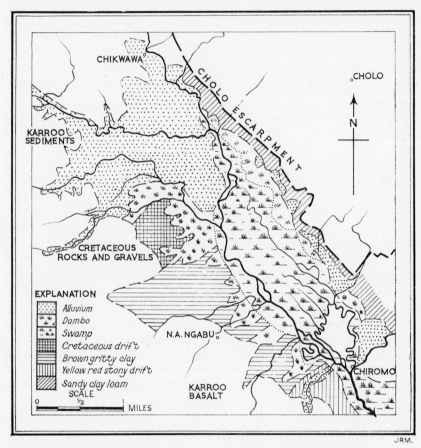

Fig. 24.   Drift and soil map of Lower Shire Valley.

Mopanosols

This term is a convenient one given to those soils which carry an almost exclusive *mopane* (*Colophospernum mopane*) vegetation found in many of the warm, drier areas of the country. Two main types of mopanosol have been recognized in Malawi as (1) Ridge, and (2) Relic land surface. The ridge mopanosols occur in the lower Shire area where mopane woodland occurs on ridges in the low hills to the west. The soils are alkaline and have been described as 'shallow sands to gravelling sands, ill drained in the early rains'. In the upper Shire valley the *mopane*

woodland appears to occupy relics of an old land surface and there
is a clear dissection pattern to be observed by examining the air photographs of this region. The *mopane* is on the higher lying portions, on
sands to sandy loams which cement in the dry and puddle in the wet
season. The sub-soil contains calcium carbonate concretions and the
profiles show distinct mottling and small black concretions. In the glades
between the mopane the soils become heavier and carry either grassland
or *Acacia–Combretum* vegetation in complete contrast to the mopane.
These glades may, on the one hand, be highly saline with a salt efflor-
escence on the surface, but, if well drained, can be fertile, and are
cultivated.

Dunes and Beaches

There is a distinct sandy beach or dune to Lake Nyasa in many places,
particularly along the Salima, Kota Kota, and Karonga lake-shore.
These beaches often overlie fossil soils which continue into the lake and
are usually covered in dense *bango* reed (*Phragmites mauritianus*). At
higher elevations on the Lake Nyasa littoral and surrounding Lake
Chilwa, fossil sand beaches or terraces up to levels of 160 feet and
115 feet above the present lake level respectively have been identified.[1]

SOIL NUTRIENTS

By African standards, Malawi soils are generally regarded as fertile, although their nutrient status shows wide differences. In general it
may be said that the soils of the southern part of the country are more
fertile than those of the northern part of the country.The higher potassium
and potash content in southern Malawi is undoubtedly the result of
the underlying Moçambique series of gneisses, granulites, and crystalline limestones with dolerite dyke swarms. Potassium is derived chiefly
from orthoclase felspar which is an abundant mineral of the igneous
rocks, and phosphate is probably derived from the crystalline limestones
or such minerals as apatite also found in igneous rocks. In the northern
areas of the country the basement rocks of the Mafingi system are made
up of quartzites and schists, the crystalline limestone and dolerite dykes
being usually absent.

Representative Malawi soils have been analysed and the table on
page 91 compiled from these data shows the relative nutrient status of
these soils.

It clearly shows the differences in availability of nutrients between
the southern and northern areas. Although organic carbon is sufficient
in most areas the loam sands of the Kasungu area show a deficiency,
due possibly to the poor humic content of these soils.

VEGETATION

Very little of the vegetation in Malawi is in its natural state. With
a density of population higher than in any other country of the

[1] See Chapter II.

TABLE X
Soil Nutrient Status of Some Representative Malawi Soils

Locality	Organic Carbon	Total Nitrogen	Potassium	Phosphate	Soil types
Cholo Highlands	High	Medium	Medium	High	Red latosol
Tuchila	Medium	Medium	Very high	Medium	Clay loam
Lake Chilwa	High	Medium	High	High	Black clay
Lilongwe	Medium	Medium	Low	Low	Sand loam
Kasungu	Low	Low	Medium	Medium	Loamy sands
Vipya	Medium	Low	Low	Low	Latosol series
Mzimba	Medium	Low	Low	Low	Loamy sand with quartz

Classification	Low	Medium	High
Organic Carbon %	Less 1	1–2	Over 2
Nitrogen %	Less 0·1	0·1–0·2	Over 0·2
Potassium per 100 grs.	Less 0·4	0·4–0·8	Over 0·9
Phosphate p.p.m.	Less 15	15–40	Over 40

woodland savannah areas of southern Africa, the demands for subsistence agriculture and pastoralism have repeatedly disturbed the natural vegetation to a greater degree than is found in adjacent territories.

Subsistence agriculture by primitive hand methods on shifting plots is carried out on woodland or the drier forest soils wherever rainfall is adequate. Densely populated areas have, as a result, been largely cleared of timber. The soil in many areas is steadily becoming impoverished and eroded so that vegetation has difficulty in reasserting itself. In sparsely settled areas woodland is often re-established between periods of cultivation, but even here it is many years before the earlier ecological complex is restored. P. Topham, writing in 1936, stated that some 90 per cent. of the woodland area of Malawi bore signs of having been cultivated by the indigenous peoples at some time or other. This high proportion is questionable as more than 10 per cent. of the area of the country is unsuitable for cultivation owing to infertile soils, steep escarpments, or to the lack of water. Nevertheless, while this proportion is open to question, there is no doubt that a very large percentage of the arable land of Malawi has been or is under cultivation.

VEGETATION PATTERN

Malawi's vegetation pattern is comparable with the diversities of topography, geology, climate, and soils in the country, and may be said to consist of (1) Mixed savannah woodlands, (2) *Brachystegia–Julbernardia* woodlands, (3) *Combretum–Acacia–Piliostigma* woodlands, and (4) Montane forests and grasslands. For this purpose it would be convenient to consider the vegetation under these four main headings.

Mixed Savannah

In the mixed savannah the tree, thicket, and grass types are varied, there being no dominant species except in special localized areas. As in all savannah types the woodland may vary from open woodland to closed forest. An increase in available soil moisture along the streams or changes in soil will bring in isolated closed forest areas within the prevailing woodlands. The mixed savannah in Malawi occurs over the drier parts of the country and covers the greater part of the Shire valley, the southern lake-shore, Bwanje valley, Salima lake-shore, the fringes of the Lake Chilwa swamps, in the Lake Kazuni area of Mzimba, and along the Karonga lake-shore plain.

These woodlands are dominated by species of *Acacia, Adansonia, Cordyla, Sterculia, Ostryoderris, Pterocarpus, Sclerocarya, Terminalia* and thickets of *Grewia* and *Popewia*, and *Hyphaene* and *Borassus* palms. Within this mixed savannah there are variations dependent upon climate and soil moisture and in the drier areas the predominant trees consist of various species of *Acacia, Cordyla, Sterculia*, the baobab (*Adansonia digitata*), and stands of *mopane* (*Colophospermum mopane*). In the moister areas the most common species are broad-leaved deciduous trees such as the *ntondo-woko* (*Sclerocarya birrea*), various species of *Pterocarpus* (Mlombwa), the pod mahogany or *mkongomwa* (*Afzelia quanzenzis*), and the Ilala (*Hyphaene ventricosa*) and palmyra or *mvumo* (*Borassus aethiopum*) palms in the river valleys.

Five different vegetation types within the mixed savannah are recognizable, the distribution of which depend mainly upon climatic and soil factors. These are (1) Mixed escarpment-foothill woodlands, (2) Lowlands, lake and river plains, woodlands, thickets, scrubs, and parklands, (3) *Mopane* woodlands, (4) Alluvia parklands, and (5) *Terminalia* woodlands.

The mixed escarpment-foothill woodlands are, as the name suggests, confined to the steep, sometimes stony and shallow escarpments of the Shire Valley and the lake-shore as far north as Kota Kota. These woodlands are dominated by thickets of *Grewia* spp. (tensa)[1], *Hymenocardia, Caparia* and *Popowia obovata* (kombe) together with baobab, *Sclerocarya birrea* (mtondowoko), *Kirkia accuminata* (mtumbu), *Sterculia quinqueloba* (nsetanyani) as standards. In the foothill forests under moister conditions such as those found on the lower slopes of Nchisi and the eastern slopes of the northern Kirk range bamboo brakes (*Oxytenanthera abyssinica*) (nsungwi) occur. Bamboo is also found in drier areas associated with termite mounds and in many localities there is evidence that it occupies the site of former ever-green forest in low montane conditions. Associated with syenitic rocks are forests of *Brachystegia bussei* (mtwana) which are usually characteristic of low-lying slopes with stony eroded soil and sparse grass.

The 'lowlands, lake and river plains, woodlands, thickets, scrubs, and parklands' of the rift valley are confined to the relatively more infertile

[1] Chinyanja names in parentheses.

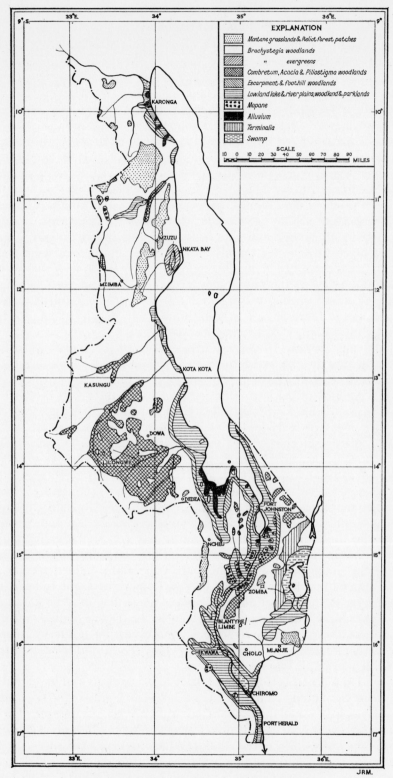

EXPLANATION

Montane grasslands & Relict forest patches
Brachystegia woodlands
"   evergreens
Combretum, Acacia & Piliostigma woodlands
Escarpment & foothill woodlands
Lowland lake & river plains, woodland & parklands
Mopane
Alluvium
Terminalia
Swamp

SCALE
10 0 10 20 30 40 50 60 70 80 90
MILES

KARONGA

MZUZU
NKATA BAY
MZIMBA

KOTA KOTA

KASUNGU

DOWA
LILONGWE

DEDZA
FORT
JOHNSTON

NCHEU

ZOMBA

BLANTYRE
LIMBE

CHIKWAWA
CHOLO   MLANJE

TCHIROMO

PORT HERALD

JRM.

Fig. 25. Natural vegetation types in Malawi.

tracts of coarse colluvial deposits and shallow soils of the Shire valley and the lake shore. Large areas have, however, been opened out for agriculture, the more fertile parts growing cotton and millets. The vegetation is characterized by *Adansonia digitata* (baobab), *Kirkia accuminata* (mtumbu), *Sterculia appendiculata* (njale) *S. africana* (mgosa), *Combretum imberbe* (mnangali), *Cordyla africana* (mtondo) with *Hyphaene* and *Borassus* palms. In areas of good colluvial soils, notably in the Lower Shire Valley, the main constituents of the woodland have been cleared for cultivation and over extensive areas only large trees such as *njale* and *mgosa* remain.

In the lower, drier, and warmer areas of the Shire Valley and in the Luwewe valley of the Mzimba area, occur almost pure stands of *mopane* (*Colophospermum mopane*) woodlands. The *mopane* or *tsanya* tree, usually associated with baobab and indicating a low atmospheric humidity and high temperature, occurs mainly on neutral or slightly acid soils overlying a compacted heavy alkaline soil, and the grass cover is characteristically dominated by *Setaria* spp. (nsenzi). Unlike most of the other mixed savannah species it can live in soils that are temporarily waterlogged, but it develops best on well-drained soils, when it may grow to about 60 feet high, with a bole 4 feet in diameter.

Then ame *mopane* is derived from the southern Bantu word for butterfly after the characteristic shaped bilobed leaves which turn their edges to the sun. For this reason *mopane* forests provide very little shade during the heat of the day. When grass is scarce the leaves of the tree provide a valuable food for game and cattle, which, although they do not form a complete feed, are rich in protein and phosphorous.

The 'alluvial parklands' are usually characterized by two species; the large spreading *nsangu* (*Faidherbia albida*) and the *mtondo* (*Cordyle africana*), although associated species such as *Albizia versicolor* (ntangatanga), and the 'sausage tree' or mvunguti (*Kigelia aethiopica*) are also found. *F. albida* has deep root suckers and is a reliable indicator of fertile light alluvium that is found mainly in the rift valley areas fringing the main rivers. Normally these areas are heavily cultivated and the woodland has largely disappeared with the exception of the *nsangu* tree, normally retained for shade purposes. A number of the above-named species of these alluvial parklands near the lake are important to the indigenous peoples for the supply of dug-out canoes. Thus they may be found in the Upper Shire Valley, more extensively in the Bwanje Valley and the Ntakataka area and on the riverine deposits occurring at intervals along the Karonga lake-shore plain, notably along the littoral courses of the North Rukuru and Wovwe Rivers.

Found in a broad belt fringing Lake Chilwa swamps and in scattered stands in the Salima and Kota Kota lake-shore areas are *Terminalia sericea* (napini) woodlands associated with *Brachystegia boehmii*. These woodlands occur gregariously on sandy soils and sand bars are colonized by it in the Lake Chilwa area. This tree, like *Acacia*, is a colonizer, grows fast and is hardy, and within a few years controls the grass which may grow under it. The venerable appearance of many *napini* is often misleading as it may represent a mere twenty years' growth. In the Lake Chilwa area, the *napini* woodland appears to be associated also with a change in rainfall and temperature found in this area.

The grasses of the mixed savannah community are usually tall, reedy grasses similar in many respects to those found in the more fertile parts of the plateau areas. On the lighter soils and in all regenerating old gardens, particularly in the Lower Shire, *Urochloa mossambicensis* (kalembalebale) and *Panicum maximum* (pokopoko) are found. On the heavier soils a *Setaria* spp. (nsenzi), *Ischaemum brachyatherum* (njogo), *Hyparrhenia* complex is found. *Njogo* grass is commonly found in *Acacia* woodlands and is an indicator of 'black cotton soils'.

The Brachystegia–Julbernardia Woodlands[1]

The most widespread vegetational type in Malawi is more or less open *Brachystegia–Julbernardia* woodland with a moderately dense grass cover. This woodland community is represented by a score of trees and, as a woodland type, is quite distinctive, keeping its leaves until the new ones nearly burst, which, during the first week, are a brilliant crimson and present a pleasing aspect. This woodland characteristically occupies all the infertile leached plateau and escarpment sites up to an altitude of approximately 5,000 to 6,000 feet, except where the rainfall is exceptionally high or well distributed and in the seasonally waterlogged depressions or *dambos* where the grassland is of a climax type. It varies appreciably in luxuriance and floristic composition according to local factors such as rainfall, altitude, drainage, soil fertility, and previous history of the site.

The plateau sites have for the most part, poor, shallow residual soils which are undergoing secular erosion and degradation, in places greatly accelerated by human mismanagement. They support a poor but distinctive woody flora in which the species *Brachystegia*, *Julbernardia*, *Uapaca*, and *Monotes* play the most important part. In southern and central Malawi these woodlands are more or less confined to the plateau areas above 2,000 feet, but north of Kota Kota they descend to lake level under the influence of a higher rainfall. Near Chinteche, where the mean annual rainfall exceeds 80 inches, it is luxuriant, and this area has been recognized as 'evergreen *Brachystegia*'. These forests are quite dense with trees reaching to 60 feet in places and with a shrubby layer of *Landolphia* (mpira) climbers which, in former years, was an economic source of rubber. Elsewhere, on steep and rocky escarpments where the rainfall is moderately heavy, the woodland is dominated by such species as *B.* boehmii, *B. microphylla*, *B. alleni* (nguti), *B. manga* (ntakata),

---

[1] Previously the term *Brachystegia-Pseudoberlinia* has been used rather indiscriminately by ecologists to describe the codominants of this woodland, but Leonard (1927): *Mem. Sci. Acad. Roy. Belg.* XXX (2) has confirmed *Julbernardia* after a new delimitation of this genus and other related genera, based on pollen and seeding studies. Thus, whenever *Brachystegia–Pseudoberlinia* woodland is mentioned in the text, this should be taken to read *Julbernardia* in place of *Pseudoberlinia* and similarly it replaces *Isoberlinia* referred to by some authors. (See J. Phillips, *Agriculture and Ecology in Africa*, Faber & Faber, London, 1959.)

B. floribunda (msumbuti), *B. spiciformus* (chumbe) and *Julbernardia globiflora* (mchenga) which probably represent the true climax, or at least one which has not been much altered by human interference.

Throughout the *Brachystegia–Julbernardia* woodlands there are various groups of types associated with soil conditions, and when the soils are arranged in a catenary sequence abrupt changes are recognizable. Characteristic of the leached quartz sand on hills are *Uapaca kirkiana* (msuku) and *B. floribunda* (msumbuti). *Uapaca* is often gregarious, particularly on the poorer sands of the westerly plateau which overlie pans of ironstone concretions. It is to be found also on many ledges on steep escarpment faces where there still remains a surface drift of quartz not yet eroded away. In some regions then, it denotes useless soil; elsewhere, on younger soils it is unstable and gives place, after fire protection, to seedlings of *Bridelia* (msopa). Associated with *Uapaca* but more deeply rooted are *B. floribunda*. On the next soil zone down the slope *B. longifolia* (mombo), *Faurea saligna* (mseje) and *Monotes* spp. (mkakatuku) are found and denote soil of poor fertility, although in the Dedza area this type may extend down the slope to more fertile soil. Within the next soil zone of the catena, and typically on steep slopes where the soil may be naturally fertile but fragile, are *B. boehmii* and *Julbernardia globiflora* (mchenga) with associated species such as *B. appendiculata, Crossopteryx febrifuga* (dangwe) in dry areas and *Uapaca nitida* (msokolwe) in moister areas.

Throughout the *Brachystegia* woodlands the grass cover is often low, very sparse and dominated by the genera *Hyparrhenia, Andropogon, Digitaria, Setaria, Panicum,* and *Brachiaria*. The grasses show an apparent change in dominance of species with the advance of the season, there being a marked spring, mid-season, and full summer phase due to the fact that the grasses making up the sward have different flowering periods. The first to flower are *Setaria sphacelata* and *Digitaria setivalva* followed in mid-season by *Andropogon schirensis* and the summer phase is characterized by the very typical reedy *Hyparrhenia* spp. and with *Bewsia biflora* often conspicuous.

The Combretum–Acacia–Piliostigma Woodlands

On the plateau sites there are isolated areas of fertile soils evident in areas of rejuvenation and along some of the major valleys. These areas are characterized by a distinctive vegetation of *Combretum–Acacia–Piliostigma* woodland dominated by such species as *Combretum album* (chinama), *C. gazense* (kakunguni), *C. mechowianum* (naltenjere), *Acacia campylecantha* (mtete), *Piliostigma thonningi, Pterocarpus angolensis* (mlombwa, the mukwa of Southern Rhodesia and kiaat of South Africa) and *P. rotundifolous* (mbalisa).

The most extensive tract of this type of vegetation occurs in the Central Province along the Bua valley and southwards in a broad crescent towards Lilongwe, covering some 3,000 square miles. This vegetational type also occurs in the Henga valley, near Katumbi and in an area to the north of Lake Chilwa and in the northern section of the Chileka plain.

These areas are extensively cultivated and produce the greater part of the country's dark-fired tobacco crop. As a result of this intensive cultivation, large areas have been cleared of the constituent species with only large trees remaining. On some of the stonier residual eroded soils *Acacia macrothyrsa* (nafungwe) and *C. gueinzii* are frequent. On fairly permeable soils are found *Albizzia versicolor* (ntangatanga). Wherever there is a surface layer of drift soil to a depth of 18 inches or more, *Acacia campylecantha* is a most vigorous tree. Though generally an indicator of good agricultural land, it is surface rooted and for this reason cannot be relied upon as a sure guide.

Owing to intensive cultivation, grass cover in these woodlands is patchy but normally of the tall, reedy type dominated by the same genera of the *Brachystegia–Julbernardia* woodlands. They are often tall, generally coarse and reedy grasses and although they may reach over 9 feet in height, the ground cover is very low and heavy grazing is not possible for long periods. The seasonal succession is much the same as for the *Brachystegia–Julbernardia* woodlands except that *Panicum maximum* appears to be the most dominant grass during the mid-season phase.

Dambo Vegetation

On the plateau surfaces the monotony of the woodland is broken by broad, grass covered drainage lines, waterlogged during the rainy season and known in Malawi as *dambos*. Dambos are covered with short grassland in which geophytes and other herbs are numerous. The physiognomy of this type is similar to the 'watershed grasslands' of the Congo–Zambezi watershed and like them may be an edaphic climax type. The dominating grasses vary considerably but are generally *Hyparrhenia* types associated with clay; *Arundinellae* types with sand, *Chloris gayana* and *Ischaemum brachyatherum* with black and saline soils. *C. gayana* (kolambinzi or Rhodes Grass) is a valuable grass for temporary leys as it sets copious quantities of good viable seed, although with local strains seed setting and ripening takes place over a protracted period and good seed requires hand picking.

Montane Vegetation

The montane areas above 5,000 to 6,000 feet in Malawi support a flora and vegetation that has little in common with the miombo[1] woodland of the plateau areas and are characterized by open montane grasslands interspersed with relatively small patches of evergreen forest.

The most extensive grasslands in the country are those of the Nyika plateau where they cover an area of some 400,000 acres. Most of the landscape on these high plateaux is dominated by a herbaceous vegetation which, over large areas, is almost pure grassland. Within this

---

[1] *Brachystegia-Julbernardia* woodlands.

patches of low, seasonally yellow flowered, *Helichyrysum* scrub or very open woodlands with small widely spaced *Protea* may be found. The dominant species in these grasslands are *Loudetia simplex, Exotheca abyssinica* and *Andropogon schirensis*. Many opinions have been expressed as to the status of the montane grasslands but few are supported by careful investigation. It is assumed that much of the grassland is secondary and owes its origin to the destruction of the forest by fire. At the edges of the surviving patches of forest, evidence of their recent diminution through fire and subsequent replacement by tall *Hyparrhenia* grassland can often be found, and most of the taller grasslands have probably originated in this way.

The primary montane forests of the highland areas of Mlanje, Zomba, Cholo, Nchisi, Vipya, Nyika, and Misuku are usually found in small patches at the heads of valleys, on the edges of the plateau rims and frequently on the crests of ridges. These remnant forests are often rich in timber species such as *Widdringtonia whytei* (Mlanje cedar), *Parinari excelsa* (muula) *Syzygium guineense* s. spp. *afromontanum, Podocarpus milanjianus* (*nkanguni*), *Entandrophragma stolzii* (mukarikari), *Albizia gummifera* (mtangatanga), *Ficalhoa laurifolia* (mlunganya), and, very locally on the Nyika only, *Juniperus procera* (mlanji).

It is interesting to note that *Widdringtonia*, which occurs in relic patches along the eastern part of southern Africa, reaches its extreme northern limit of natural distribution on Mlanje mountain. Similarly, the small remnant forest of *Juniperus procera* in the Uyagaya valley of the eastern Nyika represents the extreme southerly limit of the distribution of this species. The Mlanje cedar is the most outstanding tree of Mlanje mountain, and is approached in size only by *Podocarpus milanjianus*, a less common conifer of the forests. Old Mlanje cedars may be over 100 feet tall and their straight trunks coated with a very thick fibrous bark, attaining 6 feet in diameter at the base. They tend to dominate the forest in pure stands on the sides of ravines or steep slopes; in more open country they form a conspicuous super-canopy thrusting grey boles and lichen-draped crowns well above the mixed stands of broad-leaved trees that form the actual canopy of the forest. The broad-leaved trees, thick of stem in proportion to their height of 30 to 60 feet, form a canopy so dense that on dull days visibility under it is normally too poor for details of the tree tops to be made out.

Swamp Vegetation

In areas adjacent to Lake Nyasa there are numerous swamps and lagoons held back from the Lake by ridges of resistant rocks lying parallel to the shore. These exhibit a typical swamp vegetation. South of Lake Nyasa the most extensive swamps are those associated with the Shire River in its lower reaches, e.g. the Elephant Marsh, and the fringes of shallow Lake Chilwa. Half of its area of 1,000 square miles is covered in vegetation which may be classified in three broad groups:

(1) Tall reed or sedges.
(2) Floating mats or sudd.
(3) Open lagoon communities of bottom rooted or free-floating aquatics.

There are three species of reed, *Typha australis*, *Phragmites mauritianus* (bango) and *Cyperus papyrus*, making up the bulk of this vegetation, though the latter is found only in small scattered clumps. The sudd, confined mainly to the Elephant Marsh and Lake Chilwa, is composed of tall mats of grasses *Vossia cuspidata* (duvi or hippo grass) and *Echinochloa* spp. (ndanga). These originate around the margins of lagoons tending to become detached, so floating into the main stream or open lake. On the seasonally dry land and fringes of the swamps sedge mats occur of which the main constituents are *cyperus* spp. and the 'Shire cabbage' or kakombwe (*Pistia stratiotes*). The open lagoons and lake areas very often support a dense aquatic vegetation of which the commonest plants are *Nymphaea lotus*, *Pistia*, and the floating fern *Azolla*. Very often, particularly in parts of the Elephant Marsh, these plants become so thick that it is impossible to force a boat through them.

Around the edges of many marshes, lagoons, and seasonally flooded land occur *Hyphaene* spp. parklands with the superficially similar species of *Borassus* palm. In the Elephant Marsh these palms often occur on islands. They are often pollarded for the making of palm wine.[1] The young *Hyphaene* palms are utilized for the making of mats.

VEGETATION PROBLEMS

An outline of certain problems for agriculture presented by the natural vegetation is necessary to an understanding of the hazards and potential of agricultural development. Malawi possesses relatively few indigenous plants of outstanding economic value. While there are certainly valuable indigenous cereals, roots, tubers, grasses, and fruits, agricultural production and subsistence depend for the most part on exotics.

The more important kinds of indigenous food, commodity and economic plants are: Cereals, such as millets (*Pennisetum*, *Eleusine*) and rice; numerous pulses, among them the valuable pigeon pea, *Cajanus*; watermelon (*Colocynthis citrullus*); certain gums and resins (*Acacia*, *Commiphora*) and yielders of rubber (*Landolphia*); a small number of hardwood timbers such as mlombwa (*Pterocarpus angolensis*) and mbawa (*Khaya nyasica*) and limited amounts of coniferous *Podocarpus*, *Juniperus*, and *Widdringtonia* as sources of soft woods. Some of these and various other indigenous species are invaluable in a subsistence economy, and some are of potential use for the development of better varieties for both subsistence and commercial production. However, it is to a very limited number, notably sorghum, the more promising indigenous strains of rice and a few timbers, that progressive agriculture and forestry can

---

[1] This kills the palm, and is more wasteful than the West African practice of tapping the tree at the top of the trunk.

look. On the other hand, exotic plants such as maize, cassava, bananas, tea, coffee, groundnuts, tobacco, and cotton have proved their value in the present economy and it is in these exotic plants that the future of agriculture lies.

The Nature and Origin of the Brachystegia–Julbernardia Woodlands

When viewed superficially, much of the plateau *Brachystegia* woodland has a uniform appearance but closer examination reveals that the most outstanding feature of these woodlands is their great diversity. One may repeatedly pass through relatively dense small pole stands into open stands of old trees with little or no reproduction. The composition may change from pure stands of a single species into complexes of many species. This paradox of inconsistency of composition, age, and condition from one stand to another, provides the clue to the origin of these woodlands. They do not constitute a natural forest vegetation. Rather they are the result of fire and the repeated clearing under shifting agriculture. For each clearing has its own individual history that has determined the appearance of the present regenerated tree cover. Early clearings were cultivated for different periods of time in different degrees. Some gardens, favourably sited with regard to climate and soil, were repeatedly cultivated, while others less favourable may only have been cultivated once or twice in the last century.

Next to shifting agriculture and fire, these woodlands have been further modified, at least during modern times, by the constant collection of small wood products essential in the daily life of the African people. For hut poles, for example, only the best and straightest are taken and woodland areas adjacent to heavily settled areas are characterized by the absence of straight stemmed trees. It is possible that some five to eight million poles are removed annually for this purpose alone in Malawi. Other practices, such as the stripping of bark for string, have resulted in stunted and crippled trees of the desired species over hundreds of acres.

Cattle also generate vegetation problems, foremost being the sensitivity of the apparently robust grass pasturage to continued heavy trampling, leading to the replacement of the more palatable and nutritious grasses by inferior ones. In over-stocked woodland an intricate meshwork of ecological change is set in motion. Over-stocking removes much of the grass, hence burning in the dry season is either retarded or made impossible. In the absence of fire over a protracted period, the increase in woody elements during the plant succession is uncontrolled and is accelerated towards a more densely stocked woodland with an ultimate loss of grazing. On the other hand, heavy concentration of cattle near water holes, or on slopes close to villages to which they are herded daily, often results in the complete disappearance of the original woodland and grass and the establishment of low thorn scrub characteristic of dry desert regions. In certain areas, notably the Karonga lake-shore, woodland consisting of *Acacia* spp., *Zizyphus* and *Gymnosporia* is increasing at the expense of the grass in overstocked areas. The spread of this thorn scrub has been assisted by the large numbers of cattle in this area. The cattle are dependent upon the thorn for sustenance in the dry season in the form of edible pods and by eating the pods and spreading the undigested seeds in their droppings, account for the dense establishment of seedlings.

Few facts are known regarding the time of origin of the first extensive *Brachystegia* woodlands in Malawi. Certainly there has been a great increase in the amount of re-clearing for agriculture during the past fifty years, associated with the large increase in population over this period. There is evidence that a closed tree cover of reasonably good quality extended over most of the plateau areas of the Central and Northern Provinces within the last century. Reliable observers, such as Dr. Robert Laws of Livingstonia, who travelled throughout the Northern Province for many years, testified before the Lands Commission in 1920 that he had personally witnessed in his lifetime the destruction of well-wooded land by shifting agriculture. Today, this same region presents the largest continuous expanse of poor quality *Brachystegia* woodland in Malawi.

This rapid devolution from closed forest to poor open woodland is considered by some observers to be due to profound soil changes initiated by the clearing of land and burning of logs and debris together to sterilize and prepare the soil for the growing of finger millets. The resulting sterilization and physical changes in the soil brought about by this 'slash and burn' practice may well explain the rapid vegetation change that has taken place in Malawi in the last five decades or so. The extensive low quality *Brachystegia* woodlands encountered today are a retrogressive succession induced by continued deterioration of the soil and the climate controls at the ground surface. Under present agricultural practices this deterioration is proceeding at an accelerated rate.

The Woodland as Pasture

The natural grazing grounds of Malawi vary in composition very greatly from place to place, but generally speaking may be divided into two groups, being (1) natural dry land pastures, and (2) *dambo* pastures.

The natural dry land pastures put forth a scanty spring growth before the onset of the rains by drawing on root reserves. This process is accelerated once the rains begin and within three months most grasses have reached maturity, after which the mixed mineral content of their foliage rapidly wanes. These natural dry land pastures are continually competing with trees, scrub, and cultivation for the occupation of the land. Thus for three to four months of the year the natural grasslands provide adequate pasture provided there is no overstocking. During this period the minimum phosphoric and protein requirements of an ox are met, but during the dry season there is usually a serious deficiency of both nutrients. During the dry season, therefore, resort is had to the limited areas of *dambo* pasture, which are normally waterlogged during the rainy season and provide pasture only during the dry season. The soil in these *dambos* is usually sandy and, being unsuitable for cultivation, provides valuable pasture during this period.

Unfortunately, the position in Malawi is not just a simple matter of rotational grazing from dry land pastures to *dambo*. The population of the country is dense and is increasing; as a result more and more land is coming under cultivation with a consequent reduction in the dry land pastures. Increasing use is being made of the *dambo* grasslands throughout the year and these limited areas are rapidly becoming overgrazed and eroded.

BIBLIOGRAPHY

L. J. Brass, 'The Vegetation of Nyasaland', *Mem. New York Bot. Gard.*, Vol. 8 (1953).

P. Brown, 'Modern Trends with Pastures and their Management', *Nyasa. Far. and For.*, Vol. 4 (1959).

C. V. Cutting, 'Survey of Soils Investigation. C.C.T.A. Report, Nyasaland Protectorate'. *Proc. 2nd Inter Afr. Soils Conf.*, Leopoldville (1954).

F. Dixey, J. B. Clements, and A. J. W. Hornby, 'The Destruction of Natural Vegetation and its relation to Climate, Water Supply and Soil Fertility', *Agric. Dept. Bull.*, No. 1, Zomba (1924).

C. R. Hursh, *The Dry Woodlands of Nyasaland*, I.C.A. Publication (1960).

G. Jackson, and P. O. Weihe, *An Annotated Check List of Nyasaland Grasses*, Dept. of Agriculture, Nyasaland (1958).

A. Muir, and L. Stephen, 'The Superficial Deposits of the Lower Shire Valley', Nyasaland, *Col. Geol. & Min. Res.*, Vol. 6, No. 4 (1957).

——, *Annual Reports*, Part II, Dept. of Agric., Nyasaland, 1954–60.

J. Philips, *Agriculture and Ecology in Africa*, Faber & Faber (1959).

P. Topham, *Check List of the Forest Trees and Shrubs of the British Empire, No. 2, Nyasaland Protectorate*. Imp. For., Inst., Oxford (1936).

CHAPTER V

DRAINAGE SYSTEMS

MALAWI occupies the major part of two separate drainage systems; the Lake Nyasa–Shire system of the rift valley and the now endoreic system of Lake Chilwa lying to the east of the Shire Highlands that at one time probably formed the headwaters of the Lujenda River, flowing northwards to join the Rovuma River. The Lake Nyasa–Shire system occupies a narrow drainage basin elongated in a north–south direction along the course of the rift valley and is essentially a tectonic basin. Although the Shire River finally joins the Zambezi River in its lower reaches, the confluence is too far downstream to play any significant part in the regimen of this larger river.

The total area of the Lake Nyasa–Shire system is 61,100 square miles of which 11,430 square miles are occupied by the waters of Lake Nyasa. In land catchment Malawi occupies some 35,600 square miles or nearly three quarters of the area, and the history and economy of the country have always been affected by the lake's regimen. As a result of meteorological and hydrological variations the environs of the lake and large areas of the lower Shire Valley have been subjected to spectacular alternate periods of drought and flooding in past years which has damaged or sterilized arable land and hindered navigation. From the hydrological aspect, the country is therefore dominated by the entire Nyasa–Shire system and we should extend our study to include those parts of the catchment that lie beyond the political borders of Malawi.

DRAINAGE DEVELOPMENT

The present day hydrographic pattern of both the Nyasa–Shire and the Chilwa systems is closely bound to the formation of the rift valley in this area, but along the margins of the rift on the older surfaces there is evidence of an older pre-rift drainage that was developed in a north-easterly direction towards the east coast of Africa. Since all but the coastal borders of southern Africa is considered to have been dry land since the early Jurassic, the original drainage must date back to that epoch. Towards or shortly after the close of the Karoo sedimentation in the early Jurassic, there occurred gentle flexures of the land surface that appear to have been influenced by older structures trending in a north-east direction in the south-eastern part of Africa. Many of the larger rivers of the sub-continent, or important sections of them, follow this direction (e.g. the Gwembe–Zambezi trough and the Upper Limpopo).

In the Nyasa area it is probable that during the Jurassic age, when relatively stable conditions prevailed, a drainage system that flowed predominantly in a north-easterly direction developed on the extensive and mature Jurassic peneplain. As a result of successive cycles of uplift and faulting in a north–south direction along the line of the rift valley, these rivers probably maintained their courses across the rising margins by the incision of deep gorges at first, but were later captured by the Shire–Zambezi system. This is well exemplified by the character of the Lilongwe, Bua, and Dwangwa rivers that lie to the west of Lake Nyasa, which all follow remarkably parallel courses in a north-east direction and, at one time, probably formed the headwaters of the Rovuma River to the east of Lake Nyasa. These rivers exhibit features of senility in their upper reaches with broad valleys, frequent meanders and ox-bows, but on entering the gorges of the rift margins they assume youthful characteristics with deep youthful valleys and steep immature gradients. The rivers of the Northern Province, in particular the South Rukuru, exhibit similar characteristics, but the latter's general north-easterly course has been considerably modified by having had to skirt the remnants of the late Jurassic and late Cretaceous surfaces of the Nyika and Vipya.

The South Rukuru river traverses the Miocene and end-Tertiary peneplain of the Mzimba district in a NNE. direction and on changing direction to the north-east to the south of the Nyika Plateau it cuts through the southern extension of this plateau and later through a gorge in the highland area overlooking the lake, north of Uzumara. The history of this river is analogous with that of many of the rivers to the west of Lake Nyasa that flow from the Miocene and older surfaces of the lake. This river probably originated on the Jurassic surface and flowed eastwards towards the sea, and probably formed the headwaters of the Ruaha and Luwegu rivers; when uplift and probably up-tilting of the trough margin intervened, it continued its course across the edge and into the trough which was being rapidly deepened by erosion of the Karoo sediments. There followed in succession, submergence, infilling of the trough with Cretaceous sediments, Miocene peneplanation, and further uplift; and as the Cretaceous sediments were removed as a result of the uplift the river re-established itself in its old course. Therefore throughout its long history it is possible that this river, and others like it, were captured twice by the rift after successive cycles of erosion and deposition.

While the majority of the main tributaries of Lake Nyasa lying to the west in Malawi are seen to be the upper parts of beheaded rivers or those that have matured on a much older surface, the rivers of the Shire Valley, Dedza, Vipya, and Livingstonia escarpment, are all true consequents of a later age, having developed as a direct result of the rift faulting. At the northern limit of Lake Nyasa there is the Pleistocene volcanic infilling of the rift that has also given rise to a number of consequent rivers flowing south eastwards to Lake Nyasa, all of which exhibit youthful ungraded profiles.

Thus the tributaries of Lake Nyasa and the Shire river are of two distinct types, being (*a*) rivers of an ancient pre-rift drainage system that have been captured and rejuvenated by rift faulting and (*b*) those youthful rivers of the northern area, the western escarpments, and parts of the Shire Valley that have developed as a result of the rift faulting. In some parts of the Shire Valley, however, the tributaries are of a consequent type developed much earlier than the consequents of the north, probably at the time of the early Cretaceous valley form erosion cycle.

Lake Nyasa

Lake Nyasa has been shown to have originated in or near the middle Pleistocene as a small lake at the northern extremity of the present basin at an elevation fully 750 feet above its present level. As a result of local faulting and the removal of the dinosaur sediments from the Nyasa trough it was lowered in stages to near its present level and, at the same time, elongated southwards, finally, with the development of the Ruarwe fault and the associated down-warping, it reached its present southern limits by flooding the former head of the Shire Valley. The southern half of the lake basin and the present Shire Valley are but parts of one great trough, and they differ only in the degree of warping imposed upon the floor of the trough.

The following paragraphs outline in more detail what appear to have been the principal events in the evolution of the Lake Nyasa–Shire and Chilwa systems.[1]

(*a*) At about the beginning of the Pleistocene period, Lake Nyasa stood at about 1,000 feet above its present level and does not appear to have extended further south of Deep Bay, but it reached much further west than it does today. During this period there were alternating wet and dry periods with associated faulting that brought the level of the lake down to about 750 feet by the end of the middle Pleistocene. To the south of this small lake the rift trough was composed mainly of Cretaceous deposits that were still being steadily removed by the Shire River working its way northwards.

(*b*) Further faulting in the late middle Pleistocene lowered the floor of the rift and the lake level to approximately 650 feet above the present level. This faulting extended the lake to a point some miles south of the present South Rukuru river mouth, possibly capturing the river at this time.

(*c*) After this pause the major Ruarwe fault along a north–south line with concomitant volcanic activity at the northern limit of the lake occurred. The Ruarwe fault, maintained on a more or less north–south line, gave rise to the tilt of the floor of the trough opposite in direction to that of the north. This major fault, together with associated later fractures, enabled the lake to extend southwards, practically as far south as its present limits; but southwards of Nkata Bay it was then considerably wider, standing about 400 feet above the present level of the lake. At this time the ancient Shire river, instead of following the course of the modern Shire Valley, left the valley north-east of Liwonde and

[1] For the detailed geological evidence for this sequence of events see F. Dixey (1926).

followed a more easterly course by way of Lake Chilwa, Tuchila Plain, and the Ruo valley. This stage probably occupied a considerable duration of time, enabling the wide, mature valley plains of the Lake Chilwa area to develop, which are comparable with those of the modern upper Shire valley, and to bring the floors of several intersecting rifts or down-warps into complete accordance. At the close of this stage no great changes had taken place in the form of the old river course beyond a slight warping that has resulted in the formation of the broad, shallow depression in which Lake Chilwa now lies, and possibly also led to the ormer connexion of this lake with the head of the Lujenda River.

(d) Following upon this period of comparative stability renewed faulting along the line of the Shire valley took place; this resulted in the intersection of the old eastward drainage course running past the western foot of Mlanje mountain into the Ruo valley, by the Makongwa fault scarp. The lake probably occupied the head of the Shire and Bwanje valleys during this period and, as a result of contemporary faulting along the line of the present middle Shire valley, the effluent of the lake was diverted to its modern course.

(e) The final stage in the development of the Lake Nyasa–Shire system is considered to have extended into Recent times when there was a renewal of intermittent faulting bringing the lake down to its present limits and causing the Shire to cut more deeply into the rocky bed of the early Cretaceous valley floor in the middle river area, where faulting has strongly controlled the course of the river.

THE LAKE NYASA CATCHMENT AREA AND ITS TRIBUTARIES

The Lake Nyasa basin is about 48,850 square miles in extent, and of this area some 11,430 square miles are occupied by the waters of Lake Nyasa, thus giving a ratio of land catchment to water of about three to one. To the east of the Lake the land catchment is narrow, about ten miles wide, and extends from the southern limit of the Lake to about latitude 11° South. Along this narrow strip of country the drainage is by short, steep, consequent type rivers and streams that fall directly to the Lake, none of which individually contribute any appreciable flow. At about latitude 11° South the eastern watershed widens out to include the Ruhuhu River that drains a large basin of Karoo deposition and the south-eastern valleys of the Livingstone Mountains. From the north-western corner of the Ruhuhu basin near Njombe, the watershed follows the Kipengere Range in a north-westerly direction and then turns westward along the 7,000 feet summit ridge of the Poroto Mountains to include the high rainfall area of North Nyasa centred upon Tukuyu; thereafter continuing across the northern part of the Bundali Range to the Mbozi Plateau. From this point the watershed runs south along the Malawi–Zambian border to a point near Fort Jameson. From here it turns westwards along the Dzalanyama hills to the Kirk Range and hence to the southern limit of the lake.

Throughout the catchment there is a high variation of altitude, ranging from 1,550 feet to over 9,000 feet, and this has produced a wide range of natural conditions ranging from dry semi-arid woodlands to thick closed forests with heavy rainfall. The largest part of the land catchment lies to the west in Malawi and is drained in the main by the Songwe, North Rukuru, South Rukuru, Luweya, Dwangwa, Bua, Linthipe, and Livelezi Rivers. To the north short, steep, consequent rivers such as the Kiwira, Mbaka, Lufirio, and Rumbira drain the Poroto and Livingstone Mountains, and as the result of a high rainfall in that area all have a high average flow. To the east, the only river of any consequence is the Ruhuhu which, with a catchment area of 6,000 square miles, is the largest river draining into Lake Nyasa.

All the rivers of the Lake Nyasa basin are comparatively small by African standards, the longest river being only 180 miles in length. As a result there are no large groundwater reservoir areas within the catchments and a large number of rivers are seasonal in character. The most highly perennial rivers issue from the eastern slopes of the Vipya, Nyika, and the Poroto Mountains in Tanganyika, which are all areas of heavy rainfall, with relatively well preserved catchments and have steep gradients. Perhaps the best method of arriving at an understanding of the hydrographic conditions of the Lake Nyasa basin and Central and Northern Malawi will be to examine the characteristics of the rivers of the two main types; firstly, the older plateau rivers that have been rejuvenated, and secondly, the more recent consequent rivers of the rift margins.

The Plateau System

This system is represented by the rivers that find their source on the Luangwa–Nyasa watershed and flow for the greater part of their courses across the Miocene and end-Tertiary surfaces of the plateaux and in their lower reaches drop rapidly to Lake Nyasa. On the plateau all these rivers display features of maturity and senility, draining wide, planed-off valleys with a tributary system of broad, flat drainage lines or *dambos*, whereas in their lower reaches youthful valleys, profiles, steep gradients, and rapids are characteristic. In their final stage from the foothills to Lake Nyasa a number of these rivers traverse the lake littoral, and where this is wide, have deposited much recent alluvium and built up deltas on the lake shore. Where the littoral is wide such as the north Karonga lake-shore, these larger rivers have also built up river bank *levées*, these being the highest points of the generally flat, low lying plain.

On the central plateau and the Mzimba Plain this type of river is well exemplified by the Linthipe, Bua, Dwangwa, South Rukuru, and to the north of the Nyika Plateau, by the North Rukuru, Lufira, and Songwe Rivers. To the south of the Nyika the catchments are generally flat and the average annual run-off amounts to between 6 and 11 per cent. of the annual rainfall. The more northerly rivers, however, exhibit steeper characteristics and, coupled with a heavier and more prolonged rainy season, the run-off factors are considerably higher, being between 18 and 22 per cent. Many of these rivers have a tapering flow, the point of maximum increment being either on the plateau itself or where the rivers disgorge on to the lake littoral. If this is wide there is usually a high loss of flow in the dry season from absorption and it is common to find these rivers flowing in the foothill areas with no flow reaching the lake.

The Rift Margin Consequent Rivers

Extending along the whole course of the rift margins there is a large number of consequent type rivers that have formed as a result of rift subsidences and in many cases these rivers are youthful and with small catchment areas. In three main areas, however, these rivers have managed to develop under heavy rainfall conditions and contribute a large proportion of the perennial inflow into Lake Nyasa, their run-off factors ranging from 16 to 43 per cent. of the annual rainfall.

At the northern limit of the lake, three large rivers, the Kiwira, Mbaka, and Lufirio drain the high rainfall area of the Poroto mountains and during the dry season these rivers probably account for more than half of the total inflow into the Lake. These rivers exhibit youthful profiles and have dissected the volcanic tuffs and lavas of this area to a considerable degree.

The second main area is along the eastern flanks of the Nyika Plateau where the North Rumpi and its tributaries have succeeded in eroding a deep valley in the softer Karoo formations back to the main plateau wall of the Nyika. The average annual run-off from this river is high, about 43 per cent. Of a similar nature is the Luweya river, draining nearly 1,000 square miles of the eastern flanks of the wet Vipya Plateau. With the Songwe and Linthipe rivers it is one of the highest yielding tributaries of the lake in Malawi and the average run-off amounts to approximately 30 per cent. of the mean annual rainfall.

The third main area lies along the eastern flanks of the Dowa–Chitembwe Highlands to the south-west of Kota Kota. This plateau is drained to the east by a number of swift-flowing rivers, the Lingadzi, Limpimbi, Chirua and, to a lesser degree, the Kaombe. Rainfall in this area is considerably lower and the rivers traverse a wide littoral prior to flowing into the lake; dry season flow is therefore considerably depleted. During the rains, however, the peaceful streams often become raging torrents at times causing considerable damage to bridges in the lower reaches.

In a category on its own, and probably the most important tributary of Lake Nyasa, is the Ruhuhu river draining an area of some 6,000 square miles of the north-eastern catchment in Tanganyika. The upper tributaries of this river draining the south-eastern flanks of the Livingstone Mountains have probably been captured by the main river, cutting back eastwards along the Karoo basin from the lake; they explain the considerable flow of this river, which otherwise occupies an area of low rainfall. Flow data for this river are meagre, records only having been collected over one year in 1954 when observations were made by the Nyasaland Government in connexion with investigations into the hydrology of Lake Nyasa. During this year, however, the total volume of flow contributed to Lake Nyasa exceeded that of any other tributary.

THE SHIRE RIVER AND ITS TRIBUTARIES

The Shire river may be divided into three main sections in accordance with the physiography of the valley it occupies, and which has been described in detail in previous chapters. The upper section covers a distance of 82 miles from the outlet of Lake Nyasa to Matope at an average gradient of 0·28 feet per mile; the middle section is where the river plunges through the cataracts of a total fall of 1,258 feet in 50 miles; and finally, the lower river section extends from the foot of the cataracts to the Zambezi river over a distance of 174 miles, 54 miles being in Moçambique, at an average gradient of 1·06 feet per mile.

Five miles south of Fort Johnston the Shire river enters Lake Malombe which is, at present, about 18 miles long and 9 miles wide. This lake is shallow, its bed remarkably level, and in Recent times it probably formed part of Lake Nyasa. In 1915, when the Lake reached its lowest recorded level, all flow in the Shire river ceased except in the wet season, and bars of sand and silt overgrown with reeds were formed at the mouths of the main tributaries. The main barriers were at the outlet of the lake, at the north end of Lake Malombe and at the confluence of the Nkasi River, south of Lake Malombe. These bars contained the waters of Lake Nyasa, the water level of which rose considerably between 1915 and 1934. Early in 1935, however, the water began to rise over the bars and flow down the Shire river was resumed, its volume increasing until it reached a maximum flow in 1937.

The general features of the banks of the Shire river from Lake Malombe to Matope are distinctive. While on one side of the river there may be high banks, on the other there are swamps and old ox-bow lakes. The most extensive of these swamps is at Chigaru upstream of the first of the middle Shire cataracts.

From Matope to a point twelve miles upstream of Chikwawa the Shire River falls in a series of spectacular gorges and cataracts, but nowhere are there any high waterfalls. The main rapids occur near Matope, at Nkula near Walkers' Ferry, at Tedzani 5 miles downstream of Nkula, at Mpatamanga, and finally at Hamilton Falls. There are also lesser rapids at Nachimbeya, about 10 miles downstream of Matope.

At Chikwawa the hills bounding the valley recede and the Shire River enters a plain some 20 miles wide extending to the Zambezi. Much of this plain is covered by seasonal and perennial swamp of the Elephant Marsh, some 160 square miles in extent. At Chiromo, some 70 miles downstream from the Hamilton Falls, all flow is concentrated into one channel by the railway embankment on the south bank and a natural *levée* thrown up by the Ruo river on the north bank.

At Chiromo, the Ruo river joins the Shire river, and from this point the river flows southwards bordering on a further large area of swamp lying to the east in Moçambique. The channel is less obstructed in this reach than is the section upstream of Chiromo and the fall from here to Port Herald, a distance of 31 miles, is 30 feet. South of Port Herald the swamp area is mainly on the western side of the river in Malawi and is known as the Ndindi Marsh.

Beyond the border the river flows for several miles in a very tortuous course until Vila Bocage where it is well defined between high banks. The fall from Port Herald to the Zambezi is about 30 feet, but when the Zambezi River floods, water pours through a north-easterly channel, known as the Ziu Ziu Channel, towards the Shire, and if the volume of flow in the Shire River is high, the effects of Zambezi flooding are discernible as far north as Port Herald. With the completion of the Kariba Dam in the middle Zambezi the danger of high floods in the Zambezi–Shire area has greatly diminished.

The flow of the Shire River has been measured over the past decade at Liwonde, Matope, Chikwawa, Chiromo, and Port Herald. Flow measured at Liwonde is taken to represent outflow from Lake Nyasa, the loss from evaporation in Lake Malombe being offset by minor tributary flow between Lake Malombe and Liwonde. Table XI shows the mean annual flow in cubic feet per second (cusecs) at each of these stations. In some years, it will be noted, the flow at Chiromo is less than that at Chikwawa, and this may be attributed to the large loss incurred by evaporation from the large tract of marsh lying between these two stations.

TABLE XI

Mean Annual Flow in Cusecs—Shire River—1948–61

Year	Liwonde	Matope	Chikwawa	Chiromo	Port Herald
1948–49	10,557	10,265	—	10,798	9,459
1949–50	10,392	10,804	—	11,480	9,677
1950–51	10,474	10,754	—	11,089	9,534
1951–52	12,090	12,808	14,243	14,743	11,022
1952–53	10,468	10,754	11,165	11,545	10,023
1953–54	7,855	8,179	8,215	7,729	7,349
1954–55	7,179	7,828	8,309	9,108	8,529
1955–56	8,106	8,616	9,493	9,633	8,475
1956–57*	2,667	2,810	3,424	3,091	4,932
1957–58	14,070	14,317	14,674	15,168	10,875
1958–59	11,422	11,497	11,644	12,300	10,106
1959–60	9,942	10,064	10,186	9,983	9,819
1960–61	9,342	9,613	10,388	10,374	10,191

* During this year all flow from Lake Nyasa ceased owing to the construction of a bund across the Shire River at Liwonde. This bund was breached in August 1957.

The tributaries of the Shire river are mainly seasonal and erratic. As is the case with most Malawi rivers, about 80 per cent. of the annual flow occurs in the wet season from November to April. The few perennial rivers lose much of their flow in their sandy beds before entering the Shire river. To the west the main tributaries are the Rivi Rivi, Lisungwe, Wankurumadzi, and Mwanza, of which only the Wankurumadzi and Lisungwe are perennial. These two rivers rise on the Kirk Range and flow through broken, sparsely inhabited country. To the east the main tributaries are the Lisanjala, Lirangwe, Likabula, Maperera, Mwamphanzi, Masenjere, and Tangadzi East, of which only the latter two are perennial. It is of interest to note that many of these eastern tributaries drain country that is physically similar to the catchments of the Lisungwe and Wankurumadzi rivers to the west under a similar rainfall, but there are wide differences in their regimens. The eastern catchments support a dense population and with the demands for cultivation there has been a deterioration of sustained yield. Records of flow over the past seven years for the Lunzu and Lirangwe rivers show that this tends to cease earlier with each succeeding year.

The Ruo is the largest of all the Shire tributaries. It drains a catchment area of some 1,900 square miles which includes most of the Mlanje Mountain and the eastern Shire Highlands south of Limbe. The heavy rainfall of the catchment area and the swift-flowing nature of the tributary streams often results in serious flooding in the lower Shire area.

In February 1952, when the Shire river was carrying some 30,000 cusecs, the Ruo river discharged a flood of some 70,000 cusecs into the Shire at Chiromo, causing the latter river to flood over its banks and inundate large areas of the surrounding country. In April 1956, as a result of heavy rainfall in the catchment from cyclone 'Edith', the Ruo River discharged a peak flood of approximately 190,000 cusecs. On this occasion the flow in the Shire river had not yet had time to build up owing to storage in the Elephant Marsh upstream and at one stage the flood waters from the Ruo were flowing upstream from Chiromo into the Marsh area. Needless to say, flooding of the surrounding country was severe and the railway embankment was washed away.

THE RÉGIME OF THE LAKE NYASA–SHIRE SYSTEM

Throughout this study it has been seen that Lake Nyasa dominates the physiography of the country; equally so the hydrology. Its probable evolution, bordering physiography, climate, and bathygraphy have all been described in previous chapters and we should now turn to the aspect of its régime. This should be considered from two aspects; the thermal relations of the lake waters which control the movement of water within the lake exercising an ecological control, and secondly, the fluctuations of level as influenced by such factors as rainfall, run-off, evaporation, and outflow into the Shire river.

Limnology

The statement that we can designate the thermal relations as a pivotal point of every limnological investigation has been found to be equally true for both tropical and temperate region lakes, despite their large differences in temperature range. The annual temperature range in

Lake Nyasa is only 4° C but being high on the temperature scale this has a considerable effect on the limnology. The temperature relations control the stratification of the water mass and the currents of the lake basin indirectly through changes in the density of the water.

The largest source of heat is solar radiation and is taken up by the water by absorption and to a lesser degree by heat transfer from the air or from the bottom. The condensation of water vapour at the surface can also provide quantities of heat. The loss of heat takes place by radiation, evaporation, and through conduction to the air and to the bottom. If heating of the lake by solar radiation is taking place one would expect the distribution of temperature to decrease sharply just below the surface and gradually decrease in depth. However, from temperature observations at various depths it is found as in all large bodies of water, that the temperature decreases slowly for some depth when there is a sudden decrease, and thereafter it is more or less constant. The concentration of oxygen shows a similar pattern, there being little to no oxygen below the point where the temperature decreases rapidly.

The simple absorption of radiant energy cannot produce a heat distribution of this nature, and it has been shown that the energy which distributes heat in a lake is derived chiefly from wind. The wind pushes water particles lying on the surface and generates a current. When it reaches the shore, the moving water mass is deflected by the resistance of colder, heavier strata, resulting in a current in the opposite direction just below the surface. This current produces turbulence which leads to a vertical interchange of water particles to a certain depth, and the stronger the wind the deeper will this mixing take place.

The specific gravity of water decreases at an increasing rate as the temperature rises from 4° C, and under tropical conditions, a small temperature change can cause considerable differences in density. Owing to the wind's causing turbulence and warming of the upper water there is therefore a change in density between the heated surface strata and the quieter water below, and a boundary between these two strata—the epilimnion and the hypolimnion—is formed. This interface is known as the thermocline or the discontinuity layer and indicates the lowest limit of mixing currents generated from the surface. The equalization of temperature in the epilimnion is further enhanced by evaporation and radiation and conduction at night in cold weather.

Stratification of the waters has an important effect upon the limnology because of the barrier created by the thermocline between the level at which assimilation of energy occurs, i.e. the epilimnion, and that of the major source of nutrients, the bottom deposits. The abrupt change in density of water at the region of the thermocline gives this region the properties of a slippery surface and therefore facilitates horizontal movements of water but tends to suppress vertical movements across it. This stratification of the lake waters therefore divides the lake into two separate layers of fundamental differences; the epilimnion, being highly oxygenated and kept in motion by the turbulent currents, promotes the

movement of phytoplankton and fish life and, as a result of the assimila-
tory activities of the phytoplankton, becomes progressively impoverished of organic plant nutrients. The water in the hypolimnion, on the
other hand, having no source of oxygen and frequently a high oxygen
demand, becomes rich in plant nutrients. This lower layer, with its reserves of food which most animals cannot obtain, however, frequently
becomes oxygenated by the internal movements of water in the lake
known as the seiche movement, this movement being fundamental to
the problems of productivity in any lake.

A seiche movement is normally initiated by the action of the wind on
the surface of the lake. Strong winds over a period of days cause a temporary 'pile up' of surface water on the leeward shore and cause an
apparent depression of the thermocline to a greater depth under increased oxygenation. On cessation of the wind this pile up of surface
water tends to recede and an oscillatory movement is set up both on the
surface and internally. The surface seiche on Lake Nyasa has been
measured by automatic limnographs at various stations since 1954 and
the most marked is found at Monkey Bay where the seiche occurs at
regular intervals of 6 hours with an amplitude of some 3 inches.

The internal wave or temperature seiche is, however, very different
and the period may vary from 20 to 40 days depending upon the depth
of the thermocline, the respective densities of the two layers, and the
length of the lake. This vertical displacement of the layers on the passing of an internal wave is also accompanied by both lateral and longitudinal movements of water, giving rise to horizontal currents in the
stratified layers, and this movement often assists in carrying down oxygenated water to the hypolimnion without materially disturbing the
thermocline. Investigations into internal seiche movements in Lake
Nyasa were first carried out by R. S. A. Beauchamp in 1939, and more
recently on a more extensive scale by the Joint Fisheries Research
Organization. Unfortunately no results have been published by the
latter organization, but Beauchamp's observations are of interest. He
found that the probable period of the internal seiche was about twenty
days and that at one period the lake very nearly became isothermal or
'turned over'. This is a normal occurrence in temperate region lakes but
uncommon in deep tropical lakes, and he considers that Lake Nyasa
may become isothermal once every few years as a cumulative effect of
successive windy, dry seasons.

Therefore one would expect to find, during the dry season when the
trade winds are most prevalent, the thermocline to be well established
and on cessation of the wind a continuance of the internal wave motion
but with a breakdown of the thermocline. In Lake Nyasa this does not
appear to be the case, as the thermocline usually becomes more marked
during the calmer period of October and November. This is brought
about by the fact that when the winds cease temperatures are increasing
and the lake receives the maximum amount of heat from the sun which
leads to a more marked thermocline but at a much shallower depth than

I

that found during the dry season. Towards the end of the rains, calm periods and variable winds cause the thermocline to be less well defined, causing further mixing between the epi- and the hypolimnion.

These seasonal variations of stratification appear to have a marked effect on the fishing in the shallow south-east arm of the lake; during the dry season months there is a marked absence of fish from the fishing grounds with a reappearance at the beginning of the rains. It is possible that because of oxygenation to a greater depth during the dry season there is a correspondingly wider dispersal of fish, whereas during the hot, wet months fish are forced into shallower waters through de-oxygenation of the deeper water. There is, as well, the possible attraction offered by the additional supply of nutrients that are at this time beginning to be discharged into the lake from the rivers.

Hydrology

The seasonal variation in the level of the lake averages 3 or 4 feet but has been as much as 6 feet in a single year. Over long periods of years, however, the accumulative rise or fall may be much greater and since accurate records were commenced in 1896 the level of the lake has fluctuated from 1,538 feet above sea level, to just over 1,556 feet above sea level, a range of over 18 feet.

Prior to 1896 there is considerable evidence, in the form of writings by early travellers on Lake Nyasa and the Shire river, to show that this fluctuation is a phenomenon that has persisted for some time. From this evidence it has been suggested that the lake level was very low in

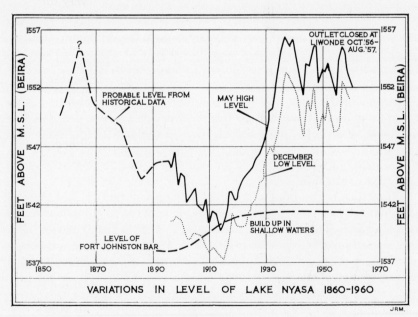

Fig. 26.

1830, very high in 1857–63, high in 1873, falling in 1875–78, high in 1882, very low in 1890, but rising rapidly in 1892–95. Since records were begun in 1896 the level declined and reached a minimum recorded level of 1,537·8 feet in 1915. Almost all flow down the Shire had ceased by this time, the upper reaches of the river channel becoming blocked by sandbars, often formed by the tributaries in flood, and covered with a dense growth of reeds. From 1915 the level rose gradually and in 1937 reached its maximum recorded level of 1,556·4 feet. Some two years prior to this, the rising lake waters overtopped the various bars in the river and an open channel was again formed, although this is still partially obstructed by the remains of these old bars. After 1937, the lake level fell slightly, but in 1948 reached a high level that was but half a foot below the 1937 level. Since then there has tended to be an overall continuing decline in level.[1]

These long term changes in level have given rise to many theories that have included speculations as to 'underground connexions with other great lakes', but it was F. E. Kanthack who first drew attention to the balance that exists between rainfall, run-off, evaporation, and outflow from the lake, and that these long term fluctuations could be attributed to purely normal meteorological phenomena.

By utilizing a considerable amount of further data collected in recent years this problem has been examined in more detail, confirming the delicate natural balance which is primarily attributable to high evaporation losses from the lake relative to rainfall and inflow. The annual evaporation from the lake area amounts to between 75 and 80 inches, whereas the average rainfall over the whole catchment probably only amounts to some 48 inches or possibly less.

The amount of water contributed by run-off and reduced by evaporation during the period of rise is therefore the surplus amount of water made available for flow down the Shire River or storage in the lake. Thus with a ratio of land catchment to lake area of 3·3 to 1 and with high fixed losses from the lake area, the effect upon the amount of surplus water in the lake in any one year would be a magnification of the variation of annual rainfall and run-off over the catchment. It has been calculated that only about 5½ per cent. of the rainfall eventually becomes available as surplus water, although the run-off factor over the land catchment is probably of the order of 20 to 22 per cent. of the rainfall over the land.

In an effort to extend the record further back in time, N. J. Cochrane has sought to effect a correlation between sunspots and climatic changes, following the work of C. E. P. Brooks and F. Dixey. Brooks showed that, for a period of 19 years (1902 to 21), there existed a striking qualitative relation between sunspot numbers and the level of Lake Victoria. From this correlation it was assumed that sunspots, by influencing the intensity

[1] Post-script: Since 1962 there has been a cumulative rise in lake level and in May 1963 a maximum level of 1556·6 was reached, 2½ inches higher than the previous maximum reached in 1937.

of the sun's rays, caused changes in such meteorological factors as rainfall and evaporation sufficiently to effect periodic changes in the levels of lakes, whether or not they lie in enclosed basins.

In 1924, Dr. F. Dixey extended these investigations to Lake Nyasa for the period 1894–1923 and showed a similar relationship between sunspots and lake level. More recently the same author furthered his observations in the light of recent information from Lakes Albert, Victoria, Tanganyika, and Nyasa. These data were submitted to mathematical analysis and while a significant correlation was obtained in the cases of the two former lakes no significant relationship was found in the cases of Lakes Tanganyika and Nyasa. Dixey concludes, however, that the odds are between ten to one and four to one 'that lake level peaks do coincide with sunspot peaks more often than they would if there were no relationship present'.

While Cochrane found that there was little real correlation between sunspots and climatic changes and other phenomena he has sought to establish a relationship in another form, that of the *rate of change* of sunspot numbers and surplus water in the lake. This method of hydrological analysis is certainly unique, but it is doubtful if this correlation is of much significance as, by utilizing the same data statistically, it can be shown that only about one sixth of the variation of the 'surplus' water can be related to changes in sunspot numbers. The short period of observations used in this analysis—twenty-eight years, less than three sunspot periods —would not be enough to establish a periodicity of the lake unless the period was very definite, and as has been shown, many supposed periodicities have proved to be merely transient.

With the present delicately balanced régime of Lake Nyasa with its unstable outlet, the hydrology of the Shire river will always be subject to wide variations. For instance, in a group of three wet years there is a probability that the amount of water made available in a year (assuming that there was no outflow) might be equivalent to some $7\frac{1}{2}$ feet in three years or equivalent to a flow of 26,000 cusecs down the Shire river. In a period of three dry years, however, there might be no surplus water at all, but a net deficit of some 7 inches on the lake area, equivalent to about 5,600 cusecs. Under these conditions the construction of harbours on the lake, navigation, the development of power in the middle Shire area and reclamation in the lower Shire area, all become precarious, if not impossible, without some control on the outlet of the lake.

In recent years considerable investigation into the problem of controlling Lake Nyasa and the Shire river for these purposes has been undertaken under a scheme known as the Shire Valley Project. The scheme envisages the stabilization of the lake to bring the fluctuations of lake level within reasonable limits to facilitate the construction of harbours to ensure a regulated flow down the Shire River, the development of power in the middle Shire cataracts and the reclamation and irrigation of large areas of flooded land in the lower Shire area. Although the stabilization of the lake and the regulation of the outflow to the Shire

SCALE (Approx.)

1 3/4 1/2 1/4 0   1   2   3   4 MILES

Fig 27. The Upper Shire River between Lake Nyasa and Lake Malombe.
Reproduced by permission of Her Majesty's Stationery Office.

are interrelated, these various aspects are mutually antipathetic and an overall solution to an integrated scheme must essentially be a compromise.

Since the natural phenomena influencing the erratic behaviour of the level of Lake Nyasa cannot be controlled, complete stabilization is impracticable and the degree of stabilization depends upon the amount of water allowed to flow down the Shire river. To constrain the lake level within a range of six feet would require the alternate release of large and small amounts of water into the Shire River which, besides being incompatible with a regulated demand for power purposes, would make conditions in the lower Shire at least as bad as they are naturally, if not worse. On the other hand, to release a regulated flow of 5,000 cusecs down the river at all times would require a lake level variation of 7 feet and probably 14 feet at long intervals, and at low stages recourse would have to be had to pumping this out of the lake and dredging of the upper Shire channel where the gradient is extremely flat. The simplest solution to overcome these difficulties and ensure a regulated flow down the Shire river would be to raise the lake level by at least 6 feet above the highest recorded level (i.e. 1,562·4 feet) as, in this event, pumping and dredging would be unnecessary. But, at the same time, this would flood areas of the lake-shore in three territories that are densely populated and cultivated and would be difficult from a political aspect.

THE LAKE CHILWA–CHIUTA DRAINAGE AREA

Lakes Chilwa and Chiuta occupy part of the elongated depression that extends from the northern foot of Mlanje Mountain in a NNE. direction into the Lujenda valley of Moçambique. Lake Chilwa, now lying in an enclosed basin, at one time probably formed part of a larger lake that originated following upon down-warping of the Miocene peneplain in this area after the diversion of the Shire river to its modern course. In pre-Miocene times it is thought that the ancient outlet of Lake Nyasa flowed south-eastwards through the present Lake Chilwa area to the Ruo valley, and upon diversion of the Shire the drainage of the section of the valley, now occupied by Lake Chilwa, was reversed northwards into the Lujenda down-warp and in time developed into a shallow lake. After a long period of deposition and falling lake level, resulting either from climatic changes or headwater erosion, along the course of the Lujenda river, or a combination of both, Lake Chilwa became separated from its northern section by an east–west barrier of deposited silt, known today as Kwituto. This northern part, known as Lake Chiuta, remains, however, connected to the Lujenda river through a further series of lakes and swamps that go to make up Lake Amaramba in Moçambique.

Lake Chilwa today covers an area of approximately 1,000 square miles, but less than half this area is open water. The remainder is made up of shallow, reed-covered swamp or seasonally inundated grasslands. The maximum depth is about ten feet only. The lake and swamps are the focus of an endoreic system that drains the north-eastern section of Mlanje Mountain, the Palombe, and Chilwa plains and, to the west, the Zomba and Chikala mountains. The main rivers of this system are the Sombani, Palombe, and Likangala. While a number of these rivers are perennial in their upper reaches all are known to dry up in their lower reaches where they traverse large tracts of highly permeable lacustrine sands and silts.

Over the past fifteen years the level of the lake has shown an annual variation of as much as $7\frac{1}{2}$ feet, but normally this annual change is in the region of two to three feet. The presence of fossil beaches and wave-cut platforms testify to higher levels in the past, although the lower terraces are thought to be modern.

Dr. Livingstone noted that in 1859 the lake extended almost to the northern foot of Mlanje mountain and this is partly confirmed by an early map of the Shire Highlands by O. C. Bollinger which shows Njalu Island some 5 miles from the shore. Today this island is surrounded by marsh at the southern extremity of the lake. This map indicates that Lake Chilwa was probably 30 feet deeper at this time.

Being an enclosed lake, the waters of Lake Chilwa are distinctly saline and become increasingly so towards the end of the dry season owing to a high evaporation rate at this time of year. Inshore waters in the swampy areas, which are fed by seasonal streams, are, however, relatively pure for the greater part of the dry season, becoming saline only in October and November. Sampling carried out during the dry season of 1951 shows that the concentration of alkaline carbonates and bicarbonates increased from 340 parts per million in April to 590 parts per million at the end of October.

The waters of Lake Chiuta are, however, relatively pure by reason of their effluent into Lake Amaramba and thence to the Lujenda river. Lake Chiuta is a large seasonal lake covering some 440 square miles, the area of permanent water covering only some 10 square miles in the northern reaches. This small body of water is connected to Lake Amaramba by a wide channel near Ngokwe which, during the dry season, is reduced to a trickle. The difference in level between these two lakes is very small and this gives rise to a régime that is of interest. Lake Amaramba is supplied by a number of perennial streams and rivers which drain the Namwera plateau. During the rainy season inflow often exceeds outflow northwards into the Lujenda and Lake Amaramba rises at a faster rate than Lake Chiuta, which is supplied by small seasonal streams only. Once the level of Lake Amaramba exceeds that of Chiuta water flows southwards through the Ngokwe channel into Lake Chiuta, and this flow is usually maintained until March. When outflow from Amaramba northwards into the Lujenda River exceeds inflow from the tributaries, the level of both Amaramba and Chiuta begin to fall and, during the months of April and May, flow through the Ngokwe channel is reversed and Lake Chiuta drains into Lake Amaramba.

BIBLIOGRAPHY

R. S. Beauchamp, 'Hydrological Data from Lake Nyasa', *Jour. Ecol.*, 41 (1953).

C. E. P. Brooks, 'Variations in the Levels of the Central African Lakes Victoria and Albert', *Geophys. Mem.*, No. 20, p. 9 (1933).

C. E. P. Brooks, and N. Carruthers, *Handbook of Statistical Methods in Meteorology*, H.M.S.O. (1953).

N. J. Cochrane, 'Lake Nyasa and the River Shire', *Proc. Inst. Civil Engrs.*, Paper No. 6178, Vol. 8 (1957).

F. Dixey, 'Some Aspects of the Geomorphology of Central and Southern Africa', *Trans. G.S. of S.A.*, Annex. Vol. 58 (1955).

——, 'The Nyasaland Section of the Great Rift Valley', *Geog. Jour.* (1926).

——, Annual Reports, Water Development Department, Nyasaland, 1954–60.

——, 'Variations in the Level of Lake Nyasa', *Nature*, Vol. 114 (1924).

M. S. Garson, 'The Geology of the Lake Chilwa Area', *Nyas. Geol. Surv.*, Bull. No. 12, 1960.

F. E. Kanthack, 'The Hydrology of the Nyasa Rift Valley', *S.A. Geog. Jour.*, Vol. 24 (1942).

E. W. Latham, 'Some Points of Interest in the Hydrology of the Shire Rivers', *Proc. Vth Informal Conf. Hydrology*, Blantyre (1960).

J. G. Pike, 'Northern Nyasaland: A Regional Geographical Study with Special Reference to Hydrography and Hydrology', Blantyre (1955).

——, 'The Movement of Water in Lake Nyasa', *Nyas. Jour.*, Vol. X (1957).

F. Ruttner, *Fundamentals of Limnology*, Univ. of Toronto Press (1931).

PART TWO

HISTORICAL, SOCIAL, AND ECONOMIC GEOGRAPHY

CHAPTER VI*

HISTORICAL GEOGRAPHY

EARLY SETTLEMENT

THE prehistoric climates of Central and Southern Africa were marked by an alternation of very dry periods with wet periods. It was during the dry periods that Malawi offered conditions most congenial to human settlement. Then, because of the high mountains, it tended to be wetter and cooler than the surrounding hot, arid regions. During wetter periods the surrounding lands were more attractive.

The earliest evidence of human settlement in Malawi is thought to belong to one of the drier periods, the Kanjeran-Gamblian inter-pluvial period, between seventy thousand and one hundred thousand years ago, when concentrated settlement in the more favoured lake-shore plain in Karonga and the Luangwa valley was evident. These people were Middle Stone Age hunters and food gatherers, who had probably followed the larger animals as they migrated to Malawi grazing areas.

The wetter Gamblian Pluvial period, between ten thousand and seventy thousand years ago, favoured the dispersal of human settlement. There was little to attract people to the cold, higher lands, though there may have been some settlements in the Great Rift Valley. The increasing aridity at the close of this period, however, brought about the migration into Malawi of groups of hunters out of areas no longer able to support them. There is evidence that they came into contact with some earlier inhabitants, though little is known about the latter. It is probable that there was some tendency to concentrate in the more favourable areas occupied during the earlier arid period, but with the increasing use of more specialized tools, such as arrowheads and knives, population was much more generally dispersed throughout the Nyasa highlands.

Out of the Post-Gamblian settlement there developed what Dr. J. D. Clark calls Nachikufan man, who inhabited large areas in and around Malawi, and had a Later Stone Age culture. Evidence of Nachikufan settlement in Malawi has been found in the vicinity of Hora mountain in the Mzimba district, at Mphunzi mountain in Dedza district, and on the raised beaches at Monkey Bay. It is doubtful if any of these settlements were more than temporary, for the people were primarily hunters, roving the countryside in small groups. The numerous grindstones, mullers, and pestles and mortars unearthed, however, show that between four thousand and five thousand years ago vegetable foods were being consumed, though evidence is not sufficient to show whether

* Chapters VI–XIV have been written by G. T. Rimmington.

the vegetables were collected or cultivated. It is possible that cultivation in Malawi had its beginnings with Nachikufan man.

Nachikufan people were neither Bantu nor Bushmen, but seem to have combined other physical features in their make up, similar to those of the long-headed stock seen today in Somalia. Some were predominantly negroid in type, and their descendants may be seen in the isolated groups of non-Bantu baTwa inhabiting some parts of Central Africa today.

THE BANTU MIGRATION

Early in the Christian era came the Bantu incursions into Malawi. These were to bring about major ethnographic changes over considerable areas of Southern Africa. Bantu people, a blending of Hamitic and Negro stock, and united by a common language type rather than physique, were established south of the Zambezi river by the seventh century. The Arab geographer El Mas'udi, writing in 947, described them as 'a tribe of Abyssinians', indicating their migration from the Ethiopian borders. This was no single migration, however, but a succession of movements with a general southward trend, modified by the type of country through which the people passed, the exigencies of warfare, and subsistence possibilities. Groups were still moving southward into Malawi in the fourteenth and fifteenth centuries.

While the earlier groups entering Malawi had been mainly cattle herders, using the tsetse-free high grasslands as a highway to the South African *veldt*, later groups were predominantly agriculturalists, who brought with them the simple hoe and shifting cultivation from the dense forests of the Congo Basin, in which they had probably sought refuge for a time from more warlike neighbours.

Wherever the cultivating newcomers settled they either absorbed or pushed into more isolated areas the smaller and weaker baTwa groups. There are surviving legends among the Cewa of the Central Province which record their defeat of a baTwa group near the site of the present-day town of Lilongwe. While the baTwa have retained their separate identity in some areas of Moçambique and Zambia, in Malawi they have lost their distinctiveness, but their physical characteristics may be seen in some of the small negroid people of the hilly areas.

THE LATE EIGHTEENTH AND NINETEENTH CENTURIES

During the eighteenth and early nineteenth centuries Malawi was inhabited by various branches of the Malawi tribe. With no strong tribal organization Malawi soon became sub-divided into three main groupings, the Sena, the Nyanja (or Mang'anja), and the Cewa (or Cipeta). The Sena and Nyanja inhabited large areas of the Lower Shire Valley, while the Cewa took themselves to the highlands of the Central Province, where they spilt over the rift valley escarpment into the lake-shore areas. The Tumbuka and associated smaller tribes had entered the Mzimba and Karonga areas from the north. The population was not large; enormous areas were still uninhabited. Highlands, such as the Vipya and Nyika plateaux and the Kirk Range were populated only at their margins, as also were large afforested areas such as the Dzalanyama Forest in Lilongwe and Dedza districts. Waterless areas were common. The Bwanje Valley, a dried-up arm of Lake Nyasa, was completely uninhabited for this reason, although containing light, fertile, easily-worked soils. Along the lake-shore population was limited to a narrow ribbon of settlements along the waterline. In the Lower Shire Valley population was probably fairly dense, though changing from year to year as a result of periodic flooding. On the highlands villages were more settled, but very small, and in defensive groupings, though with no tribal organization beyond loose and temporary alliances.

The relatively peaceful settlement of the Malawi groups was unsettled by the spread of the slave trade into the Lake Nyasa area. Slavery of a domestic type had been common among the Bantu for a long time, but this was different in kind from the slavery introduced by Europeans, Arabs, and those African tribes which assisted them. The former was more lenient than European serfdom; the latter was cruel, involving transportation to a new land under frightful conditions.

During the eighteenth century there was little evidence of the slave trade, only the occasional raid into the territory, although elsewhere it was at its height. The nineteenth century was different. With the suppression of the slave trade in West Africa in 1840, and the continued demand for slaves in Brazil until 1878, the half-caste Portuguese traders turned their attention to the Lake Nyasa area. Later the Arabs also extended their activities to Malawi, for slavery continued on in Zanzibar and Arabia until much later.

The main slave routes to Malawi lay along the Rovuma valley, across Lake Nyasa to Kota Kota, which grew up as a major inland staging point for the interior of Central Africa. Another important route lay along the valleys of the Matandu, Luweya, and Ruhuhu rivers to Manda on the eastern shore of Lake Nyasa, and thence across the lake to Deep Bay, with its Karonga hinterland.

The extension of slaving had two main effects. It had far-reaching effects on the settlement patterns and tribal organization of the Cewa–Nyanja and Tumbuka people; it brought other settlers into the country, some, like the Yao and Ngoni, to enslave, others, like the British, in order to prevent slavery, to spread the Christian gospel, and to engage in commerce.

The Cewa–Nyanja, with their loose tribal organization and small scattered villages, had at first no defence against the slavers, and were often forced to flee from the lake-shore settlements into the hills and woodlands. It is significant that even today the Cewa chiefdoms of Kasumbu and Kaphuka are situated very close to Dedza and Chongoni mountains. In both cases oral tradition supports the suggestion that the mountains were refuges in troubled times. Livingstone noted settlement on Zomba mountain in 1859.

The first Yao incursions into Malawi were probably peaceful. The original tribal home was to the east of Lake Nyasa, near to a grass-covered hill between Mwembe and the Luchilingo Range. During the nineteenth century there was a period of famine in this area. This, together with internal dissension and a defeat by the Lomwe, resulted in the breaking away of a number of sections. Of a total of ten sections there were four which moved westward at different times into Malawi, settling around the southern shores of Lake Nyasa, from where they fanned out, most of them towards and into the Shire Highlands. Smaller numbers moved northwards along the lake-shore, extending as far as Salima. The earlier groups were often dependent on the hospitality of the Cewa–Nyanja people among whom they settled.

The period of peaceful penetration did not last long, for the relatively peaceful Mangoche Yao were followed by the more warlike Machinga Yao, who settled in force in the Fort Johnston area, pushing the Mangoche group southwards further into the Shire Highlands. The latter in their turn made war on the inhabitants of the new areas in which they settled, resulting in substantial changes in the human geography of large areas.

Dedza district was penetrated by two waves under Ndindi and Tambala. The former settled north of the present day Ntakataka Mission, where he murdered Sosola, the local Cewa chief, and enslaved his people. The latter climbed the rift valley escarpment and settled with his people in the area which his descendants still occupy on the high plateau to the north-east of Chongoni mountain, the local Cewa being either enslaved or driven farther west to the margins of the Lilongwe Plain.

The ease with which the Yao enslaved the Cewa–Nyanja people encouraged the newcomers to trade in slaves with the Arabs, who followed the Yao invasions and established themselves in the courts of the most powerful chiefs. The result was that slaving forays extended over considerable areas, driving Cewa, Nyanja, and weaker Yao groups into more inaccessible areas.

Human geography was further complicated by the Ngoni invasions, which influenced much wider areas than the Yao invasions. Indeed there were few areas entirely unaffected by them. Warlike pastoralists, the Ngoni became, like the Zulu from whom they had fled, highly efficient fighting units. Two distinct groups moved northwards independently across the Zambezi river in the 1830s, both entering Malawi near to Domwe mountain, on the present frontier with Moçambique to the west of Dedza township.

Zwangendaba's Ngoni entered Malawi earlier than Maseko's Ngoni. They encamped for a time on the Lilongwe Plain, depopulating the area by their destruction of Cewa villages, in which they killed the adult males and took away the women and children. They continued northwards along the Luangwa–Nyasa watershed to the headwaters of the Luangwa near the southern shores of Lake Tanganyika. Some sections of this group were later to return to Malawi, where they settled in the Henga valley in 1851. Mombera's Ngoni, as this group became, carried out numerous raids on the Tumbuka, Tonga, Cewa, and Nkonde tribes living in the area. The Tumbuka, who were more numerous than the others, and who had been densely settled in the fertile Henga valley, suffered most of all. The result was that they fled to the Nyika and rift valley escarpments.

Following on the heels of the earlier migration Maseko's Ngoni arrived at Domwe mountain to find Zwangendaba encamped only a short distance to the north. There were, therefore, few cattle left in the area, and Maseko moved eastwards over the escarpment, where for a time he camped near to the present site of Mua Roman Catholic Mission, at the northern edge of the Livulezi step fault overlooking the lake littoral. This was not an area with many cattle, and it was only a short time before he crossed the Shire river and headed northward into Tanganyika, thereafter wandering in Portuguese territory, before eventually returning and settling on the Kirk Range and the Ntakataka area of the Dedza lake-shore. Others moved in a splinter group to the margins of the Lilongwe Plain.

The Ngoni were not a party to the slave trade in the same way as the Yao, but they subjected many of the defeated to the status of the domestic slave. It is significant that many chiefs of the Central and Northern Provinces today can trace their descent from Ngoni invaders, while the majority of people in their chiefdoms are members of other tribes. The Ngoni lived in densely populated village clusters under strong chiefs, while others too, such as the Cewa, began to organize themselves similarly, bringing about significant changes, not only in settlement patterns and tribal organization, but also in economic organization.

Wherever the Ngoni went they increased the numbers of their cattle. It was for this reason that they followed watersheds as far as possible on their journeys, for highlands were more likely to be free of *trypanosomiasis* and to possess richer grasslands. Their cultivation methods were wasteful of natural resources, as the crowding of people into larger groups of settlements had resulted in little regard being paid to the need for soil regeneration. Monocropping of maize and the overgrazing by very large numbers of poor quality cattle soon produced soil exhaustion and erosion on a large scale. This soon brought about the need to move on to other areas. Professor P. Gourou, in *The Tropical World*, states that the Ngoni had 'an advanced system of agriculture in which erosion was checked by the construction of banks of earth along the contours . . .' On the whole this is not true, for Gourou has generalized from a particular instance. In a few instances in the Kamenya–Gwaza area of Dedza district and the Gomani area of Ncheu district the Ngoni were practising a more advanced form of agriculture before British rule, but this was because they had domestic slaves from the local Cewa, whose own agricultural practices were fairly advanced. In most areas the Ngoni economic system was far from advanced.

Yao and Ngoni were followed by the British. Dr. David Livingstone made four journeys into the Lake Nyasa–Shire valley areas between 1858 and 1866, being the first European to take news of Lakes Chilwa

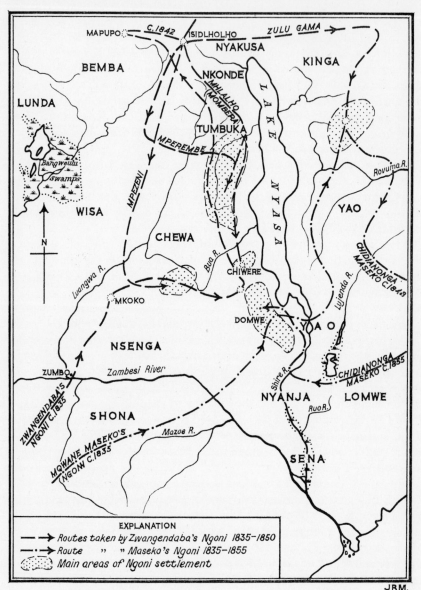

Fig. 28.   Ngoni movements during the nineteenth century.

and Nyasa to the outside world. He was also the bringer of Christianity and European concepts to Malawi. Appalled by the chaotic social and economic conditions brought about by the slave trade he felt that the introduction of Christianity should be accompanied by commerce.

Following Livingstone's precepts the aim of the early missionaries was to survey the country geographically and to establish a number of mission stations which combined evangelism with commerce, but their work had other geographical influences too. New settlement patterns

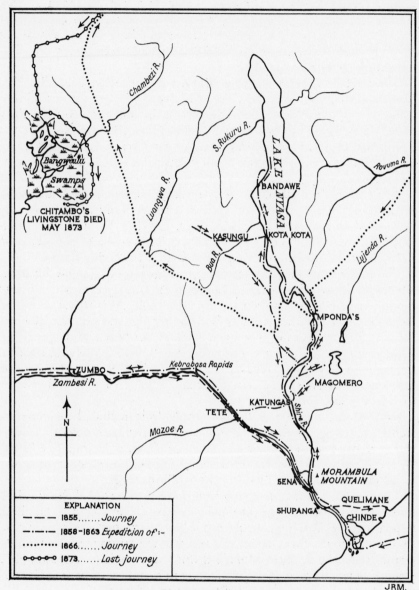

Fig. 29. Dr. Livingstone's journeys.

were brought about, and conflict with slave traders and the Portuguese was finally to bring about the declaration of British protection in the area. Thereafter were to come the definition of boundaries and settled administration that have been such important factors in bringing about a national consciousness among the territory's inhabitants.

K

The first mission settlement was not a success. A party of seven, headed by Bishop Mackenzie, the vanguard of the Universities Mission to Central Africa, established itself at Magomero, between Blantyre and Zomba. Magomero lay at the edge of an area recently invaded by Yao, and it was soon found necessary to used armed force to prevent the slaving activities of these people. It was not long before a series of disasters culminating in the death of Bishop Mackenzie forced the withdrawal of the mission in 1876.

Other missions were entering Malawi in the meantime. The Free Church of Scotland and the Church of Scotland were anxious also to follow in the footsteps of their compatriot, in order to sever the slave trade routes which Livingstone had indicated. In 1875 Dr. Robert Laws established the Livingstonia mission. A year later a second and larger mission was established in the Mudi valley, and named Blantyre, after Livingstone's birthplace.

While the Scots missionaries were settling themselves the Universities Mission to Central Africa had retreated temporarily to Zanzibar. By 1886 they had worked their way back towards Malawi and established a mission station on Likoma Island. They had also put a boat on Lake Nyasa for the interception of Arab dhows carrying slaves.

The missionary activities encouraged a group of Glasgow businessmen to found the African Lakes Corporation, the object of which was to promote trade in goods to replace the slave trade. As it aimed to supplement the missionary activities its first trading post was near the Blantyre Mission, but it soon put a steamer on to Lake Nyasa and opened up another station at Karonga. The latter developed rapidly with the construction in 1883 of the Stevenson road, linking it with the London Missionary Society's stations in the Lake Tanganyika area, and opening up a hinterland for trade.

By 1883 the number of British people, who included missionaries, traders, and some planters, had increased so much that a British Consul was accredited to the 'Kings and Chiefs of Central Africa'. The British Government headed by Lord Salisbury refused, however, at this stage, to declare the country a British sphere of influence.

There were two factors which were soon to reverse Salisbury's decision. The first was that the missions needed to be protected. It had been hoped that physical force would not be necessary, but it was quite clear that armed conflict was inevitable, and that the missionaries and traders would be forced to leave Malawi if this was forbidden. Accordingly a private Defence Force, including among its members the young Captain (later Lord) Lugard, was raised to fight in Karonga.

The second factor was the realization by 1888 that the Portuguese were hoping to extend their hegemony to include Malawi. An expedition under Serpo Pinto was then being prepared. Its ostensible purpose was scientific investigation, but its real purpose may well have been imperialistic. The 'scramble' for Africa was under way. To thwart the Portuguese H. H. Johnston was despatched (with financial support from

Cecil Rhodes) to Moçambique as British Consul, with instructions to 'proceed up the Zambezi and report on the extent of Portuguese rule in the vicinity of that river'. Approval was later given for the securing of conditional treaties with tribes beyond the limits of Portuguese jurisdiction.

In July 1889 Johnston's gunboat sailed into the recently discovered Chinde mouth, and through the delta, into the main Zambezi river beyond. Successfully forestalling Pinto *en route* Johnston reached the Shire river determined that 'our Nyasaland will become a kind of African Servia or Paraguay, an inland state with direct fluvial communications with the sea'. Before the end of 1889 he had concluded treaties with the chiefs of the Lower Shire, the Shire Highlands, and the western shores of Lake Nyasa. At Karonga he had negotiated a truce between the Arabs and the African Lakes Corporation.

As Johnston planned to continue northwards into the Lake Tanganyika area disquieting news came from the south. Following a skirmish between the Makololo and the Portuguese expedition on the Ruo river, the Acting Consul in Blantyre had, as earlier instructed by Johnston, declared a British Protectorate over the Makololo and Yao areas in southern Nyasaland. The Portuguese had crossed the Ruo and occupied Katungu's area (now Chikwawa), and given notice of their intention to occupy the Shire Highlands. This was forestalled, however, by an agreement between the British and Portuguese governments to allow all British claims to the Shire Highlands.

With the boundaries defined and the administration set up in 1891 Nyasaland came into existence as a state in the modern sense. By the end of the nineteenth century it was pacified. The Ngoni and Yao were contained in the areas they had conquered, the Cewa, Nyanja, Tumbuka, and other peoples were freed from the fear of slavery, Christian mission work began in earnest, and commerce in cash crops began to take the place of the slave trade. But the past has been stamped on the face of the country. Tribal distributions, settlement patterns and population densities, mission and trading company sites, were all to continue to reflect past struggles and opportunities. With the twentieth century, however, were to come many new developments, overshadowing and modifying the earlier human geography, making the present country seem very different from that which Livingstone and Johnston knew.

BIBLIOGRAPHY

Y. B. Abdallah, 'Chikala cha Wayao', translated and edited by M. Sanderson as *The History of the Yao* (1919).

L. J. Brass, 'Vernay Expedition Report 1946', *Nyasa. Jour.*, Vol. VII (ii).

J. D. Clark, 'The Prehistory of Nyasaland', *Nyasa. Jour.*, Vol. IX (i).

——, *'The Prehistory of Southern Africa'* Penguin Books (1959).

El Mas'udi, *Meadows of Gold and Mines of Gems, c.* 947 (translated by Sprenger, 1841).

P. Gourou, *The Tropical World*, Longmans (Second Edition, 1958).

S. Green, 'Blantyre Mission', *Nyasa. Jour.*, Vol. X (ii).

J. C. Mitchell, *The Yao Village*, Manchester Univ. Press (1956).

——, 'Preliminary Notes on Land Tenure and Agriculture among the Machinga Yao', *Nyasa. Jour.*, Vol. V (ii).

'The Nyika Plateau, Richard Crawshay's Impression in 1893', *Nyasa. Jour.*, Vol. VII (ii).

R. Oliver, and J. D. Fage, *A Short History of Africa*, Penguin Books (1962).

J. G. Pike, 'The Pre-historical Climates of Nyasaland', *Nyasa. Jour.*, Vol. XIII (ii).

——, 'A Brief Note on the Upper Pleistocene Raised Beach', *Nyasa. Jour.*, Vol. XI (i).

W. H. J. Rangeley, 'Mtwalo', *Nyasa. Jour.*, Vol. V (i).

——, 'The Makololo of Dr. Livingstone', *Nyasa. Jour.*, Vol. XII (i).

——, 'The Origins of the Principal Street Names of Blantyre and Limbe', *Nyasa. Jour.*, Vol. XI (ii).

G. T. Rimmington, 'The Historical Geography of Population Growth in the Dedza District of Nyasaland', *Nyasa. Jour.*, Vol. XVI (ii).

O. H. Robertson, 'Trade and the Suppression of Slavery in British Central Africa', *Nyasa. Jour.*, Vol. XIII (ii).

P. T. Terry, 'African Agriculture in Nyasaland, 1858 to 1894', *Nyasa. Jour.*, Vol. XIV (ii).

M. Tew, 'People of the Lake Nyasa Region' O.U.P. (1950).

F. Winspear, 'A Short History of the Universities Mission to Central Africa', *Nyasa. Jour.*, Vol. IX (i).

T. C. Young, 'The Henga People in Northern Nyasaland', *Nyasa. Jour.*, Vol. V (i).

——, *History of the Tumbuka–Nkamanga Peoples* (1935).

CHAPTER VII

POPULATION

THE average population density of Malawi is higher than that of any other country in Central Africa. While in Zambia the average density is as low as eight people per square mile, in Malawi it is as high as seventy-three per square mile. Since 1921 the total population has increased rapidly, so that in forty years it has more than doubled, as Table XII shows.

TABLE XII

Population Increases since 1921

Years	Africans (de jure)	Europeans	Asians and Coloureds
1921	1,200,000	1,486	563
1926	1,291,000	1,686	?
1931	1,600,000	1,975	1,591
1945	2,180,000	1,948	2,804
1956	2,755,000	6,732	8,490
1960	2,840,000	9,500	13,200

As far as African population is concerned these figures cannot be regarded as more than estimates; often figures published in recent years by the Central African Statistical Office have conflicted with those compiled by the Nyasaland Government. For instance, the 1956 estimate by the former was 2,755,000, whereas figures published in the Nyasaland Report (1958) put the total at 2,600,000. Moreover, since 1945 annual estimates have been compiled at the same rate of increase evident between 1931 and 1945, which is almost certainly an under-estimation. The present population therefore is probably in excess of the official figures.

The increases in African population have been matched by a growth of European and Asian communities. In spite of the very large percentage increases since 1945, however, numbers are still comparatively small. Population figures published in respect of these racial groups are reasonably accurate, since they are compiled from an actual count.

In spite of the unreliability of statistical information in respect of African population there can be no doubt that numbers have increased so much that pressure on the land has become serious, for there has been no proportional increase in commerce and industry to absorb the increased labour supply.

FACTORS CONTRIBUTING TO AFRICAN POPULATION
INCREASES

It is not possible to isolate natural increase and immigration as factors in population increase, for there are no accurate figures or even
estimates which enable us to do so. Historical and sociological investigation, however, suggests that both have contributed large shares.

The rate of natural increase has become greater since the ending of
inter-tribal warfare and the slave trade. It is probable that the death
and transportation of many kept the population stable before the ad-
vent of the British Protectorate, in spite of a high birth rate, which has
for long been a feature of Bantu life.

A high birth rate has been a necessity among the African population
of Malawi and adjoining territories for so long that it has become a
part of social custom and is an essential part of the economic system.

There are few African women who remain unmarried. This stems in
part from the matrilineal and uxorilocal social system (which is typical
of all tribes other than the Ngoni, Tumbuka, and Nkonde). The man
without a wife has, in many cases, no land of his own, and therefore no
means of obtaining his living. If he marries he may share in his wife's
land; if he obtains two wives he will have an even better living. Hence
all women have their husbands, a widow being inherited by a deceased
husband's brother.

The economic system results from the man's earlier role as a hunter
and warrior, which left the woman on the land. The woman without a
husband had no protector. Moreover the childless had no support in old
age. Hence the ridicule which is often heaped on to the heads of those
women who are sterile, and the rise in status attached to motherhood.

A high infant mortality has been a further incentive to the production
of large families. In earlier times this was essential for population main-
tenance. With the growth of medical facilities and the consequent decline in the death rate it is common to find four or five children in a
family surviving to adulthood.

Medical facilities not only reduce infant mortality but enable adults
too, to live longer. Unfortunately there are no statistics to enable us to
measure significant changes in the death rate.

The substantial immigration which has also been responsible for
swelling population densities has come about through three main
causes. During the whole of the period of British Protection there has
been substantial movement of population from Moçambique. Some
came during times of water shortage and famine. During the early
1920s there was a succession of dry seasons in east-central Africa. It
brought about some drying up of water sources in Malawi, but in
Moçambique the position was much worse. This brought about the
migration of large numbers of Lomwe people into the relatively wetter
Shire Highlands and the margins of the Mlanje massif.

Other population movements were forced by the Portuguese during the 1920s and early 1930s following quarrels between Africans on either side of the Malawi borders, and the tendency for people to avoid payment of taxes by moving over the border temporarily at the appropriate time of year. The greatest increases occurred in the Central Province, particularly in Dedza and Ncheu districts.

In Dedza the District Books give a fairly clear indication of the extent of this migration. Administrative areas of the district with sections of the southern end of the Lilongwe Plain within their boundaries all increased the number of taxable huts during 1924, one showing a 17 per cent. increase.

In the Southern Province large numbers of Africans entered the country to seek work on European estates as labourers and house servants. Others sought land in the vicinity of towns because of other factors, such as the possibility of growing cash crops for the European market. The tea estates in Mlanje and Cholo districts attracted many Nguru from over the eastern border of Malawi.

DISTRIBUTION OF AFRICAN POPULATION

There is a marked irregularity in population densities throughout Malawi. Because of the lack of perennial water supplies and sharp changes in physiography areas with very high densities are often contiguous with low density areas.

The dominant physical feature of Malawi is the Great Rift Valley, in which the Shire Valley illustrates the sharp variations in population density. Entering the country from the south the Port Herald district is observed to be very densely populated between the foot of the Port Herald Hills to the west and the Shire River to the east. Average density on cultivated land is about 334 per square mile, though there is a tendency for intense wet seasons to bring about flooding in areas adjacent to the river, resulting in periodic migration to drier areas in Chikwawa district farther north. As Port Herald district has little commerce or industries, and is not self-supporting agriculturally, the Nyasaland Government has, in the past, encouraged migration to relieve pressure on the land. Between 1931 and 1945 the number of Africans in Chikwawa increased from 35,892 to 59,664, while in Port Herald there was a corresponding decrease from 81,410 to 66,746. Recent population estimates (1960) indicate that any relief then gained has been more than offset by recent population increases, for the African population of Port Herald is 92,990 and of Chikwawa 83,050. Fortunately the overcrowding in alluvial areas is not as great as may be imagined, for a programme of well digging and the drilling of bore-holes has enabled settlement to spread out on to higher ground. Nevertheless the density is still too high for soil fertility to be maintained by traditional methods of agricultural production.

North of Chikwawa the Murchison cataracts mark an area in which the soils are dry, sterile, and stony, extending beyond Matope almost to Liwonde. These areas have less than ten people per square mile, and in

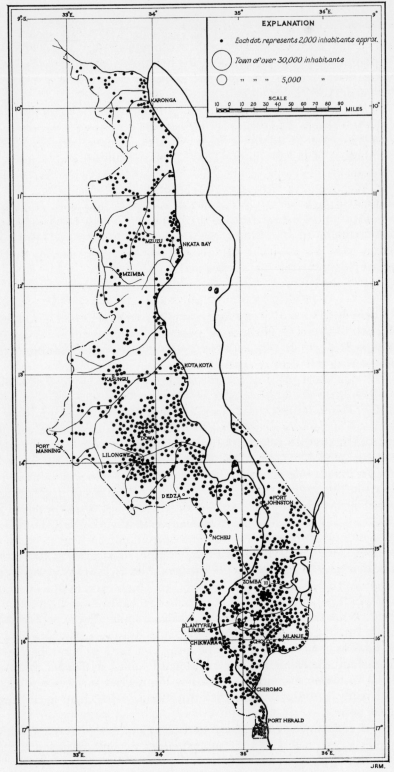

Fig. 30.   Distribution of population in Malawi.

most parts will probably remain so for some considerable time. Even where richer alluvial soils exist, however, population is still sparse, reflecting the lack of perennial water supplies and communications. There are few roads, and even the Shire river is unnavigable, so there is no outlet for cash crops. Population tends to be concentrated along rivers. For instance, in Blantyre district the Lisungwe valley has a density of 182 per square mile, while the surrounding areas are virtually uninhabited.

Between Liwonde and Lake Nyasa the riverside population increases, particularly around Lake Malombe, where rice and maize may be grown intensively as the water level recedes after each wet season. At Liwonde the chiefdom has an average density of more than thirty people per square mile, while at Nyambi (near Fort Johnston) there are more than 56 per square mile. In the latter area increases are considered to be in the region of 3·5 per cent. per annum. Outside the riverine tracts and the lake-shore areas the population is as sparse as it is in the Murchison cataracts section.

North of Fort Johnston the Great Rift Valley is largely occupied by Lake Nyasa, around the shores of which the coastal plains are densely inhabited near to the water's edge. Extending for about two miles inland except where the escarpment marking the edge of the rift valley comes close to the shore, there are many inhabitants relying at least partly on fishing for a livelihood.

Beyond the lake-shore margins, between them and the escarpment foot, population is dense in patches, with intervening areas of very sparse population. Along most of the north-western shores of the lake the plain is very sparsely inhabited because of the lack of soils and water, much of the country consisting of gravel slopes. The few people have tended to be confined to a few dry season water-holes in the beds of dried up streams.

The most densely populated sections of the coastal plain are in the south, between Kota Kota and Fort Johnston, extending into the Bwanje valley, a dried up arm of the lake. The soils of the area are often very fertile, capable of producing two crops of maize a year, while the presence of the railway enables rice, cotton, and tobacco to be grown for sale in Blantyre. Yet even within the section there are large areas devoid of surface water and, therefore, also of population. Moreover, soils vary too, from very rich alluvium in the river valleys to soils with a high saline content, the latter's use being restricted to uninhabited *mopane* woodland. Population has become of high density, locally more than 500 per square mile, alongside areas where rivers broaden out into a *dambo* formation. The future is unlikely to bring about any significant changes in density patterns for some considerable time, for away from the rivers and streams the water table tends to dip sharply away, sometimes lying at more than 150 feet below the surface. In the Bwanje valley, where few people lived until the 1930s, government water-borings have made possible the resettlement of many people from congested areas of the Southern Province.

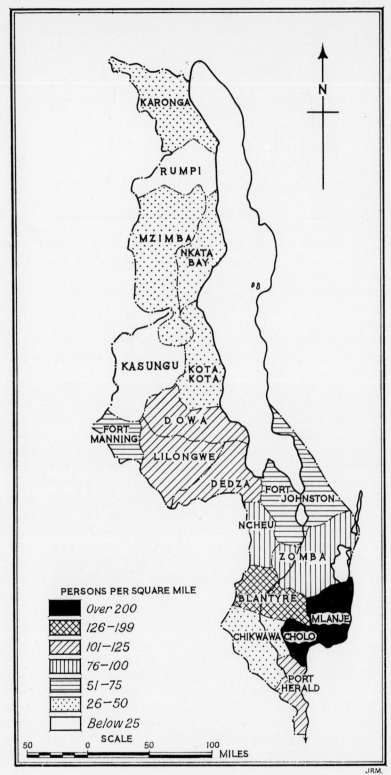

PERSONS PER SQUARE MILE

Over 200
126–199
101–125
76–100
51–75
26–50
Below 25

SCALE

50   0   50   100

MILES

JRM.

Fig. 31. Population densities in Malawi.

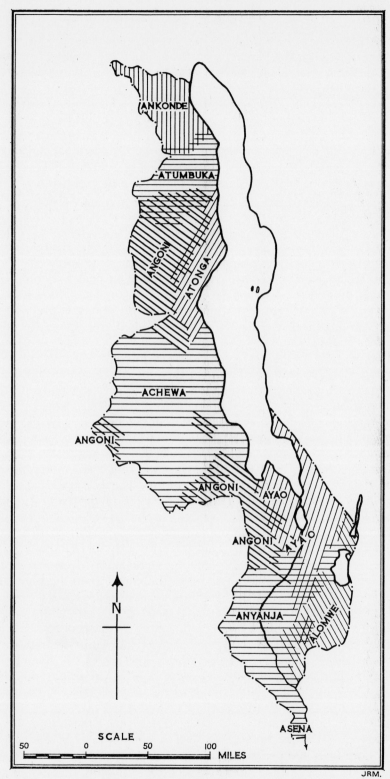

ANKONDE

ATUMBUKA

ANGONI

ATONGA

ACHEWA

ANGONI

ANGONI

AYAO

ANGONI

AYAO

ANYANJA

ALOMWE

ASENA

N

SCALE

50   0   50   100

MILES

JRM.

Fig. 32.   Tribal distributions in Malawi.

Most of the people of Malawi live on the high plateaux up to an altitude of about 5,000 feet, for climate is cooler and diseases less rampant than in the Great Rift Valley. Density variations are considerable, however.

Escarpment zones are generally without population, settlement having been discouraged in the past. Soils are poor and easily eroded. Deforestation tends to bring about an earlier drying up of streams running from them as the dry season proceeds. Occasionally, however, there are breaks of slope, where the lessening of gradient makes settlement possible. In Dedza district the main rift valley escarpment falls from 5,000 to 1,850 feet. At an altitude of between 2,600 feet in the south and 2,000 feet in the north a step fault has resulted in the formation of the Livulezi 'shelf'. Scattered settlements occur here, and population density is low, except near to the Roman Catholic mission station at the northern end, and along the road leading southwards.

The higher plateau surfaces vary in population density mainly because of soil and relief variations. In the north the population is relatively sparse. The Nyika and Vipya plateaux are almost entirely uninhabited, being bleak and relatively inaccessible. Large areas surrounding these massifs also have low densities as a result of very poor stony and sandy soils. No district of the Northern Province has more than 45 people per square mile, and most of these people live along the lakeshore, so that rarely does population exceed 20 per square mile in the higher areas.

In the upper South Rukuru river system perennial streams have encouraged a denser than average population which exceeds 70 per square mile.

The highlands of the Central Province are in general more densely populated than the highlands farther north. The Lilongwe Plain has large areas of fertile red soils. This, coupled with the frequent incidence of perched water tables beneath grassy *dambos*, has encouraged a rapid increase of population during the past three decades. Inter-tribal warfare before the present century kept the area fairly sparsely populated, but peaceful conditions brought about population movements from the Dedza–Chongoni mountain region into the more promising plain. In addition people expelled from Moçambique during the 1920s and early 1930s were settled in the area. Dedza District Books show that the native authority areas of Pemba I and Kaphuka had increases of 55 per cent. (3,651 huts) and 25 per cent. (1,546 huts) respectively in the number of huts assessed for taxation purposes between 1926 and 1933. Population density in Dedza district increased by 21·5 to 76 per square mile between 1926 and 1931. Ripple movements of population northwards were later to increase densities in Lilongwe district.

At present both Lilongwe and Dedza districts have population densities exceeding 100 per square mile. Many parts of the Lilongwe Plain have more than 400 per square mile; even on the margins, where the red soils merge with the light sands, densities probably exceed 350 per

square mile. Dowa district also has high density areas in the undulating
but fertile land surrounding Dowa township.

Beginning in Dedza district and ending at the Shire Valley in Blantyre
district is the Kirk Range, forming the watershed boundary with Moçambique to the west. There are large areas where protruding rock
massifs, with their lack of soils and high altitude, make settlement impossible. Dedza, Chongoni, Dzonze, and other large masses have no
population on their plateau summits, but in each case they are fringed
with a moderate population density attracted by the perennial streams
which run from them.

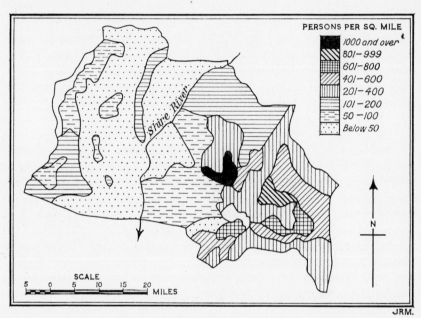

Fig. 33.   Distribution of population in Blantyre district (after C. A. Baker).
(Note that Blantyre–Limbe is unshaded.)

In Dedza and Ncheu districts there are inter-montane plateaux,
where relatively fertile soils support densities of more than one hundred
people per square mile. In Kamenya-Gwaza, to the south of Dedza
mountain, densities exceed 200 per square mile.

Further south the plateau surface rises to more than 6,000 feet between Nzama (Ncheu district) and Neno. Higher rainfall (about 50
inches), the prevalence of mists, and lack of tree shelter make the area
bleak and inhospitable. Nevertheless the development of wheat and
potato growing makes it possible for the Neno and Goche areas to support more than 50 people per square mile.

The most densely populated areas in the country are Blantyre, Cholo,
and Mlanje districts. Already fairly densely populated (probably more
than 100 per square mile) by the end of the nineteenth century the protection from slavery and employment possibilities offered by European

settlement has increased densities considerably in the Blantyre area of the Shire Highlands. By 1926 it was estimated that densities in this area were between 150 and 250 people per square mile. Today there are densities of as high as 800 per square mile in sections served by adequate roads and public transport. Even in the Chiradzulu sub-district, however, where there are many rocky outcrops, steep slopes, and thin soils, the average density is about 470 per square mile.

In the Zomba area, where there is also the possibility of work on European estates and in government departments, African population is again densely settled. The nearest Yao chiefdom, Malemia, has a density of about 250 per square mile. There are small pockets of higher densities.

The Mlanje plateau is uninhabited, but the tea plantations at its foot provide work for many people, principally of the Nguru tribal group. Furthermore, the fertile plain soils between Mlanje and the Shire Highlands support a large agricultural population. In both Mlanje and Cholo districts overall densities exceed 200 per square mile.

MIGRATION OF AFRICANS

It has been estimated that about 20 to 25 per cent. of the adult male population of Malawi find employment outside their own country at some time in their lives. As a result of this some northern districts, such as Rumpi and Nkata Bay, experience a dearth of able-bodied men. This has serious social and economic repercussions. Where few able-bodied men remain the productivity of an area is much impaired, so that food supplies raised locally are not sufficient to meet demand. This raises the price of essential foodstuffs considerably. The additional income derived from the remittance of earnings elsewhere to relatives in Malawi, or brought in by returning migrants, is not always sufficient to cope with this contingency.

An obvious social repercussion is the break in family life occasioned by the separation of husbands and wives. Marriage has come to be regarded as little more than a temporary union. To lessen the incidence of divorce the government requires unaccompanied males to return to Malawi after two years away.

Malawi Africans have for many years contributed to the labour forces of adjoining territories. Some even reach as far as the Witwatersrand, where they enjoy a good reputation for intelligence. Large numbers are recruited by agents for the mining industries, but many also migrate individually. In 1958 about 169,000 men were absent from the country. Of these 123,000 were estimated to be in Southern Rhodesia, 26,000 in South Africa, 19,000 in Zambia, and the remaining 1,000 elsewhere. Organizations recruiting labour do so under the Governor's permit. The quota of recruits and the areas from which they are taken is determined by the organizations' requirements and also by the locality's needs. The planting season, which extends from October until February, is normally a period when recruiting is not permitted.

Under the Tripartite Labour Agreement of 1947, migrant workers are required to remit a portion of their earnings for the upkeep of families in Malawi. In 1958 an estimated £1·75 million was remitted.

Throughout Southern Africa the migratory labour system is a significant factor in the social and economic systems of all the territories lying on the periphery of the industrial and European agricultural areas of South Africa and the Rhodesias. The gold mining industry of the Witwatersrand depends largely on migrant labour; in 1958 more than half a million men were drawn from Basutoland, Swaziland, Bechuanaland, Angola, Moçambique, Tanganyika, and Malawi.

Most men are absent from Malawi for a period between fourteen months and two years. On returning they tend often to prefer leisure rather than contribute to agriculture. When all their savings have been consumed they tend often to return to their former occupation, becoming migrant workers again.

There will always be migration of labour from relatively poor countries to relatively rich countries. Unless Malawi is able to develop large scale industry (which, in view of the lack of mineral resources, is very unlikely) the migration rate is likely to be maintained.

EUROPEAN AND ASIAN POPULATION

Europeans and Asians are insignificant when numbers alone are taken into consideration, for Africans outnumber all other races by more than one hundred and twenty to one. The Europeans, however, have not only brought the country into existence, but have guided its affairs over more than sixty years. The Asians were among those who helped to pacify the territory, and have built up large commercial and professional interests. These minority groups are not, therefore, unimportant as far as influence and economic development are concerned.

Europeans in Malawi tend to be missionaries, farmers, business men, or civil servants. Only in recent years have numbers increased rapidly. In 1945 there were no more than 1,948 Europeans, but by 1960 the number was 9,500.

People in all categories may be found in Blantyre district, where more than 40 per cent. of the European population is concentrated. Most of these are concentrated within the municipality of Blantyre-Limbe. Zomba district records show a European population of 1,520, most of whom are civil servants and their families. Numbers in Lilongwe district are slightly less than a thousand, most of whom are engaged in government service or commerce. Only in Cholo (790) and Mlanje (407) are there substantial numbers of Europeans engaged in agriculture, for in these districts are the large tea estates.

Throughout the rest of the country the pattern is similar. Here and there one finds the occasional European farmer, especially in the healthier highland districts. Missionary stations dotted about the countryside usually have a number of Europeans engaged in pastoral, medical, and educational work. The largest concentrations are always in the district administrative centres (*bomas*), where almost the entire European population consists of civil servants and their dependents.

The European population is predominantly British, young, and vigorous. Although the birth rate is high, its future is uncertain. 'Africanization' of many civil service posts is tending to result in the premature departure of some, though in any case most would have retired to their countries of origin in due course. On the other hand, with the rapid increase in government services, particularly education, forecast for the future, there is likely to be a rapid increase in the numbers of young Europeans unlikely to stay for more than two or three years. In course of time numbers will diminish as these posts are filled by Africans.

The Asian population consists of people originating from India and Pakistan. Sir Harry Johnston introduced Asians to Malawi in 1891, when his small military force consisted mainly of Sikhs. Asian immigration was thereafter encouraged for the purpose of filling minor government posts. It was not long before Africans were capable of undertaking this type of work, and Asians, having no land, became mainly storekeepers and professional people.

As Africans are rarely able to accumulate capital the bulk of the country's trade is in Asian hands, so that Asians can be found in all populous centres, and indeed wherever any volume of trade can be handled.

The largest Asian communities are found significantly in those areas where both African and European population densities are greatest. In Blantyre district there are almost 5,000 Asians, most of whom are resident in the Blantyre–Limbe municipality. In Zomba, Cholo, and Mlanje districts the numbers are more than a thousand in each case. Lilongwe has about 900 Asians.

Asian numbers are significantly small in the sparsely populated and economically poor Northern Province, though no district administrative centre is without its near-by Asian trading centre.

The total Asian population now exceeds the number of Europeans, being more than 11,000. Their birthrate is high, and many Asians are now permanently domiciled, so population is likely to increase rapidly in the future.

BIBLIOGRAPHY

C. A. Baker, 'A Note on Nguru Immigration in Nyasaland', *Nyasa. Jour.*, Vol. XIV (i).

——, 'Blantyre District: A Geographical Appreciation of the Growth, Distribution and Composition of its Population', *Nyasa. Jour.*, Vol. XII (i).

S. J. K. Baker and R. T. White, 'The Distribution of Native Population over Southeast Central Africa', *Geog. Jour.*, Vol. CXII.

F. Dixey, 'The Distribution of Population in Nyasaland', *Geog. Review*, Vol. XVIII.

——, 'The Nyasaland Section of the Great Rift Valley', *Geog. Jour.*, Vol. XCII.

——, *A Practical Handbook of Water Supply* (1931).

J. C. Mitchell, *The Yao Village* (1956).

W. B. Morgan, 'The Lower Shire Valley of Nyasaland: A Changing System of African Agriculture', *Geog. Jour.*, Vol. CXIX.

Nyasaland Census Reports, 1921, 1926, 1931, and 1945.

G. T. Rimmington, 'The Historical Geography of Population Growth in the Dedza District of Nyasaland', *Nyasa. Jour.*, Vol. XVI (ii).

L

CHAPTER VIII

RURAL SETTLEMENT PATTERNS

IT has been seen in the previous chapter that population in Malawi is to a great extent dependent on relief, soil types, and the availability of water supplies. These factors are also important in the determining of settlement types, but to them is added the culture of the people. The history and social organization of a people is as important as physical and economic factors.

The basic unit of African society is the extended family, a kinship group which has its geographical expression in the village or hamlet. A small cluster, often modified by the past need for defence, or by the development of communications, or by other factors, the village has often been regarded as a mere crowding of huts. It is more than this, as we shall show.

The traditional village is small. Duff MacDonald observed in the later nineteenth century that settlement in the Shire Highlands consisted mainly of small villages about a quarter of a mile apart. Hynde observed in 1895 that the villages in the Domasi area varied from five or six huts to about thirty. When villages grew beyond these points there was a tendency for fission to occur, and a small group would go into the bush to form the nucleus of a new village. This is consistent with the function of the village as an agricultural economic unity, for as it grows larger there is an increasing distance between the huts and the furthest limits of the cultivated land, so that unless there is a strong desire among the people to maintain unity there is a tendency for groups to break away. Often this is initiated by a violent quarrel with the headman, or by a disaster, such as the burning down of huts.

Except where affected by warfare the settlement pattern of earlier times may be envisaged as a mosaic of small nucleated settlements, distributed according to relief, water supplies, and soils. Villages on the Shire Highlands tended to be much more closely packed than settlements elsewhere.

One can still see the basic pattern in many areas, even though the superimposition of other settlement types has taken place. Moreover it can be seen in transition. There are hamlets with only two or three huts, clearly a result of 'calving' from a nearby larger village, and still recognizing, even if grudgingly, the authority of the headman of the parent village. Others have grown to six, seven, or eight huts, and have their own recognized headman, no longer subservient to the headman of the parent village. Others have a dozen or more huts, and have reached the stage at which 'calving' is imminent, or is actually taking place.

There has been little study of settlement patterns over the country as

a whole, so that for detailed consideration we are limited to samples
taken mainly from Dedza district.

SETTLEMENT ON A PLATEAU

Some of the level Miocene plateau surfaces tend to have a more complex settlement pattern than the relief would suggest. As an example of
settlement in this type of landscape we consider here the Dedza section
of the Lilongwe Plain, where historical influences are clearly seen.

Before 1900 most of the Lilongwe Plain was sparsely inhabited, large
areas being entirely devoid of population. Only in the south-east, on the
margins of the region, were settlements large. Earlier nineteenth century
Cewa villages had been very small and widely scattered, sited on *dambo*
margins. Within the *dambo* formations were 'perched' water tables yielding perennial water supplies, except in exceptionally dry years. On the
level plateau surface between *dambos* the woodland was cleared for
shifting cultivation.

The scattered nature and small size of the Cewa villages, together
with the lack of any permanent tribal organization, made these settlements vulnerable to attack by larger and well organized enemies. Before
the arrival of the Ngoni warfare was mainly the outcome of squabbles
between villages or groups of villages similarly organized, but it made no
significant changes in settlement patterns.

Far-reaching changes were made as a result of the Ngoni invasions.
Zwangendaba's group plundered the cattle and took away many of the
women before moving on northwards, so that population was reduced.
The ensuing settlement pattern was based partly on the agricultural
needs of the people, which had changed little, and the need for better
defence. *Dambo* margin sites were still favoured, though some villages on
the occasional rocky intrusions which rise above the level surface of the
plateau were founded during this period. Whereas there had formerly
been little contact between one village and the next, the new sites tended
to be nearer to other villages, so that help could be sought more easily.
Groups of villages, the individual settlements being small and not
usually more than six or seven huts in size, began to appear. As they
were linked together by recognition of a common chief, so these settlements, between seven and fifteen in number, were linked geographically, each village within a group being sited little more than half a mile
from the next. Between these groups forest and woodland and grassy
dambo country, uninhabited, stretched for as much as seven or eight miles.

The Cewa response to the new needs was similar to movements of the
same kind taking place in other parts of Africa. The Mende towns of
Sierra Leone were brought into existence by the agglomeration of
villages on the same site, all subject to the same paramount chief. The
Yoruba built walled towns to house villagers in large numbers. A similar development in Bantu Africa is evident in the Zimbabwe ruins of
Southern Rhodesia.

The main difference of the newer Cewa settlement pattern was the tendency to spread more, and to have no definite focus. The small village was nearer to its neighbours, and its headman acknowledged an authority in the group chief higher than his own, but there was no merging within a larger settlement. This was probably because the Cewa chiefs tended to be weak. They had no traditional authority. There is no evidence that any of them in this area distinguished themselves as great warriors; strong chiefs in Africa have been produced by long periods of

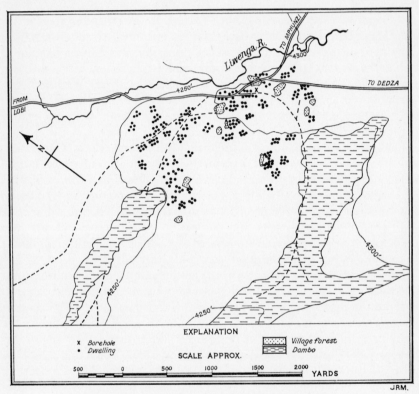

Fig. 34.   Kachere's village, Dedza District.

warfare, and the Lilongwe Plain was left relatively peaceful when the Ngoni warriors passed on.

Before the coming of European rule there was a further change in the basic settlement pattern, brought about by a second Ngoni invasion. Maseko's Ngoni became split into two chiefdoms. Gomani's people occupied the plateau areas between the present Dedza township and Ncheu, while Kachindamoto's people occupied the Dedza lake-shore area. A quarrel between the leaders of these groups resulted in Kachindamoto driving a wedge across the plateau which separated the main body of Gomani's people from a smaller group encamped around the site of Dedza township. The latter group, now called Kachere's Ngoni, moved westwards into the Lilongwe Plain, where they had no difficulty in subduing the Cewa.

The Ngoni chiefs were stronger than any of their Cewa predecessors, and their own villages were larger than any others in the area. Pemba's village in 1926 was one of three with a population of more than three hundred, and there are indications that it was once more populous. The larger village was a direct response to the growth in chiefly authority. Ngoni chiefs ruled over subject peoples far outnumbering their own followers, and needed the trappings of authority, warriors on hand to subdue any rebellion, slaves to cultivate their land, courts in which to try and condemn those who tried to flout authority, and counsellors to advise them. Thus the chiefs' villages tended to be large, and to consist of the chiefs' own huts, the huts of their counsellors and other Ngoni, and huts belonging to subject peoples enslaved.

Apart from the establishment of large chiefs' villages, of which only one now remains (Kachere's village), the Ngoni conquest resulted in other settlement types. To the south-east the villages consisted of two main types. There were those which had been in existence previously, and which remained much as before. There were others which were more complex in that they reflected in smaller measure the chiefs' villages. They were larger than the Cewa villages which they replaced, and consisted of a section inhabited by Ngoni and other hut clusters inhabited by subject people.

Cewa people in the north and west of the plain tended to move into the Dzalanyama forest, where they settled in small villages little different from those of pre-invasion times.

There was little disturbance of the settlement pattern resulting from the Ngoni invasion until after the end of the First World War, when a series of migrations from Portuguese territory began. This brought about very large increases in population and the establishment of the settlement patterns to be seen today. Although there were migrations between 1918 and 1923 the increase in numbers seems not at first to have resulted in the building of new villages. These migrations were mainly of individuals joining relatives and friends in existing settlements. In the area of Pemba I the number of huts registered for taxation purposes had increased by 30 per cent. between 1918 and 1919, and by a further 17 per cent. between 1919 and 1920. The increases were mainly in the villages of the south-western margins.

Later migrations from Moçambique were of whole communities, increasing considerably the numbers of villages in the native authority areas affected.

TABLE XIII

Village Increases in Dedza Section of the Lilongwe Plain

	1923	1927	Increase
Pemba I	126	158	32
Pemba II	34	37	3
Kaphuka	138	153	15
Total	298	348	50

As Pemba II consisted of the northern sections of the Lilongwe Plain the indications are that this area was little disturbed, and continued to be sparsely inhabited. The large number of villages in that area nowadays has come about by a northward flowing ripple movement between 1931 and 1945 on to the richer soils.

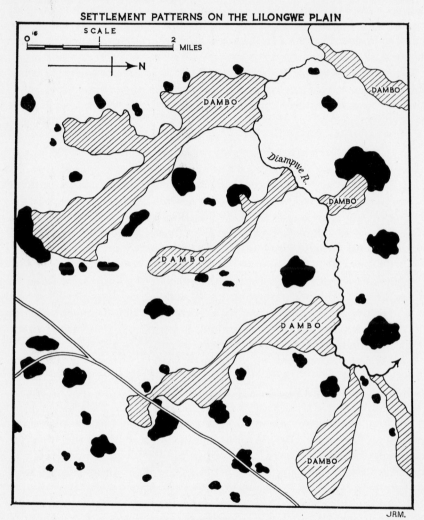

Fig. 35.

The above historical survey shows that settlement patterns today are based on tribal movements and conflicts, as modified by more recent developments, such as the alienation of land to Europeans, the establishment of forest reserves, natural increase, the development of communications, and the tendency for larger villages to disintegrate. Some of the latter factors will be mentioned in the sample studies of village types described below.

The most common village site is the *dambo* or river margin. Over most of the northern and western sections of the Lilongwe Plain the *dambos* usually have settlements stretching around their upper ends. Many of the larger villages are sited on the narrow isthmus often found between *dambos*, or between a *dambo* and a river course. The advantages of such a site are obvious. Water, either from a river or from a shallow well within a *dambo* bottom, is close at hand. It is rare for water to be more than a mile in distance from any hut in a village. Moreover, wet season grazing land within the *dambo*, as well as good arable land on the plateau beyond, is close by.

Village sites vary remarkably little, but there are considerable variations in shape and structure. Six distinct types have been observed in the red soil area. They have been classified by the present writer as follows:

'*A*' *type*. These are very small isolated villages with only four or five huts.

'*B*' *type*. These are larger than 'A' type villages, but the huts are huddled closer together, with no separation of family groupings.

'*C*' *type*. These have responded to the development of paths connecting with other villages or with cultivated land by developing in ribbon fashion along one of them.

'*C1*' *type*. These are similar to 'C' type villages, but there is a tendency for the village to follow a *dambo* margin in a long curve. There is invariably a road or path running the whole length of such villages.

'*D*' *type*. These are villages with a central nucleus from which paths extend radially. Newer development is taking place along the paths, along which there are hut clusters.

'*D1*' *type*. These are large villages formed by small hut clusters linked together by paths, but differ from the 'D' type villages in that there is no central nucleus.

'A' type settlements are the oldest village types, but they are comparatively few in number. With huts huddled closely together they are often situated in drier areas away from the well-watered river valleys, but very close to *dambo* margins. Where there is an uninterrupted level surface between *dambos* of more than a mile villages of this type tend to be sited centrally on the most productive land.

It is usual for 'A' type villages to have a population of less than 25. A sample count in four villages revealed figures of 24, 18, 12, and 14, an average of 17. The people, normally Cewa by tribe, are fiercely independent in attitude from other villages near by. In few cases are they of any great age. All of those visited by the author had come into existence as separate villages since 1945, and had resulted from quarrelling within a larger village. Thus the oldest settlement *type* is represented by the youngest villages.

In spite of the independent attitude of people living in 'A' type villages the splitting away from the older settlement is often so recent

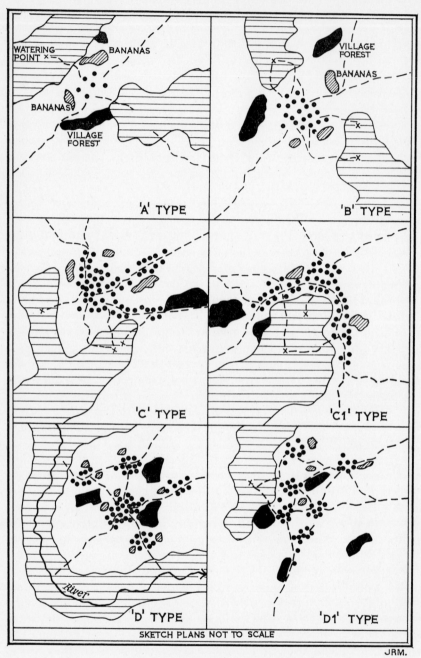

Fig. 36.   Dambo Village types on the Lilongwe Plain.
(Note shaded areas are Dambos.)

that agricultural holdings have not yet become separated, except where the 'offspring' is more than 4 or 5 miles away from the parent.

Indicative of longer existence as a separate unit are the larger isolated villages of the 'B' type, which are the most common settlements on the Lilongwe Plain. It is possible to find villages of this type with as few as a dozen huts, and differentiated from the 'A' type village only by their slightly larger size and longer existence. Others may have as many as three or four dozen huts. Separation from the parent village is complete in every sense.

'B' type settlements may be divided historically into three groups, those which were settled before the 1920s, those settled by migrations from Moçambique during the 1920s and early 1930s, mainly between 1926 and 1933, and those settled during the later 1930s and early 1940s.

The earlier 'B' type villages are indeterminate in age. In each of four villages the original headman's name was remembered in the present name of the village. In three of them the originator was three generations back, and in the other it was unknown. In the case of the latter it is thought that the history of the village is older than the occupation of its present site, oral tradition suggesting migration from the east as a distinct community.

Most of the 'B' type settlements that were studied were established on or near the present site between 1920 and 1945, seven by migration from Moçambique, and six by 'calving' from other villages. In some of the older villages the expansion and change of settlement type associated with expansion was forestalled by the breaking away of a group, and the founding of another village some miles away. Thus the single nucleated settlement has survived. As communities change through time, so the number of 'B' type settlements is being maintained, for as some grow into other types, so others are coming into existence as they grow from 'A' type settlements.

As trade has grown during the twentieth century, so has the inter-village communications system been improved. The paths extending from the village to the *dambo* or to the agricultural holdings have become a network, linking villages with each other. It is by the building of huts in relation to these paths that the 'C' and 'C1' types of settlements have been initiated. With the 'C' type village the old nucleus remains with its 'higgledy-piggledy' hut arrangement, but newer huts face the pathways or roads.

It is probable that 'C' and 'C1' types owe their development to European influence. It is customary for a large proportion of men to return at intervals from their work in other countries. With some of their savings they often build themselves a bigger and better dwelling. As many of them have seen, and even worked in, the homes of Europeans, it is not surprising that many of them build in a fashion which is a compromise between African and European styles. The difference between old and new building styles is sometimes startling. The round hut tends to become rectangular. 'Wattle and daub' tends to be replaced by baked bricks. Corrugated iron replaces grass roofs. The pit latrine is improved. The hut becomes a house.

In walking through both 'C' and 'C1' types the spacing between houses increases the further one moves away from the original nucleus. Houses along the main path or road are usually set back from the highway. In the first place each house is reached separately along a small 'drive', sometimes tastefully bordered with flowers, a feature which is rarely found in the old nucleus. This tends to change in course of time.

The returning migrant worker has responsibilities to others beyond his immediate family of wife and children. He may be responsible by custom for the education and well-being of his sister's children. Moreover, generosity towards even quite distant relatives is a distinctive feature of African life. Thus a man who has earned himself a small fortune is looked upon as a contributor to the well-being of a large number of people, who will soon remind him of these responsibilities. It is not long therefore before relatives begin to arrive and to build their own huts around his new house, so that it soon becomes the centre of a new cluster. If it were not for its very close proximity to the old village nucleus this cluster would tend to break away to form a new village.

The typical 'D' type settlement is large, sometimes with more than three hundred huts. These villages often consist of a central nucleus situated centrally within a large river meander. Radiating from the nucleus are paths leading to the river, and to other villages. Along the paths are clusters detached from the main nucleus, so that the general appearance is that of a 'B' type village surrounded by 'A' type satellites.

The origins of 'D' type villages are twofold. A number of them are villages of the 'C' type, which have grown in the manner described above. Others, however, have an interesting history, for sometimes the village headman and many of the people within the central nucleus are of Ngoni origin, while Cewa people inhabit most of the smaller surrounding clusters. While many such settlements broke up during the 1930s in response to the weakening position of Ngoni headmen under British rule, there were other settlements of this type where regard for a wise headman, or the non-availability of land for settlement further away, or sheer inertia, retained this interesting survival.

Similar to the 'D' type is the 'D1' type of village, which differs, however, in that there is no central nucleus. It consists basically of 'A' and 'B' type clusters in close proximity, and appears to be wholly Cewa in origin. It may be an early linking of small settlements for defensive purposes, although this is difficult to confirm. The position of the headman, who is little more than a *primus inter pares* with the familial heads of each cluster, suggests that these settlements have a continuous history of Cewa settlement, which is one reason why no cluster has become the central nucleus. There are so many villages of this type that it is thought that they represent a distinctive phase of Cewa settlement between the two Ngoni invasions.

SETTLEMENT IN A HIGHLAND AREA

Dominated by great syenite massifs and a large number of lesser intrusions rising above the Miocene peneplain surface of micaceous schists and gneisses the Ngoni Highlands in Dedza district have for long been

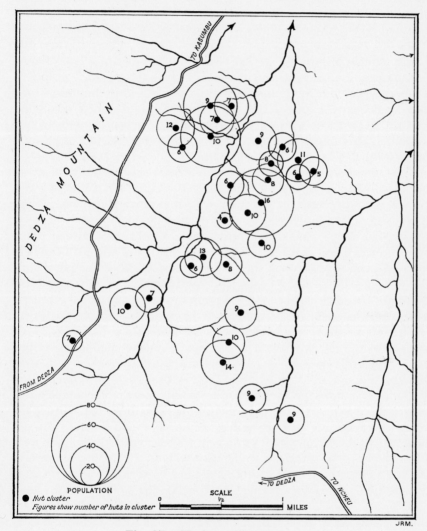

Fig. 37. Kudzoe village group.

a place of refuge for small and weak tribal groups. Here the early Cewa–Nyanja people were able to find abundant perennial water supplies in the swiftly flowing mountain streams and pockets of comparatively fertile soils, as well as means of defence or escape in the rocky heights of the higher massifs.

Around Dedza mountain one finds a number of interesting settlement types. To the east are the Kudzoe and Kasumbu village groups, the former of which is similar to the 'D1' type of the Lilongwe Plain. The hut clusters tend to be small and yet close enough together to have been able to provide help to each other in time of war. Indeed the clusters were once closer together.

There is a significant gap between the Kudzoe group and the nearest Ngoni villages of the Kamenya–Gwaza area, which reflects past enmity between Ngoni and Cewa, and the tendency of the latter to flee up the mountain slopes on the approach of the former. The suspicion with which visitors are regarded even today has its basis in the past fear of war-parties.

The Kudzoe group consists of twenty-nine hut clusters, representing family groups, all of which are subservient to one headman. The headman is the familial head of the largest group, which has sixteen huts inhabited by sixty-seven people. Only ten groups have more than ten or more huts.

Oral tradition suggests that the present hut groupings are of recent origin, but are nevertheless a reversion to a much older pattern temporarily rendered obsolete by warfare during the nineteenth century. Some of the older hut clusters appear to have been larger than they are now, the present village being represented by two hut clusters within half a mile of each other at the northern end of their present territory. They were significantly nearer to the chief's village of Kasumbu than most of the hut clusters are today. During the present century pacification brought about a renewed emphasis on the smaller scattered groups, but with a new orientation, for the newer hut clusters have tended to site themselves progressively nearer to Dedza township.

Increasingly the women of Kudzoe are turning to market gardening for a large proportion of their income. Maize yields tend to be low here, but potatoes and other vegetables eaten by Europeans grow well. Market days in Dedza township are characterized by the early morning hurrying of women with large head-loads of vegetables along the numerous tracks from Kudzoe. Thus they prefer to site their hut clusters as near to the township as is consistent with an agricultural economy. Though the furthermost groups are no more than $3\frac{1}{2}$ miles from Dedza the greater emphasis on vegetable growing by the nearer groups is quite noticeable.

In recent years the original village kinship links have been breaking down as immigrants from other tribes with employment in Dedza have moved in. In one group the majority of the people and even the headman are Ngoni. In another slightly less than half are Yao newcomers. But these affect only those hut clusters on the south-western periphery, the rest being almost entirely Cewa.

Over the 8 square miles occupied by Kudzoe the total population was 993 (448 male and 545 female), a density of 121·6 per square mile.[1] In an area where deep soils are limited this population is unable to support

[1] G. T. Rimmington's survey was in 1961.

itself by agriculture alone. A number of men are away working for the
Witwatersrand mines.

On the other side of Dedza mountain and extending for a considerable distance northwards villages are very similar in character to Kudzoe, though one notes that the chief's village of Kasumbu has retained
its strongly nucleated character. Similarly the villages between Dedza
mountain and the Chongoni forest reserve to the west have remained

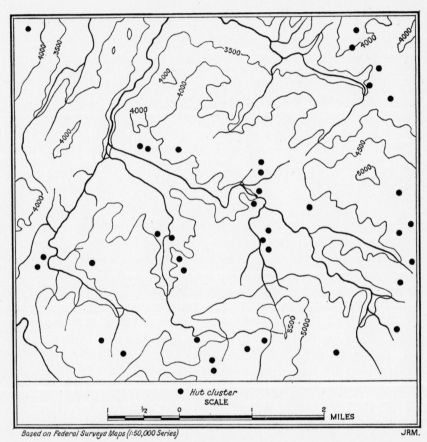

Fig. 38.   Settlements in the Dadzi–Nguwo area of Dedza District.

integrated. Even here, though, the separate familial sections can be
seen. They are merely closer together than at Kudzoe. The reasons for
this are not difficult to discover. In the first place these villages were
probably subjected to raids by Yao war-parties from Tambala even
after British protection. There has been considerable Yao migration
south of the Mpatha–Milonde pass into the adjoining areas to the north
of these villages. They would therefore tend to remain prepared for war
over a longer period. Nevertheless, considerable dispersion might have
been expected over the past thirty years which has not in fact been
evident.

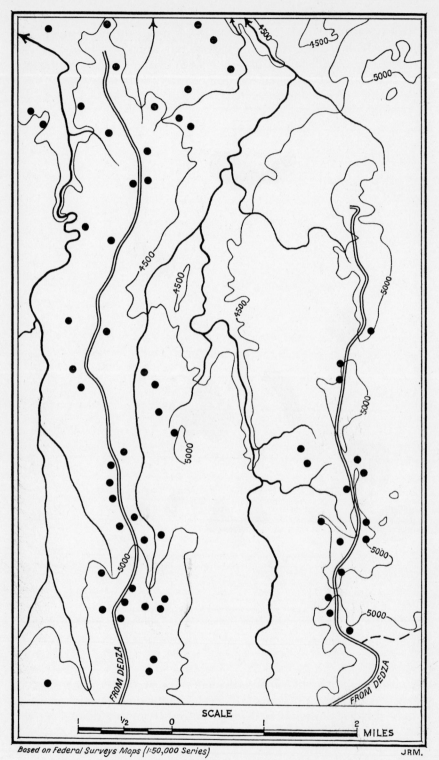

Based on Federal Surveys Maps (1:50,000 Series)   JRM.

Fig. 39.   Settlements in the Kanyama area of Dedza District.

African villages in Malawi tend to break up in the interests of agriculture, which is more efficiently carried out when people live near to their holdings. Since land is usually held in scattered strips throughout the village lands the isolated dwelling is rarely practicable, and in the

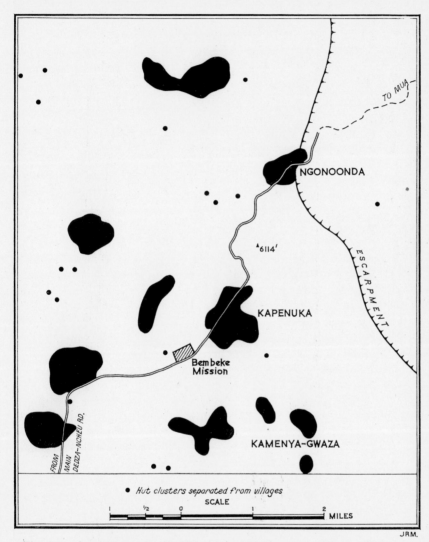

Fig. 40. Settlements in the Kamenya–Gwaza area of Dedza District.
(Large villages shaded.)

circumstances the best form of settlement is the small hut cluster. Nevertheless once a large nucleated village has been established it will not usually disperse unless it is deemed desirable for rebuilding to take place, or a violent quarrel breaks out, or an abundance of fertile but unoccupied land is available some distance away. For villages like Ngwere, Nkomeko, and Tomo, none of these conditions has been applicable. In Kudzoe, on the other hand, the people had not only a reputation for being quarrelsome, but also an incentive for re-orientation.

To the north of Dedza mountain the soil fertility gradually diminishes, for one approaches areas where the older rock structure has been almost completely worn away, except in a few small pockets, and the younger syenites have been exposed. Soils are generally infertile and tend to remain uninhabited in the most hilly areas.

Between Dadzi mountain (5,188 feet) and Nguwo mountain (5,266 feet) the villages are few and the hut clusters widely dispersed within the village areas. These settlements are entirely Cewa in origin and present occupation, and, with the lack of any motor roads, have tended to remain backward. In travelling through the area it is quite common to find the whole village population fleeing at one's approach, an indication that slave raids have not been forgotten. The hut clusters rarely have more than five or six huts.

A few miles farther south two roads from Dedza peter out. These have brought about some modification of the settlement pattern in the area which they traverse. It has been difficult to assess, however. Before the roads were constructed there was certainly a large number of villages, inhabited in some cases by outlying Ngoni and in others by Cewa people, but there seems to have been a greater degree of dispersion than is apparent now. Today almost all the hut clusters are within a mile of one of the roads, a series of roadward movements having taken place during the past three decades.

To the east and south-east of Dedza mountain is a broad plateau surface reaching to the edge of the Great Rift Valley escarpment. Some two miles from Kudzoe one comes across the closely knit Ngoni villages of the Kamenya–Gwaza area. These villages tend to give an impression of much greater neatness than the Cewa villages, although in fact the majority of the people are of Cewa origin. One finds the planting of trees, a much greater care in hut building, flower gardens planted before some houses, and sisal hedges around many plots. In one village, Kulemeka, it has been the proud boast for some years that no cattle have been kept, so that property is not spoiled.

The original nucleation of the Ngoni villages was characteristic of a conquering people, who surrounded each of their own hut clusters with those of their domestic slaves. Even today dispersal has not developed to any great extent, except where the terrain has discouraged the continuance of a large number of hut clusters. Nkhungumbe, Kanchito, and Kapenuka, for instance, are sited on land with a gentle slope and fairly deep soils, and have remained integrated. Kamenya–Gwaza, though, is in a more rocky area with poorer and thinner soils, and has begun to disperse itself over a wide area of the western slopes of Ngoma hill. Nevertheless a large central nucleus has remained.

It is surprising to find Ngonoonda, a large village spilling over the plateau on to the upper slopes of the rift valley escarpment, with very little dispersion in spite of the poor soils. One familial group has moved in isolation to a patch of fairly good soil on an escarpment shelf more than a mile away. A further three hut clusters have remained contiguous with each other. In this case it seems that there is a good spirit

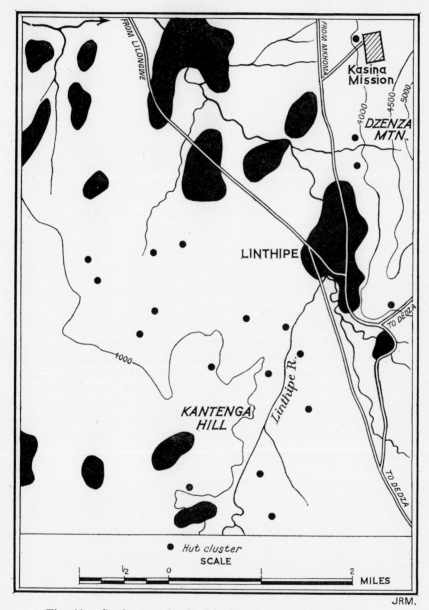

Fig. 41. Settlements in the Linthipe area of Dedza District.
(Large villages shaded.)

in the village. The people built themselves a church in 1961. There has therefore been little evidence of the usual factor in dispersion, violent disagreement.

M

Another factor in the retention of the nucleated pattern may well be the relatively happy relationship existing between Ngoni conqueror and Cewa subject. Not everywhere in Malawi were relationships between former conquerors and slaves so good that there was little desire to break away when British administration made it possible. In other areas government pressure to retain integrated villages to prevent wastage of valuable agricultural land was disregarded. In the Kamenya–Gwaza area the egress was less than elsewhere.

Standing on the summits of Chongoni mountain and looking northward one may see two distinct physical areas. To the north-west one notices the Linthipe valley, an eastward extension of the Dedza section of the Lilongwe Plain; to the north-east is the broken country of the Kaphuka and Tambala areas. The Linthipe valley shows evidence of the complex settlement pattern described above. A modification occurs in the normal pattern at Linthipe itself however, for here Dzenza mountain is a 'peninsula' of the hill region. This hill mass and the occurrence of outlying hills farther west beyond the Linthipe river has resulted in a convergence of routes on Linthipe, a trading centre which has grown up at the junction of the road system. On this point roads converge from Lilongwe, Mkhoma, and Dedza, bringing about a settlement pattern not seen elsewhere.

Linthipe is more than a trading centre. It consists in part of a row of Asian stores crowding between two road junctions, but there are also African settlements in existence in some cases before the trading centre was founded. They had been attracted by the perennial water supplies of the rivers, fertile soils around them, and the supplies of firewood from the woodland surrounding Dzenza mountain. Some of these villages are extraordinarily large, the number of hut clusters being as high as fifteen in one of them. Some are beginning to re-orientate themselves roadwards, setting up small stores and canteens for the convenience of travellers, or merely siting themselves close to a bus route.

The area to the west of Kaphuka village is fairly densely populated, with Cewa and newer Yao villages crowded closely together. Many of the settlements on either side of the Mpatha–Milonde road are considerable in size, with the mutual tribal distrust expressed clearly in the huddling together of hut clusters within each village. Many of them cap the summits of the many small hills. Farther to the east as the land becomes rockier and the soils correspondingly poorer the number of villages diminishes until the Tambala chiefdom is reached.

Kaphuka itself is a Cewa chief's village, and is sited on a fairly extensive plateau surface, around which the land slopes away gently. Standing in the midst of an extensive area of barely cultivable heath and scrubland it is clear that defence was primary in the selection of the site. It is also clear that the economy of the village is now precarious, for the soils have been extensively degraded. Indeed the livelihood of the settlement's inhabitants (about 1,000) is only maintained by temporary male migration and by a 'calving' process which falls short of the final break so apparent in many areas. As each of the seven hut clusters has grown too large, they have tended to send out young men and women to areas with better soils. The people in the newer, smaller, and socially dependent villages send back food from time to time to their relatives in Kaphuka.

Between Kaphuka and the villages of Tambala chiefdom is an area with very few villages. This area was once densely populated, but now has badly degraded soils. Migration westward to the Linthipe valley in search of better soils and water supplies as well as to escape the attentions of Yao intruders has left it as a small 'no-man's land' similar to that separating Kudzoe and the Ngoni villages of Kamenya–Gwaza.

In discussing the origins of Arab urbanization Dr. Hamdan states that 'the precepts of Islam urge a life of close association . . . its obligations may best be discharged in a collective, preferably urban society. Dispersion is deprecated because it makes for laxity and heterodox deviations'. Among the Muslim Yao people, however, urbanization was not possible because the other factors apparent in Arab urban growth have not been apparent in Malawi. The interests of the Arabs were primarily commercial; Yao interests were largely agricultural except during the relatively short period of slave trading. Nevertheless the villages of Tambala tend to be large, with hut clusters barely distinguishable one from another. Apart from the past needs of defence, the tribal mores discourage village disintegration, which is linked with the idea of death.

Tambala is typical of the integrated Yao villages. It is sited in a bowl between Ntatha hill, Tambala hill, and a number of lesser peaks. The site has defensive possibilities, and there were once palisades around the settlement. Here, though, the degree of hut crowding is greater than usual, because the fertile soils are limited in extent and there is little level land. The present writer had great difficulty during 1961 in finding a suitable site for the primary school now established there.

On the whole there is little interest in formal education among the Tambala Yao, mainly owing to prejudice arising out of the Christian origins of the educational system of Malawi. There are few schools now, and none at all two decades ago. So that it is rare to find anyone with more than a couple of years of primary education. This is tending to leave the Yao people old-fashioned in their way of life, and this is a further factor in the cohesiveness of the hut clusters.

The size of most of Tambala's villages varies partly from historical causes, but also in relation to the quality of the soils. A few villages are the result of breaking (not 'calving' as with the Cewa–Nyanja), and these reflect their recent origin in their small size. Others are small or large as they are sited on small or large patches of good soils.

SETTLEMENT IN AN ESCARPMENT AREA

An example of escarpment settlement patterns may be seen on the Livulezi 'shelf', a complex step fault within the Dedza escarpment area

overlooking the Great Rift Valley. The basic settlement pattern consists of small scattered villages at the foot of the main escarpment to the
west, where streams disappear below fan gravels in the dry season. Only
two of these have any distinct nucleation.

A cluster of nucleated villages lies around Mua Mission, where there
is a perennial river used as a source of power for a small saw mill. It is
clearly the mission station, as an employer of labour (carpenters, hospital orderlies, house servants, etc.) and as a means of obtaining reli-
gious, medical, and educational benefits, which has influenced the
growth of these villages.

From Mua to the south, and running the whole length of the 'shelf', a
road follows the Livulezi valley to Ncheu. From a junction near to the
Ncheu and Dedza district boundaries another road climbs the escarpment and joins the main Lilongwe–Blantyre road a few miles south of
Dedza township. There are small settlements along the roads wherever
local water supplies permit. Some houses advertise themselves as places
of refreshment. The largest village, a distinct ribbon development, has
been sited significantly at the road junction.

SETTLEMENT ON A FLOOD PLAIN

In some areas there are settlements which are occupied seasonally, or
during a period of a few years. The Shire River, with its seasonal flow
reduced during the dry season, has many temporary islands of *dimba*[1]
land in the Lower River, on which small temporary villages of grass-
walled huts spring up. These people revert to drier land during the
wet season, taking up for occupation again the huts of the previous year.
These are more permanent in type, being mud-walled.

During periods of intense wet seasons the margins of cultivation are
pushed farther away from the river, and new villages grow up on the
dry land farther out. Small and haphazardly built, with clearly no
interest in a future of more than a few years hence, these villages are
deserted as the dry seasons become longer and the margins of cultivation
move riverwards again.

Some Lower Shire villages are permanently occupied. A large number of these are sited alongside the river. These tend to be long narrow
villages, confined to the upraised dry land of the *levée*, and are large,
often with more than one hundred huts, reflecting the greater agricultural possibilities surrounding the site and the permanent water supply.
Other permanent villages are of a type found commonly in Malawi,
being located along the foot of the hills on the well-drained gravels of
alluvial fans at the points where surface water disappears underground
during the dry season.

THE IMPORTANCE OF WATER SUPPLIES

In a country where rainfall is comparatively unreliable the villages
are often of a temporary nature, as water supplies may become non-
existent during a severe dry season, causing a movement of the settle-

[1] A *dimba* is a fertile alluvial flood plain often inundated during the wet season.

ment. In recent years thewell-digging programmes of the Nyasaland Government have changed the nature of settlement patterns, making village sites permanent rather than temporary, and grouped around wells and bore-holes rather than in defensive positions.

In Chigaru's area of Blantyre district many villages moved from stream bank sites to new watering points. Some villages moved over considerable distances. Masamba's village, for instance, moved from the

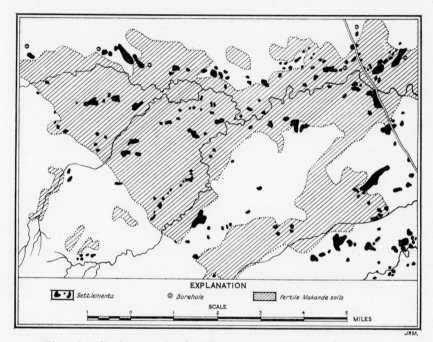

EXPLANATION

Settlements   ⊚ Borehole   Fertile Makande soils

SCALE

MILES

JRM.

Fig. 42.   Settlements in the Ngabu area of Chikwawa District.

Zomba area in 1936 and settled in a previously uninhabited area. Villages already in existence which had wells dug were increased in size by the immigration of people from European estates. Many of these people were of different tribes. In London village there were less than a hundred people, mainly of the Mang'anja tribe, in the late 1920s. In 1958, after the provision of two wells, there were 1,350 people, the majority of whom were Yao (45 per cent.) and Lomwe (36 per cent.).

It needs to be noted, however, that in areas where soils are very fertile, such as the Ngabu area of Chikwawa district, where much cotton is grown as a cash crop, settlements do not necessarily move to the vicinity of the bore-holes. Of twelve very large villages in the area five are within half a mile of a bore-hole, the others being sited in relation to soils rather than water supply.

The great majority of villages are situated on the *makande* soils, but it is interesting to note that some villages, especially the larger ones, are sited on poorer soils overlooking *makande* series. In this way they gain an advantage in that none of the richer soils are rendered agriculturally useless by the sprawl of huts over them. Most settlements are within one mile of a perennial stream or water-hole dug in the bed of a seasonal stream.

BIBLIOGRAPHY

C. A. Baker, 'Chigaru's: A Study of its Population', *Nyasa. Jour.*, Vol. XI (i).
Dedza District Books (unpublished).
G. Hamdan, 'Medieval Urbanism in the Arab World', *Geography*, Vol. XLVII.
R. S. Hynde, 'Among the Machinga People', *Scottish Geographical Magazine*, Vol. VIII.
D. MacDonald, *Africana* (1882).
J. C. Mitchell, Manchester U.P. *The Yao Village* (1956).
W. B. Morgan, 'The Lower Shire Valley of Nyasaland: A Changing System of African Agriculture', *Geog. Jour.*, Vol. CXIX.
Nyasaland Census Report, 1926.

CHAPTER IX

URBAN SETTLEMENT

TRUE urbanization was unknown in Malawi before the entry of Europeans and Asians into the country, for African life was almost wholly dependent on subsistence agriculture. In some cases there were very large villages or groups of contiguous villages which arose out of the need for protection from enemies and the rise of the slave trade. Mponda, for instance, was placed in a strategic position near the point where the Shire river flows out of Lake Nyasa, and was the chief's village in a strong Yao chiefdom. Thus it grew into a village with more than a thousand inhabitants before the arrival of Johnston. Kota Kota was a group of villages acting as a collecting centre for the slave trade, and from which the Arab *dhows* sailed across Lake Nyasa with their human cargoes. Karonga was the stockaded fortress of the Arab slaver Mlozi. But none of these represented true urban development, for at both Mponda and Kota Kota agriculture continued to be the most important means of sustaining life. Karonga was little more than a fortress and depot.

Urban development is entirely a result of the growth of administration, commerce, and industry during the period of British protection. And this has been dependent upon the arrival of Europeans and Asians, people with little direct interest in agriculture, many of whom tended to become professional administrators or traders, accustomed to urban life in the countries from which they originated.

BLANTYRE–LIMBE

Blantyre and Limbe now form one municipality for administrative convenience, and the area between them, five miles distant, is being filled in by new buildings, such as the Malawi High Court, the Provincial administration block, a new teacher training college, small factories, and new housing estates. Their origins are, however, quite distinct, and some separate consideration is necessary.

Blantyre stands on the Shire Highlands at an elevation of between 3,400 and 3,500 feet, and occupies a hollow formed between the Ndirandi, Michuru, and Sochi mountains. The town owes its inception to the arrival in 1876 of a party of Scots missionaries under Henry Henderson. He had chosen the site earlier in the year because of its position between the Nasolo and Likabula streams in the bowl formed by the surrounding hills. Henderson was fortunate in that on the site he had chosen were some derelict huts of a deserted African village, whose people had fled from the southward thrusting Ngoni war-parties. These huts were repaired and used temporarily by the missionaries, who were welcomed by the Yao chief Kapeni, and allowed to purchase the site of the mission station.

The establishment of the mission station was not sufficient, however, to bring about the establishment of an urban centre, and it is doubtful if Blantyre would have been much more than this had it not been for its choice as the headquarters of a trading company. The largest trading company in Malawi today is the African Lakes Corporation, which had its beginnings in the Livingstonia Trading Company, founded by a group of Glasgow businessmen and established by the Moir brothers near the mission. The Moirs arrived in 1878 and the first store was opened during the following year in a mission bungalow. A more permanent building (which still exists) was erected to the south of the Mudi stream, about two miles from the mission.

The fortified store opened by the Moirs was several times used as a place of refuge from Yao and Ngoni raids, which were indirectly responsible for the subsequent development of Blantyre. In 1884 the Maseko Ngoni had raided as far south as the mission and stores. Although eventually persuaded to withdraw they did not go far away, for they proceeded to harry the Yao people to the east of Sochi and Ndirandi. Chief Kapeni feared their return, and, in an effort to strengthen his own position encouraged the further immigration of Europeans.

The Livingstonia Trading Company was followed by the establishment of Eugene Sharrer's Kubula stores, first of many commercial ventures by its founder. Other traders followed.

Administrative interest in Blantyre began in 1892 with the purchase of land in the centre of the present urban area by John Buchanan on behalf of the Crown.

The area now occupied by the centre of Blantyre was formerly divided into a few large estates, but fragmentation of these commenced as the settlement grew. By 1895 there were many houses, and streets were in evidence. The original street pattern, on which the present streets and roads are based, was merely a series of tracks linking the earlier and most important properties.

Before the end of the nineteenth century Asian traders had also begun to settle in Blantyre. Osman Adam acquired a quarter of an acre in the predominantly Asian trading section as early as 1894. Others soon followed the aptly named Adam.

In spite of its earlier development and the fact that it became the railway terminus for a while, before the northern extension to Salima was constructed, Blantyre has not become the most important railway centre. This function is carried out by Limbe, which is more favourably sited.

Before the railway from Port Herald reached Limbe in 1907 there was no trace of urban development, and little trace of rural settlement. A survey plan made in 1896 showed that there were two European agricultural estates. The Limbe estate had only one house on it.

Subsequent urban development had the advantage of lands already having been alienated to non-Africans, and was aided by the lack of any need
to displace African rural settlement. The arrival of the railway brought
about such rapid development that in 1909 a township was established.
That it was completed before the station at Blantyre and was nearer
to the capital, Zomba, enabled Limbe railway station to achieve an
early precedence. Moreover, the establishment of the large Malawi
headquarters of the Imperial Tobacco Company in Limbe soon after
railway construction encouraged the immigration of Europeans and
Asians. Today Limbe is larger than Blantyre.

Although Blantyre–Limbe is a European and Asian creation the
majority of its inhabitants are African. At the 1956 Census Europeans
numbered 2,457,[1] Asians 2,686, Coloured (persons of mixed race) 355.
The number of Africans was estimated to be 50,000, or about 90 per
cent. of the total. A fairly large number of the latter live in the European
housing areas in servants' quarters adjacent to the houses, but most of
them live in clearly demarcated areas elsewhere.

At Sochi, the area lying between Blantyre and Limbe at the foot
of the mountain of the same name, a high density African housing area
is being developed. Here the houses are more permanent than traditional housing and the layout pattern is similar to that in some of the
African townships adjoining the cities of Southern Rhodesia, and as
monotonous as that of some local authority housing estates in England.
Nevertheless is is interesting to see over 1,700 African houses, each
fronting on to a road, and equipped with mains electricity, reticulated
water supplies, and flush sanitation, together with markets, shops,
schools, churches, playing fields, an urban court, a police post, and a
community centre forming the background to a new social system
which is a blending of the European and African ways of life. The people
of Sochi, unlike Africans in most other areas, have no agricultural land.

Africans elsewhere live on the fringes of the municipal area in areas
unfavourable to European and Asian settlement. For instance the higher
and cooler slopes of Nyambadwe hill are covered with European[2]
civil servants' houses, but at the foot, where the railway to Salima
winds its way through a mass of low hummocks, and the summer heat
is greater, traditional 'wattle and daub' dwellings are arranged in
groups wherever the land surface permits. There is a tendency for those
huts nearer the railway to follow the direction of the line, but others
have a less formal siting. This area differs from Sochi not only in the
hut arrangement but also in density, having only about 400 people per
square mile, whereas Sochi has more than 1,000 per square mile. A
small amount of cultivation is carried on to supplement wage incomes.

[1] The more recent count in 1961 showed that the number of Europeans had grown to
4,160, a 69% increase ... G. T. Rimmington, 'The Drift to the Towns of the European
Population in Rhodesia and Nyasaland', *Geography*, XLVIII, ii (1963), p. 322.

[2] There is now a growing number of African senior civil servants, so that some houses
formerly reserved for Europeans are now occupied by Africans.

It is curious to note that the area is not as densely populated as the Chileka–Likabula–Lunzu area farther away from the municipality. Here densities are over 1,000. As the soils are more fertile farther north, and bus services are frequent, it is clear that many Africans employed in Blantyre still include agriculture as a significant factor in their economy, and choose the siting of their houses accordingly.

Near to Blantyre Mission is the peri-urban area of Ndirandi, where the process of urbanization has proceeded further than in the area mentioned above. The pattern of settlement is different from that in Sochi, however, in that, being on African Trust Land, it has had little European direction.

Ndirandi has developed out of villages which grouped themselves near to the Scottish mission for protective purposes during the later nineteenth century. Village headmen between 1876 and 1888 encouraged dense settlement as a deterrent to Ngoni raids and to enhance their own positions by the accumulation of subordinates.

In recent times the impetus of population growth has continued because of Blantyre's commercial development. On the positive side many Africans have arrived from other areas to seek work in the municipal area. On the negative side the construction of the Mudi dam and the closing to settlement of its catchment area, as well as the encroachment of public utilities sited between Blantyre and Limbe, have reduced the area of Trust Land. The resulting population density is very high, being over 2,500 people per square mile.

The history of Ndirande has given it the appearance of a large number of hut clusters based on the earlier village structure. Around each cluster every piece of available land is used for maize patches, but the population is too dense, and the area is too hilly and the soil too barren for the point of subsistence to be reached anywhere. Small kitchen gardens are the rule. Moreover more houses are being built each year, and many of the newer houses are more spacious and more permanently built.

ZOMBA

The capital, with its population (in 1956) of 798 Europeans, 671 Asians, 34 Coloured, and an estimated 13,000 Africans, lies along the lower slopes of the south-eastern end of the Zomba massif. Of little commercial importance, it is a civil service creation, the site being chosen for its beauty rather than its accessibility.

The area lying between Lake Chilwa and the Zomba massif was a junction of the slave trade routes, which the British Government pledged itself to put down. Even before the declaration of the British Protectorate Consul Hawes had chosen a site on the mountain slopes for the erection of an official residence, which was the first permanent building on the site of the present day town. From this spot the slaving route could be kept under surveillance.

With the growth of administration after 1891 government departments grew up below the Residency, and the mountainside above them became dotted with the houses of civil servants. The main road through the town has developed commercial services in recent years. These consist of a bank, a number of modern shops, Asian stores, and a remarkable number of petrol filling stations and garages. Below the main road are several streets of Asian and African stores, all with attached living accommodation. Near these are the junior civil service quarters and traditional African housing. Ribbon development of African housing and stores is tending to develop along the main road, particularly on the southern side of the town in the direction of Blantyre–Limbe.

OTHER URBAN DEVELOPMENTS

Outside the administrative capital of Zomba and the commercial and industrial capital of Blantyre–Limbe there is little more than incipient movement towards urbanization. Lilongwe is the only real town in the Central Province; there is no large centre in the Northern Province.

With the development of the Lilongwe Plain as a major producer of tobacco, maize, and groundnuts as cash crops there is a need for a marketing centre. Lilongwe has had advantages in this respect in that it is in the centre of the fertile red soil region, and has developed, because of its command of an important bridging point over the incised Lilongwe river, as the most important nodal centre of the Central Province. From the town main roads lead southwards to Zomba and Blantyre–Limbe, westwards to Fort Jameson, where the Great East Road to Lusaka is joined, northwards to Mzuzu, and eastwards to Salima, the railhead. Its commanding position has resulted in its choice as administrative centre for the Lilongwe district and Central Province. Compared with Blantyre–Limbe the town is rather dull, for there are no beautiful mountains surrounding it, only a gently undulating plain. Nevertheless its housing and shopping areas have been well planned.

Elsewhere the beginnings of urbanization may be seen in the administrative townships and trading centres which have been sited at strategic points. In each district there is an administrative centre which tends to be urban in type, for the inhabitants consist mainly of European and African civil servants of varying grades and Asian (and sometimes Portuguese) storekeepers. Each township tends to consist of a number of well-defined zones. Typically these are the *boma* (or administrative offices), the low density housing area for senior civil servants, the medium density housing area for clerks and civil servants of similar grade, the high density housing area for low-grade civil servants, public service areas (hospital, post office, etc.), a trading estate, and church and mission areas (including schools). Normally the *boma* and housing areas are sited away from main roads, while the public services and trading estates are on or near main roads. Sometimes there is a considerable distance between zones, as at Ncheu, where nearly two miles separates the two above-mentioned groups.

Quite often townships are purely administrative in origin, and the site has been chosen for its position within the district, the availability of water supplies, and sometimes a healthy aspect. Dowa, for instance, is placed centrally within the Dowa hills, where water supplies are available from perennial streams and the heat is moderated by altitude. Dedza is sited on the old main road between Ncheu and Lilongwe at the point where there is a gap of only two miles between Dedza mountain and the Moçambique border. Its site at the foot of the mountain enables it to benefit from perennial streams and the healthy mountain breezes.

Other townships have been developed out of earlier settlements. Fort Johnston and Fort Manning are examples of townships growing up alongside a place chosen as a defensive point for use during the country's pacification. In other cases the development of communications has brought a trading estate into existence, as with Balaka, which is sited at the point where the railway from Blantyre to Salima crosses the main Zomba–Lilongwe road, and Salima, at the railhead. In these cases the development of the *boma* and civil service housing has followed rather than preceded the growth of trading settlements.

Being a predominantly agricultural country Malawi is unlikely to have a very large urban population in the foreseeable future, though with the development of light industry serving local demand in Blantyre–Limbe and Lilongwe these two urban centres will continue to grow at a fairly rapid rate. Elsewhere significant urban increases are likely to be small.

BIBLIOGRAPHY

D. G. Bettison, and R. J. Apthorpe, 'Authority and Residence, in a Peri-urban Social Structure, Ndirande, Nyasaland, *Nyasa. Jour.*, Vol. XIV (i).

F. Debenham, *Nyasaland, the Land of the Lake*, H.M.S.O. (1955).

Extracts from the Diary and Letters of Peter Moore, 1888, *Nyasa. Jour.*, Vol. XI (i).

S. Green, 'Blantyre Mission', *Nyasa. Jour.*, Vol X (ii).

A. Hetherwick, *The Romance of Blantyre* (1931).

W. H. J. Rangeley, 'Early Blantyre', *Nyasa. Jour.*, Vol. VII (i).

——, 'The Origins of the Principal Street Names of Blantyre and Limbe', *Nyasa. Jour.*, Vol. XI (ii).

R. Walker, 'A Survey of Early Buildings in Nyasaland', *Nyasa. Jour.*, Vol. XIII (i).

J. H. E. Watson, 'Some Historical Notes on Zomba', *Nyasa. Jour.*, Vol. VII (ii).

DEDZA
AN EXAMPLE OF A SMALL TOWNSHIP

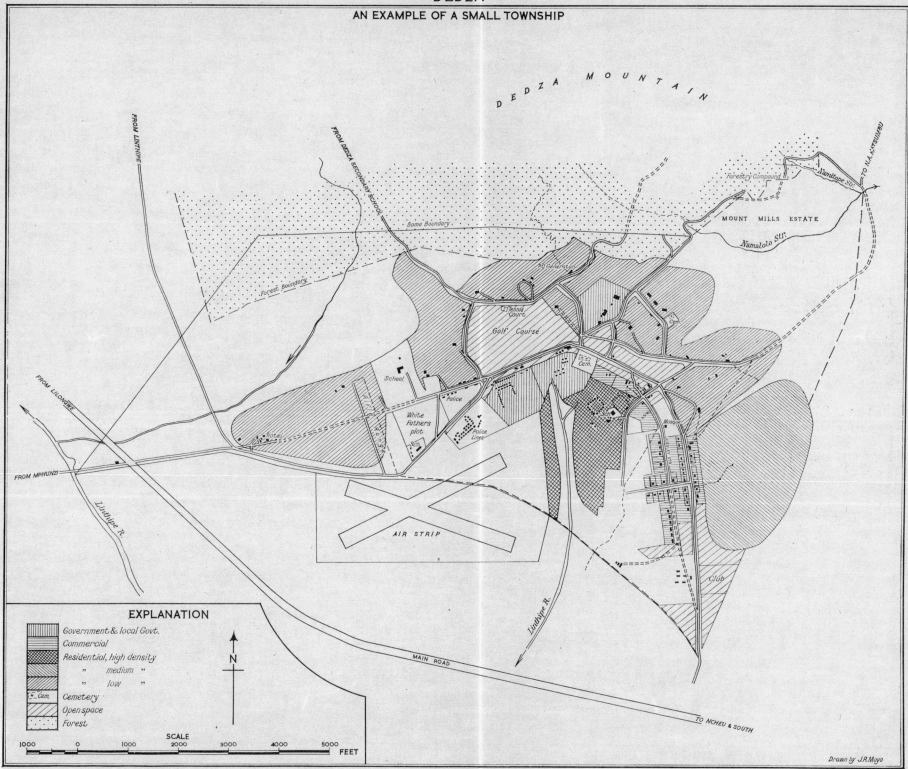

DEDZA MOUNTAIN

FROM LINTHIPE

FROM DEDZA SECONDARY SCHOOL

Boma Boundary

Forest Boundary

Forestry Compound

Namitope Str.

TO H.A. NTSUMBU

MOUNT MILLS ESTATE

Namalolo Str.

PD Generator

Tennis Court

Golf Course

Cem.

School

Cem.

Police

White Fathers plot

Sch.

Police Lines

Mosque

FROM LILONGWE

Hotel

Lindhipe R.

FROM MPHUNZI

AIR STRIP

Club

Lindhipe R.

MAIN ROAD

TO NCHEU & SOUTH

EXPLANATION

Government & local Govt.
Commercial
Residential, high density
   "   medium   "
   "   low   "
Cem.   Cemetery
Open space
Forest

N

SCALE

1000   0   1000   2000   3000   4000   5000
FEET

Drawn by J.R.Mayo

Fig. 43.

CHAPTER X

THE AGRARIAN ECONOMY

STUDIES in settlement patterns reveal clearly the importance of agriculture in the economy of even the peri-urban wage earner. In rural areas agricultural production varies between that for pure subsistence in remote hill areas and the mixture of subsistence and cash crop farming to be found in the areas with relatively good communications and soils. As almost all Africans in Malawi derive at least part of their livelihood from the soil agriculture is a vital part of the country's economy.

LAND CLASSIFICATION

At the time of the World Census of Agriculture, organized by the Food and Agricultural Organization in 1950, it was concluded that out of a total of 36,000 square miles of territory only 10,000 square miles were considered as suitable for arable agriculture, 1,000 square miles for tree crops, and the rest, 25,000 square miles, were classified as woodland, swamp, rough grazing land, steep escarpment, and hillsides. Of the latter, 5,000 square miles consist of marginal arable land and a further 2,000 square miles are suitable for permanent pasture or rough grazing. The remaining 18,000 square miles are quite unsuitable for any form of agriculture.

The Census shows that rather less than one-third of the total land surface of Malawi is to be regarded as permanent farmland, while the marginal land amounts to about another sixth. It is possible, however, that some of the marginal land may in the future be made suitable for permanent farming, and the marginal land may therefore be an under-estimate.

Most of the population of the country is crowded on to the best agricultural land, so that the average density in these areas is about 270 people per square mile. Actual densities vary from over 1,000 to less than 100 according to soil fertility. This is reflected in the size of family holdings, which tend to be large in the areas with sparse population and poor soils, and small in areas with dense population and fertile soils.

LAND TENURE

There are three systems of land tenure within the country. These consist of those in respect of African Trust Land, Public Land, and Freehold Land.

African Trust Land comprises 87 per cent. of all land in the country, and is administered and controlled by the Governor, for the benefit and use of Africans. Some of this land is leased for a maximum period of ninety-nine years, but the area involved is only a small part of the total. About 90,000 acres have been leased for agricultural purposes to non-Africans and a few thousand acres for other purposes.

Under African custom there is no land ownership by individuals; there is only the right to cultivate. On the death of the cultivator cropping rights pass (in most tribes) through the female line, and often result in fragmentation between several daughters. A man acquires land only by marriage to a woman possessing cultivation rights. The result is that men often seek paid employment elsewhere, while women cultivate the land. Men therefore have little interest in the future of the land, and are concerned only with the immediate benefits likely to

TABLE XIV

Acreages Cultivated per Family*

District	Number of families	Cultivated acreage per family
Karonga	20	4·1
Rumpi	15	7·2
Mzimba	25	7·1
Lilongwe	1,060	5·0
Blantyre	82	3·0
Cholo	36	3·0
Mlanje	72	4·3
Chikwawa	30	5·1

* The sample families were taken at random.

accrue to them. There are few literate women, so that agricultural methods have to be taught almost entirely by personal instruction, and this is a slow process. Most of the African Trust Land is administered in this manner.

Public Land, about 10 per cent. of the total land surface, includes forest reserves, land in townships not in private ownership, and land used for public buildings. Some Public Land is under lease, while other plots are occasionally sold, becoming freehold plots.

Freehold Land is very small in area, amounting to no moie than 3 per cent. of all land in the territory. It exists primarily as the result of the granting of certificates of claim during the early years of British protection. The largest concentrations of freehold land are in the Shire Highlands, where plots are intensively cultivated by European and Asian planters.

Of all the cultivated land in Malawi more than 90 per cent. is in the hands of Africans, most of whom live in the traditional manner on unalienated trust land. A fairly large number, however, occupy Public Land as tenants-at-will, without any obligation to pay rent and with no security of tenure. There are a number of Africans in the Blantyre–Limbe area who have purchased Freehold Land.

A system to be found in the Central Province only is the scheme whereby Africans may become 'visiting tenants' on estates owned by or leased to non-Africans. The owner or lessee allocates part of his land to Africans, supplies seed, fertilizer, and building materials. At the harvest time he buys the crop, which he grades and markets. Tenants often prove to have cultivation rights elsewhere on trust land, to which they eventually return. While living on the estate they are assured of at least a small cash income.

To the African who is a subsistence farmer the main incentive to grow crops is the hunger of himself and his family. Once this need is satisfied leisure tends to be preferred to the extra benefits which might accrue from additional crops raised for marketing. This in itself brings about inefficient land use, but the system of land tenure under which most Africans live adds to it. It is not surprising that some thought has been given to land reorganization, some schemes having been put into operation.

SUBSISTENCE AND CASH CROPS

Subsistence crops are almost always preferred by Africans to the raising of cash crops. The custom is to grow what is needed by the family, and then to sell anything that may be left. In the immediate areas around towns food is often expensive for those with no garden, for the peri-urban areas are inhabited by wage earners with only small gardens, insufficient to provide the whole of their own subsistence.

In areas where few employment possibilities exist there is a tendency to turn to the growing of cash crops or to migrate to other areas where there is the possibility of paid employment. A feature is that the choice does not appear to depend on the possibility or otherwise of producing cash crops. Migration is usually preferred. In Lilongwe district, for example, where conditions are more favourable than in most other areas for the production of cash crops, the migration rate is also high.

There are two main reasons for the lack of any clear-cut division between subsistence and paid employment. In the first place the demand for labour by European estates brought about the practice of providing estate labourers with sufficient land for the growing of their own food requirements. More important still is the tendency to regard the owning of cultivation rights as a kind of 'insurance policy'. Few Africans can look forward to a pension at the end of their paid employment, and in any case many of the people working in unskilled employment are liable to the termination of their work at short notice. Thus land gives them a sense of security, for they can return to it at any time, and eke out a living.

The economic effect of the combination of subsistence with paid employment is to bring about a serious lack of efficiency, for the employer tends to suffer from a seasonal lack of labour at the beginning of the rainy season, when many Africans return to their villages to prepare subsistence gardens. Because insufficient attention is paid to the latter the tendency is for bad methods to be employed, and a soil-degrading monoculture is often apparent. Frequently the opening of gardens is delayed too long for the crops to be able to grow and ripen properly.

The alternative division between a cash crop economy and subsistence is also wasteful, for most attention is paid to the latter. Even where the soils are most suitable for cash crops more than half the garden area is usually allotted to maize patches. All too often the standard of living is depressed by the lack of attention to cash crops, for poor quality cotton, tobacco, etc., is of low value. Some cash crops are even left in the field to rot, a practice which in the case of cotton, allows insect pests to remain and destroy the crops of the next year.

METHODS OF CULTIVATION

African agriculture is in transition between shifting cultivation and crop rotation of the European type. Within the boundaries of even one district one may find shifting cultivation, the bush fallow system,[1] seven year crop rotation, and continuous cropping on alluvial land over many years.

Only where population is sparse, as with some of the waterless escarpment areas, is primitive shifting cultivation now practised. Even bush fallowing is tending to become less practicable as population becomes more dense, for its success is dependent on a resting period of between five and seven years, and this is no longer possible in most parts of the country. Dr. W. B. Morgan noted that there was very little fallow to be observed in the Lower Shire valley by the early 1950s.

The main problem in agriculture is that too few people in Malawi have yet adapted themselves to the change from bush fallowing to permanent cropping. Frequently one finds maize monoculture on even the poorest soils, and no rotational pattern of any kind apart from the occasional fallow year. Animal husbandry is rarely integrated with arable cultivation, so that only by accident is soil manured with animal droppings. Moreover, insufficient attention is paid to the selection of the best seed, which, it has been estimated, could double average yields per acre, and enable more land to be fallowed at any one time.

The Malawi Government is attempting to provide solutions by two main methods, the introduction of a master farmer scheme and land consolidation. The master farmer scheme is designed to aid the planning of farms, wherever farmers have managed to consolidate their fragmented holdings into an economic unit. When a man wishes to become a master farmer an Agricultural Officer will survey his plot, advise on layout, rotation, seed and animal husbandry, and also provide some training. It has been hoped that the operation of the scheme will help to broadcast ideas.

---

[1] In shifting cultivation a plot is used for two or three years before moving on. There is no definite return to the same plot. Bush fallowing is distinguished by a fixed rotation so that within a period of several years there is a return to the same plot.

Study of a typical master farmer's holding at Kanyama, 15 miles north of Dedza township, in an area of indifferent soils, showed that a 21 acre holding had a seven year crop rotation. This consisted of maize, potatoes, groundnuts, maize interplanted with pigeon peas, pigeon peas (twice), and a year of fallow. Cassava was being grown as a reserve crop outside the rotational pattern. During 1961 only 2·5 acres of maize and 1·8 acres of maize with pigeon peas were being grown out of a cultivated total of 11·4 acres. The maize plots had had farmyard manure spread on them. A further 8·4 acres of rocky ground unfit for cultivation had been retained as woodland around the house. A hopeful feature was the partial integration of animal husbandry with a well-developed rotation. Four cattle were grazing for part of the year on the one acre strip left fallow.

Unfortunately the master farmer scheme has not been popular with the majority of the African population, who point out with some justification that master farmers tend to be those with larger areas of land than most people can ever hope to possess. On the other hand many master farmers have made an economic success of marginal land.

An advantage of the master farmer scheme is that it highlights the need for land consolidation throughout the country as a whole. By 1959 there were 745 master farmers working on 8,409 acres by improved methods.

Land consolidation is seen in the master farmer scheme on a small scale, but more important in the future will be the reorganization of whole village cultivation areas. In the areas where this has been done already the layout of individual holdings has been within the framework of an overall land use and soil conservation plan providing for rotational strip cropping. Provision is also made for grazing and forestry on poorer land.

There are now some thirty consolidation schemes in the Central and Southern Provinces, the largest and most comprehensively planned being at Kuntaja (near Blantyre), where several thousand acres are concerned. Striking improvements in crop production have resulted despite the fact that some individuals have a smaller area of arable land at their disposal. From samples taken before and after re-organization it has been shown that where four acres once yielded 7·2 bags of maize and 120 pounds of beans to a value of £7, after reorganization the same area of land yielded 7 bags of maize, 60 pounds of beans, 300 pounds of groundnuts, 200 pounds of pigeon peas, and 120 pounds of sweet potatoes to a value of £14. In addition to the short term benefits fertility is maintained by conservation measures, and the area available for grazing is increased by the withdrawal of marginal land from arable use.

In the Northern Province, where soils are generally poor, and within the *dambos* of the Central Province a destructive type of shifting cultivation is practised known locally as *visoso*. This method of cultivation is carried out by the cutting of timber and bush over a wide area, which is

N

then burned on a cleared patch of land. This pyroligneous activity destroys the weeds and produces a fine friable soil as a seed bed. It also increases the phosphates and potash in the soil, changing it from slight acidity to slight alkalinity. The crop normally grown in a *visoso* garden is finger millet, the basis of native beer.

The immediate benefits of *visoso* cultivation are readily apparent, but its long term implications must also be noted. Firing leaves fertile ashes, but it also destroys between 250 and 450 tons of organic matter per acre. This would have been more profitable in the form of timber, firewood, wood pulp, and compost. Between 600 and 900 pounds of nitrogen per acre are returned to the atmosphere, the potash is reduced to a soluble form of carbonate leached away with the first rains, and humus and bacteria are destroyed. After the first crop has been harvested and the rain has washed away the upper layer of fine ashes, a hard baked sub-soil remains, in which natural vegetation has difficulty in re-establishing itself. Infiltration of rain-water is checked, and the surface run-off increased, bringing about danger of erosion on a large scale.

EUROPEAN AGRICULTURE

Among the first Europeans to arrive in Malawi were a number interested in agriculture. Coffee, tea, tobacco, and cotton plantations were well established by the end of the nineteenth century. Many of the earlier plantations were established by private individuals, the later ones by joint stock companies employing managers.

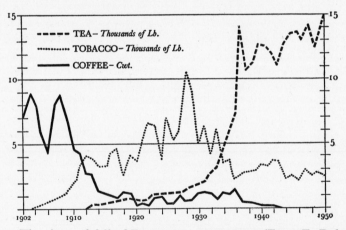

Fig 44.   The rise and fall of European-grown crops. (From F. Debenham, *Nyasaland. The Land of the Lake* (1955), p. 207)
Reproduced by permission of Her Majesty's Stationery Office.

It had at first been visualized that produce would be purchased from Africans and exported through the growing trading companies. This was impossible because the native population was then unable to grow the crops in demand. Thus it came about that the bulk of the country's production for export was soon in the hands of Europeans who were able to attain the high standards required for world markets. At the present time there are some 250 companies and individuals concerned. Most of them are highly specialized but a number near to Blantyre have developed mixed farming.

Within two fairly compact areas in the Cholo highlands and the southern flanks of Mlanje mountain are a number of large estates producing tea. The more widespread and smaller estates of the lower rainfall areas of the Shire Highlands tend to concentrate on the production of tung and tobacco. In the Central Province some seventy-four estates produce about 10 per cent. of the sun/air cured tobacco exports. In the Northern Province there were formerly a few estates producing coffee and cotton, but nowadays there is little production of these crops, although interest has been renewed in coffee recently. The province is subject to several large scale experiments. The Colonial Development Corporation has tung plantations covering an area of 6,000 acres. In the Nkata Bay area cocoa has been tried without marked success, the African Lakes Corporation has a rubber estate, and tea is being tried as an experiment at present.

The contribution of European agriculture to the economy of Malawi has been a very large one, but political and economic events have resulted in some farmers leaving the country and their estates being given over to African traditional cultivation. Thus European production is not likely to increase, but rather to decrease in the future.

BIBLIOGRAPHY

An Outline of Agrarian Problems and Policy in Nyasaland (Zomba, 1955).
A. J. W. Hornby, 'Denudation and Soil Erosion in Nyasaland', *Nyasaland Agricultural Department Bulletin*, No. 11 (1934).
C. R. Hursh, *The Dry Woodlands of Nyasaland* (1960).
D. T. Jack *et al.*, *Report on an Economic Survey of Nyasaland*, 1958–59.
J. C. Mitchell, 'Preliminary Notes on Land Tenure and Agriculture among the Machinga Yao', *Nyasa. Jour.*, Vol. V (ii).
W. B. Morgan, 'The Lower Shire Valley of Nyasaland: A Changing System of African Agriculture', *Geog. Jour.*, Vol. CXIX.
Nyasaland Agricultural Department Report, 1959–60, Part II.
G. T. Rimmington, 'Agricultural Development in the Dedza District of Nyasaland', *Nyasa. Jour.*, Vol. XVI (i).

CHAPTER XI

MAJOR CROPS

ALTHOUGH there was some trade in agricultural produce between the interior of Africa and the coastal ports before the entry of Europeans, the development of export crops on a regular basis began only with the growth of the European estates. From the 1870s planters experimented with a variety of crops, of which tea, tobacco, cotton, and coffee have become the most prominent. In the second and third decades of the present century more attention was given to the marketing of African grown crops, and produce from African Trust Land now constitutes about half the annual total of agricultural exports. The main crops grown for export are tobacco, tea, cotton, and tung. Maize, rice, and groundnuts are used mainly within the country, although oil derived from the latter is exported.

MAIZE

Maize is the most important crop grown in Malawi; almost every African family grows some maize for domestic consumption. Being a sub-tropical crop maize can be grown at all elevations, but occasional frosts at very high altitudes and the high temperatures of the rift valley areas tend to reduce yields significantly. Yields are at their best between 2,000 and 4,000 feet in areas where the rainfall is between 25 and 35 inches, with not less than 3 inches for each month during the period December to February. Intervals between falls of rain should not be more than two weeks. Optimum temperatures lie between 60° F and 90° F. Rich, well-drained loamy soils, such as those of the Lilongwe Plain, are best suited to maize.

The best physical conditions for maize growth are not always, however, the optimum social and economic conditions for a high rate of production. Research in Dedza district shows that the greatest maize surpluses are evident in soils slightly less fertile than the red soils. On the latter soils the acreage under maize is still far greater than the acreage under all other crops, but the development of a rotational pattern, and the increase in the growing of other crops, such as tobacco, beans, and groundnuts, has reduced its former extent. Outside the red soil belt the acreage under maize tends to increase, and production is remarkably high on the poor sands of the eastern margins of the Dzalanyama forest. The problem in such zones is to find suitable rotation crops. Thus maize surpluses are produced, not always in the best soils, but in those soils for which a satisfactory crop complex has not been worked out.

There are a number of maize varieties, classified by their grain characteristics. The most important types grown in Malawi are dent maize and flint maize. The essential difference between them lies in the varying density of starch granules in the endosperm tissue of the grain. In flint maize the hard endosperm comprises most of the grain, and forms a cap over the germ. In dent maize the hard endosperm is present only as an open cylinder partly surrounding the germ towards the base of the grain. The cap consists of the softer endosperm, which tends to shrink and produce the characteristic dent in the centre of the grain.

Throughout Southern Africa preference is normally given to dent maize, flint being grown only in those areas where the former will not mature under a shorter growing season. In Malawi, however, African grown maize is usually of the flint variety, because this is more resistant to weevil infestation during storage. It is also better for the preparation of maize flour by traditional methods. Moreover although yield per acre is greater in the case of dent maize the flour derived from each grain of flint maize is greater by as much as 12 per cent.

As such a small proportion of the maize grown is included in market returns it is difficult to estimate total production, and information is limited to sample surveys. From these it is concluded that the average maize acreage per family is about three acres, and that a total of about 1·5 million acres is under maize cultivation throughout the country. Yields appear to be on average 600 pounds per acre in the Northern Province, 1,000 pounds per acre in the Central Province, and 800 pounds per acre in the Southern Province. Total production probably exceeds 600,000 tons per annum in normal years.

TEA

Malawi has grown tea longer than any other country in Africa, two plants of *Thea assamica* having been introduced in 1888 by the African Lakes Company. These bushes were planted in Blantyre at first, but later one of them was taken to Mlanje and introduced to coffee plantations, where it soon replaced the coffee. By 1908 23,000 pounds valued at £538 represented the tea exports. In the same year tea estates were started in Cholo. In the past three years tea has been introduced into the high rainfall areas of Nkata Bay and the Vipya Highlands.

Tea requires, for its optimum growth, an annual rainfall of more than 50 inches, with at least 7 inches fairly well distributed during the dry season. Thus the 7-inch dry season isohyet delimits the main tea growing areas. In the Nkata Bay area dry season rainfall exceeds 7 inches, but less than 1 inch falls during the hottest period between August and October. Fortunately the heavy rains in this region are prolonged at the end of the wet season and the soils are capable of retaining sufficient moisture throughout the driest period.

Tea grows well on a variety of soils, even on those with a slight acid content. In some cases there is difficulty because the high organic content of some soils tends to immobilize available copper, which is an essential element during the fermentation stage of the tea leaves. For this reason spraying with copper compounds is sometimes practised. Some shade is also beneficial, and the planting of leguminous trees has been carried out so that nitrogen will be returned to the soil.

Annual exports of tea ready for consumption have in recent years averaged 19 million pounds valued at £3 million. The average yield of 810 pounds per acre is very high, being sometimes higher than yields in India and Ceylon.

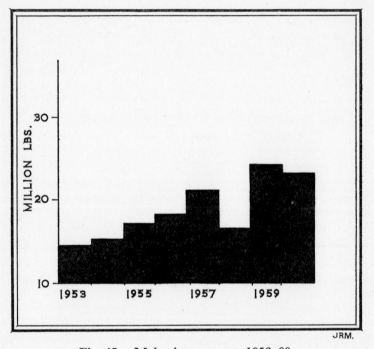

JRM.

Fig. 45.   Malawi tea exports 1953–60.

There are two main problems facing the tea industry at present. The first of these is the difficulty of expansion at a time when prosperity demands it. In 1960 the total acreage was 28,728, only about 1·3 per cent. of the world total. This can be increased to only a very small degree, for areas with suitable physical requirements are very limited in extent. Moreover much of the tea produced is of inferior quality and some bushes are of an inferior yielding type. This problem is being solved by the continued replacement of poor bush types with higher yielding Indian types.

TOBACCO

A type of tobacco, probably of eastern origin, was being grown and exported by means of the slave routes to the east coast before European planters arrived in Malawi. With the arrival of Europeans Virginia type seed was introduced in 1891, and the first recorded export of this was a small amount of 40 pounds in 1893. In 1920 tobacco was introduced into Lilongwe and Dedza districts, and the tenant system of production by Africans on European estates was developed. In the Southern Province the production of tobacco was restricted to the flue-cured types, but production in the Central Province has been more of the dark-fired and air-cured Western types.

Apart from the Kasungu area, where the soils are very sandy, most

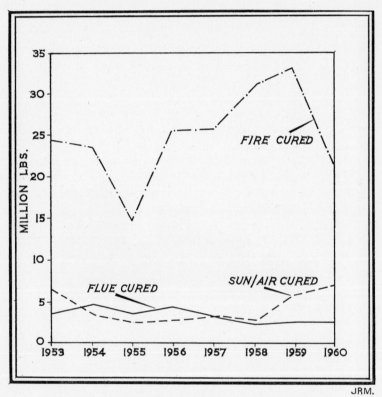

Fig. 46. Production of Virginia tobacco, 1953–60.

tobacco soils in the country are red loams, which require special care in management and manuring. The crop is fairly drought resistant, rainfall requirement being as low as 20 inches per annum. Under heavy rainfall when the soil tends to become waterlogged yields are poor. An intense wet season is therefore destructive to tobacco plants. The main tobacco growing areas in the country are those areas with low rainfall, in particular the Lilongwe, Kasungu, Tuchila, and Palombe plains, and the plains bordering Zomba massif.

Flue-cured tobacco is grown exclusively on European estates, mostly in the Southern Province, but the acreage has declined steadily until only 3,400 acres were used in 1960. This type of tobacco needs high initial capital expenditure, and high standards of cultivation, both of which are lacking in Malawi. Yields of between 500 and 550 pounds per acre are much below those of Southern Rhodesia.

Most of the production of dark-fired Western leaf is on village lands in the Central Province, where some 67,000 African farmers produced 20 million pounds in 1960 on an average of 2 acres each. In the same year African tenants on European estates produced another 5·5 million pounds.

Sun- and air-cured Western tobacco is produced in areas where dry conditions can be expected at the harvest time. It is commonly found in the Bwanje valley area of Ncheu district and the Lilongwe Plain. Production of tobacco cured in this manner was 5·5 million pounds in 1960. Most was from tenant farmers on European estates. Average yield per acre from village lands is usually about 200 pounds, but yields on European estates tend to be higher because of the supervision given. Research on agricultural stations has shown that it is possible for yields to be between 500 and 1,000 pounds per acre, so that there is scope for a much increased production from the existing acreage.

Small areas are devoted to the growing of Burley and Turkish tobaccos. The former grows mainly on European estates where Europeans grow it themselves. The latter is grown mainly in the Mzimba district, where curiously the low soil fertility lends itself to the production of a small leaf of satisfactory quality.

The market for fire-cured tobacco in Britain appears to be declining slowly, and the future is at present uncertain. The demand for sun/air-cured types is also slowly declining. In Turkish tobacco alone is there much opportunity for expansion.

TUNG

Malawi is the foremost tung oil producing country within the British Commonwealth, though production is likely to decline as demand has dropped with the discovery of a synthetic means of producing a substitute with the same quick drying properties for the paint industry. From 20,600 in 1953 the acreage had dropped to 15,800 in 1960, and further decline is expected.

Tung oil is obtained by expressing the fruit of the deciduous *Aleurites fordii* and *A. montana*. The latter variety was introduced to the country by the Forestry Department in 1927. It was found later that *A. fordii* was more prolific, and this type has now largely replaced *A. montana*. Requiring at least 40 inches of rainfall per annum, and a cool season of four months for the satisfactory growth and ripening of the fruit, it thrives best at elevations of between 4,000 and 5,000 feet in the Shire Highlands and the Vipya Highlands. It is fortunately suited to poor soil areas and does not need much rain during the dry season.

About half the acreage under tung is grown on estates specializing in the crop. Some growers have interplanted coffee bushes to spread the risk of a market collapse.

The oil is expressed locally within the producing areas, and thereafter

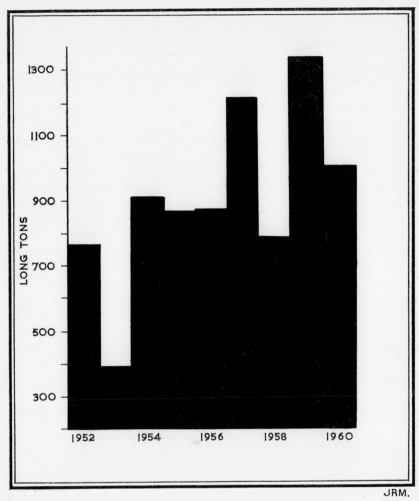

JRM.

Fig. 47.   Production of Tung Oil, 1952–60.

the whole crop is exported. The value of exports has fluctuated from
£93,000 to £142,000 per annum over the past six years.

COTTON

Cotton of the *Gossypium arboreum* type was introduced into Malawi
by the Arabs, while *G. barbadense* was probably introduced from Brazil
by the Portuguese. These varieties are of no commercial importance
nowadays, the former having become extinct. The latter is still occasionally seen in the Northern and Central Provinces, where it is cultivated as a parasitic shrub to provide the characteristic kidney-shaped
locks used in traditional funeral ceremonies. The cultivation of *G.
barbadense* is a potential danger to other commercial crops as it is host
to a number of pests.

Present commercial crops are derived almost entirely from the

G. hirsutum variety, an American type introduced at the end of the nineteenth century. It has adapted itself well to African conditions, and in hybridized form gives a better lint than similar crops in the U.S.A.

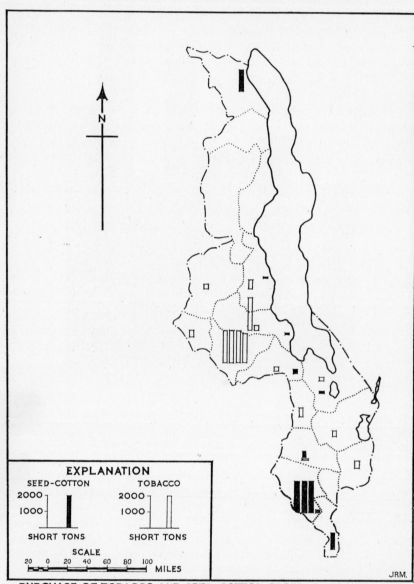

PURCHASE OF TOBACCO AND SEED-COTTON GROWN ON TRUST LAND
(Compiled from statistics in Nyasaland Agricultural Dept. Annual Reports—1957–1960)

Fig. 48.

Cotton is cultivated in the hotter and drier parts of the country, and is therefore confined to the rift valley, where it can be found intensively grown on the richer soils. About 80 per cent. is produced in the Ngabu area of Chikwawa district, where the extremely fertile *makande* soils, which are black and heavy, are used. Elsewhere it may be found on the alluvial flood lands of the lakeshore plain in Karonga district, and around the southern end of Lake Nyasa. It is also in evidence in the Lisungwe valley, an alluvial pocket in the Middle Shire.

Having had a long experience in growing this type of cash crop production of cotton by African farmers is often of a high standard. Yields vary considerably from one area to another, owing mainly to differences of soil fertility. Along the southern lake-shore plain yields varied during 1959 from 540 pounds per acre in the rich alluvial *dambo* soils of Chipoka and Ngodzi to only 190 pounds per acre in the Chinseu (near Ntakataka) sandy soils. There also appears to be an increase in quality of cotton in inverse proportion to the acreage cultivated. Those areas where average acreage is higher than one acre tend to produce poorer quality cotton than those areas with a lower average acreage per grower.

TABLE XV

Cotton Statistics for the South-western Shores of Lake Nyasa

Area	Number of growers	Acreage per grower	Total acreage	Yield per acre (lb.)	Total production (short tons)
Lifidzi	33	0·86	18	340	3·06
Chipoka	24	0·40	10 ⎫	540	13·54
Ngodzi	42	1·00	40 ⎭		
Chinseu	205	1·20	226	190	21·64
Ntakataka	106	0·74	78	446	17·02
Golomoti	330	1·10	363	360	65·35
Ndindi	406	0·78	317	463	83·25
Total	1,146	0·87	1,052	334	203·86

Cotton production has been subject to many difficulties, among them sharp weather variations, hydrological changes in the Lower Shire, fluctuations in price, and insect pests. The most important of these is the last, for ravages of the red bollworm have been particularly serious. To counter this the Agricultural Department has regulated the planting and uprooting dates to prevent the pest from re-establishing itself in the following year's crop. A further measure has been encouragement in the adopting of a cash crop complex to enable rotation to be employed. Besides maintaining soil fertility this does also help to prevent the re-establishment of any pests which have managed to remain in the soil from the previous year, for bollworms cannot survive in other crops. In addition to damage by bollworms there is frequent trouble from stainer bugs and bacterial blight.

Between 1952 and 1960 production has varied between 5,150 bales and 20,354 bales.[1] Lower quality lint is exported to Southern Rhodesia, while higher quality lint is mainly exported to the United Kingdom.

[1] A bale contains 400 pounds.

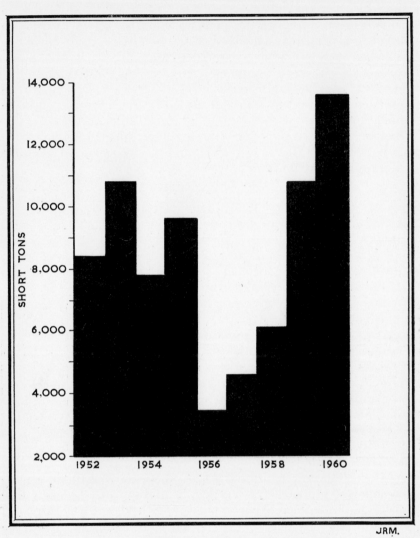

JRM.

Fig. 49.   Production of Seed Cotton, 1952–60.

GROUNDNUTS

Groundnuts form an important item of diet in the subsistence economy, as well as providing a useful cash crop. They also have a beneficial effect on the soil in rotation with maize and tobacco.

The most usual type of groundnut grown is a local semi-spreading variety, which produces large nuts much in demand by confectioners. It is grown on ridges in closely spaced double rows. This system of cultivation, together with early sowing, provides some protection against *Rosette* disease, which reduces yields. Yields vary from 400 to 1,000 pounds of shelled nuts per acre.

Groundnut plots tend to be small because labour demands are

greater than for most other crops. A survey in Lilongwe district[1] in 1956 showed that although the financial return per acre of groundnuts was much greater than for either maize or tobacco the acreage per family used for groundnut production was only 0·67. Maize and tobacco acreages were 2·72 and 1·58 respectively. Investigations in the field and marketing returns seem to suggest that average acreage per grower tends to increase with the incidence of richer soils and lower rainfall.

Annual production since 1951 has increased from 316 tons to 20,698 tons in 1960, which shows its growing importance as an essential item in a growing cash crop complex.

COFFEE

Arabica coffee was one of the first cash crops to be planted in Malawi. Introduced in 1877 by Scots missionaries at Blantyre it was soon being grown on European estates in the Blantyre and Mlanje districts. By 1899 production had reached 1,074 tons from 12,000 acres, a yield of 179 pounds per acre. From a maximum of 16,917 acres in use in 1901 there was a gradual decline during the next sixteen years until production was insignificant by 1917. This was the result of a combination of factors, among them *Antestia* attacks, severe overcropping, failure to maintain soil fertility, and the overproduction in Brazil which forced world prices down for several decades.

Interest in coffee production was revived after 1945, when prices rose. New plantings were at first mainly in the depressed tung growing areas of the Shire Highlands, but almost all present day production is centred in Karonga (65 short tons in 1960) and Rumpi (47 short tons).

Experiments in the Misuku hills have shown the importance of good soil selection and mulching. A curious feature is that the application of dung alone to the soil has little effect on production, but that if applied after mulching production is doubled. Shade is of little value, indeed is even deleterious, but shelter from strong, cold winds is extremely important. The leeside of a hill is normally chosen for planting; additional protection is provided by belts of pine trees.

During the past few years trial plots have been extended to other areas of the country, in particular to the slopes of Mlanje mountain and parts of the Kirk Range. The established coffee industry in the Northern Province is being extended. Successful trials in the Cholo highlands have resulted in a decision by the Nyasaland Government to proceed with the development of plantations in that area. On the other hand it has to be borne in mind that even the most favoured areas of Malawi are marginal for coffee production, and a continuation of the recent downward trend in coffee prices could well be disastrous. In the meantime national production is still increasing from 52 short tons in 1958 to 119 short tons in 1960.

[1] This survey was limited to one thousand families.

RICE

Rice grown in Malawi is wholly of various types of swamp rice. There is no cultivation of upland rice, such as may be found over broad tracts of West Africa. It is probable that the present strains were introduced by the Arabs.

The most important type of rice cultivated today is *Faya*, which needs a growing season of 150 days, and yields a good, firm white grain. Its attractive non-glutinous grain makes it valuable for the export trade.

The high temperatures and considerable water requirements of rice make it a crop of the rift valley, where it may be found on the flood plains, deltas, and within seasonal swamps. It prefers a growing season in which the mean temperature is 75° F or more, and between 60 and 80 inches of rain. The latter, however, is not common in Malawi, so that only in the Karonga lake-shore plain is the necessary water supplied directly by rainfall. Elsewhere rice grows under primitive irrigation.

Only in districts where plain sections of the rift valley are not included, such as Mzimba, Rumpi, and Lilongwe, is there no production of rice. The heaviest producing areas are along the Karonga, Kota Kota, and Dedza lake-shore plains, the Lake Chilwa plain, and the Lower Shire valley, where the clays, loamy-clays, and clay-with-flints are the main soils employed.

Because Malawi rainfall is unreliable and irrigation is not of a highly developed kind, consisting almost entirely of the planting of rice in places expected to flood during the rains, production of paddy varies considerably from year to year. Between 1952 and 1959 the total has varied from a minimum of 3,000 tons to a maximum of 7,200 tons. Almost the whole rice crop is sold within Central Africa.

POTATOES ('ENGLISH' TYPE)

The rapid increase in the European population of Malawi since 1945 has encouraged the production of potatoes, which will grow in poor soils, but need cool temperatures and plenty of moisture in order to swell properly. Large areas of the Northern Province highlands about 5,000 feet would be suitable for the growing of this type of tuber, but there are few Europeans in the area, so that poor roads and great distance from the markets in the Southern and Central Provinces have prohibited development.

The Kirk Range is fairly conveniently situated for the supply of potatoes to Blantyre and Lilongwe, and almost the whole crop is produced in Dedza and Ncheu districts. Eighty per cent. of the potatoes are produced around Dedza mountain, especially to the north, between it and the Chongoni and Mlunduni massifs.

By the use of *dimba* cultivation new potatoes can be supplied for marketing in Dedza township and in Moçambique, from the borders

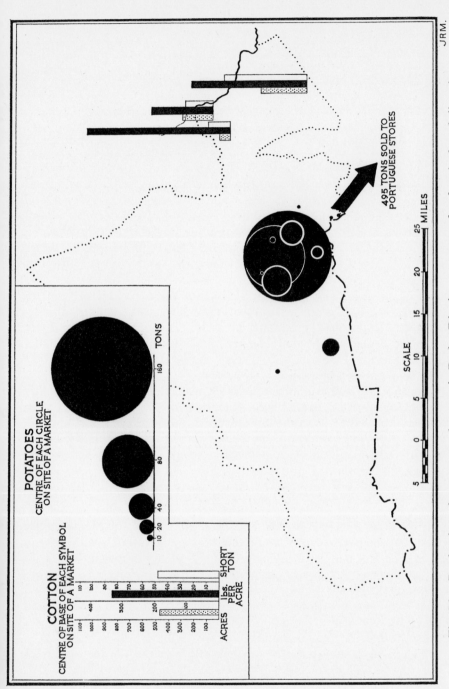

POTATOES
CENTRE OF EACH CIRCLE
ON SITE OF A MARKET

TONS
10 20 40 80 160

COTTON
CENTRE OF BASE OF EACH SYMBOL
ON SITE OF A MARKET

ACRES
100 200 300 400 500 600 700 800 900 1000

lbs. PER ACRE
10 20 30 40 50 60 70 80

SHORT TON

495 TONS SOLD TO
PORTUGUESE STORES

SCALE

5 0 5 10 15 20 25
MILES

JRM.

Fig. 50.   Production of potatoes and cotton in Dedza District—an example of agricultural diversity.

of which many are transported as far as Beira. The main *dimba* crop is harvested during the rainy season, between November and February. Between March and October a secondary *dimba* crop is grown in the drying stream beds on the exposed patches of damp alluvium. Most of the potato crop is, however, grown interplanted with maize during the wet season on land which a few years earlier would have been growing maize alone. This crop is ready for lifting between March and June.

There is a tendency for many potatoes to develop late blight since 1959. As a result of this estimated sales were 366 tons less in 1960 than in the previous year. In many cases too *dimba* land has been degraded through continuous use. This and the lack of manuring has resulted in a gradual decrease in the size of tubers.

BIBLIOGRAPHY

A Summary of Some Aspects of Agricultural Experimental Work, 1957–58, *Nyasa. Far. and For.*, Vol. 4, No. 3.

C. A. Baker, 'Nyasaland, the History of its Export Trade', *Nyasa. Jour.*, Vol. XV (i).

Crop Production Programme, 1961–62.

C. V. Cutting, 'Nyasaland Tea Soils—Their Nutrient Status', *Nyasa. Far. and For.*, Vol. 3, No. 2.

R. T. Ellis, 'The Food Properties of Flint and Dent Maize', *E. Afr. Agric. Jour.*, Vol. 24.

L. J. Foster, 'Progress in the Cultivation of Coffee in Nyasaland', *Rhod. Agric. Jour.*, Vol. 59 (1962).

——, and G. F. Craske, 'Coffee Growing in Nyasaland', *Nyasa. Far. and For.*, Vol. 3, No. 2.

——, 'Coffee-growing Prospects in Nyasaland,' *Nyasa. Far. and For.*, Vol. 4, No. 4.

G. G. S. J. Hadlow, 'The History of Tea in Nyasaland', *Nyas. Jour.*, Vol. XIII (i).

D. T. Jack *et al.*, *Report on an Economic Survey of Nyasaland, 1958–59*.

D. H. Laycock, 'Rainfall in the Nyasaland Tea Areas', *Nyasa. Far. and For.*, Vol. 2, No. 2.

S. S. Murray, *Handbook of Nyasaland* (1932).

Nyasaland Agricultural Department Report, 1960, Part I.

N. Ommanney, 'Dense Shade and its Effects on Quality of Tea', *Nyasa. Far. and For.*, Vol. 5, No. 2.

W. H. J. Rangeley, 'A Brief History of the Tobacco Industry in Nyasaland', *Nyasa. Jour.*, Vol. X (i).

G. T. Rimmington, 'Agricultural Development in the Dedza District of Nyasaland', *Nyasa. Jour.*, Vol. XVI (i).

R. C. H. Sweeney, *Insect Pests of Cotton in Nyasaland: I. Hemiptera (Bugs)*, 1961.

P. T. Terry, 'The Rise of the African Cotton Industry in Nyasaland, 1902 to 1918', *Nyasa. Jour.*, Vol. XV (i)

A. Young, *Preliminary Soil Map of Nyasaland* (1960).

CHAPTER XII

LIVESTOCK, FORESTRY, AND FISHING

LIVESTOCK

THE ratio of livestock to human population is lower than any other country of central Africa. In Southern Rhodesia there are ten cattle to every eight human beings, but in Malawi there are eight people for each animal. This is the result of a dense population, the hilly nature of the country, the tsetse fly belts, and the lack of near-by markets for substantial quantities of beef. There are indications that the cattle population in particular was much greater than it is now. On the other hand the country is not now capable of supporting such large numbers, and an increase of about 27 per cent. during the past decade is viewed with some concern.

TABLE XVI

Domestic Livestock Population

Year	Cattle	Sheep	Goats	Pigs
1948	267,000	46,000	233,000	80,000
1953	273,000	53,000	294,000	94,000
1958	343,000	62,000	413,000	82,000

The goat population has also increased at a very rapid rate, and numbers have now exceeded those for cattle. It is probable that this is a manifestation of the declining value of pastures. While the goat provides the African diet with a useful protein supplement, it is a danger to natural pastures and to woodland.

The numbers of sheep, though increasing, are doing so at a steady rate, and give no cause for concern. Pigs are subject to fluctuations caused by disease and lack of suitable feeding stuff.

Slightly more than half the cattle may be found in the Central Province, mainly in the Dedza, Ncheu, and Lilongwe districts, where the *dambo* grasslands are much used. Another 40 per cent. are grazed in the Northern Province, in the Mzimba and Karonga districts. Less than 10 per cent. are found in the Southern Province, where very high human population densities, a higher proportion of tsetse infested lowland, and a high proportion of land under crops prevents the grazing of large numbers of heavy animals.

As has been commented above, integration of animal husbandry with arable farming is rarely evident. This is resulting in arable lands being without manure, and the grazing lands being over-grazed. In the Central

o

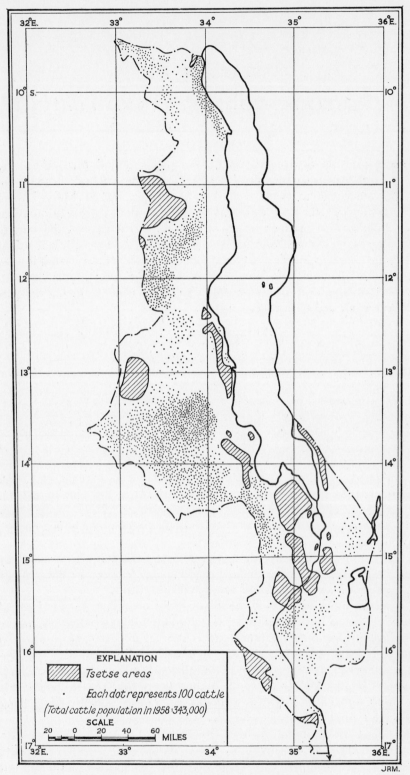

Fig. 51.   The distribution of cattle in Malawi.

Province, there is little land other than the *dambos* retained for grazing, so that the grasslands in the latter are tending to deteriorate. This is happening especially where some of the *dambo* soils are cultivated on the *visoso* system, thus crowding the animals on to an even smaller area, where the trampling of hoofs is tending to bring about a compacting of the topsoil which prevents speedy regeneration of the grass. In the Northern Province grazing is more extensive, but during the dry season the problem of watering brings about a concentration in the valleys. This is very noticeable in the Kasitu valley, where there has been considerable overgrazing.

The predominant type of cattle is the East African *Zebu*, with its thoracic hump. Some cattle, however, show that *Sanga* blood has been introduced in the past, and these are referred to locally as Ngoni cattle.

Both breeds have become adapted to African conditions over a very long period. The *Sanga* type was a fusion of the lateral horned *Zebu* introduced to Africa by Semitic tribes round about 1000 B.C. and the Hamitic longhorn. The *Zebu* was brought to Africa about 1,500 years ago by Arabs and Indians.

Types and breeds of animals vary in their ability to adapt themselves to different climatic conditions. Variations in temperature and humidity affect metabolism, respiration, reproduction, and growth. Cattle have no sweat glands, and lose heat by respiration at an increased rate. As compared with exotic breeds from Europe the African types tend to increase the respiration rate at a much lower temperature. Moreover, they also tend to lose more moisture from the skin by diffusion and evaporation. Other advantages are the shorter hair and larger skin surface area.

In spite of their greater degree of adaptation to African conditions the *Zebu* and *Sanga* types of cattle are much poorer in milk and meat yields than exotic types. Attempts have therefore been made to produce cross-breeds. On the whole these are not successful, for the exotic types tend almost immediately to eat less and soon die. Recent research has found, however, that some exotic animals are able to adapt themselves better than others, and experiments are being made by breeding from these.

European animal husbandry is generally satisfactory, but African animals are often in a poor state. Most cattle suffer from the lack of feed during the long dry season, and there are few people who make any attempt to make silage or grow grass for hay. Over-milking causes the under-nourishment of calves, and thus the degeneration of future breeding stock. The incidence of diseased animals is high, and tends to be increased by the lack of concern for high quality production among Africans. This is partly because wealth is still often measured by numbers of cattle owned, and also because even butchers do not buy cattle according to quality.

Cattle diseases in Malawi are less rampant than in East African countries farther north, but poorly fed cattle soon fall prey to enzootic and epizootic diseases. The tick-borne diseases cause the greatest losses. Gall-sickness, *anaplasmosis*, *bovine piroplasmosis* and 'East Coast Fever' are all prevalent. The last of these is very difficult to eradicate even though great care may be taken, for the carrying ticks may remain alive for as many as nine hundred days without food. The only effective means of control for these diseases is to kill the ticks on the animals' bodies by dipping them in disinfectant regularly. A large number of dipping tanks has been constructed in the main cattle areas during recent years. At the end of 1959 115 tanks were in use.

Infection of cattle by foot-and-mouth disease and *trypanosomiasis* is also prevalent. The former is extremely prevalent in Tanganyika and tends to spread southward from there. Two recent infections were effectively halted by stringent control over stock movements and quarantine regulations.

Trypanosomes are injected into the body by four main species of tsetse fly, two of which, *Glossina morsitans* and *G. brevipalpus*, are found in Malawi. About 12 per cent. of the total land surface of the country is covered by tsetse fly belts.

FORESTRY

Broken country and dense human settlement have determined the nature of Malawi forests. There are no large tracts of valuable timber trees which are indigenous. The total land area under forest and woodland is estimated at 8,936 square miles, about 24 per cent. of the total land surface. Of this about 2,943 square miles have been set aside as state forests, and another 480 square miles consist of village and local authority forests.

Although there are no good timber-producing forests of any size, there are a considerable number of first class indigenous timber trees such as the softwood types *Widdringtonia whytei* (Mlanje cedar) and *Juniperus procera* (juniper), and the hardwood types *Pterocarpus angolensis* (*mlombwa*)[1], *Khaya nyasica* (*mbawa*), *Adina microcephala* (*mwenya*), and *Chlorophora excelsa* (*mvule*). Of these the most interesting are the *Widdringtonia* forests of Mlanje mountain, from which timber has been extracted for sixty-five years. These forests occur as isolated stands, occasionally of considerable size, but more often of limited extent, and at an elevation of between 5,000 and 7,000 feet. Normally they are confined to the upper parts of the deeply incised valleys so characteristic of the mountain, or to the ravines and hollows on several shelf-like plateaux. The presence of roots and charred stumps in what has now become grassland is evidence that the present stands of *Widdringtonia* are relics of much larger forests partially destroyed by burning. After several years of fire protection the species is beginning to regenerate in areas adjacent to the older stands.

Although bearing no botanical relationship to the true cedars *Widdringtonia* resemble them in their durability, usefulness as a softwood

[1]Nyanja names in parentheses from this point.

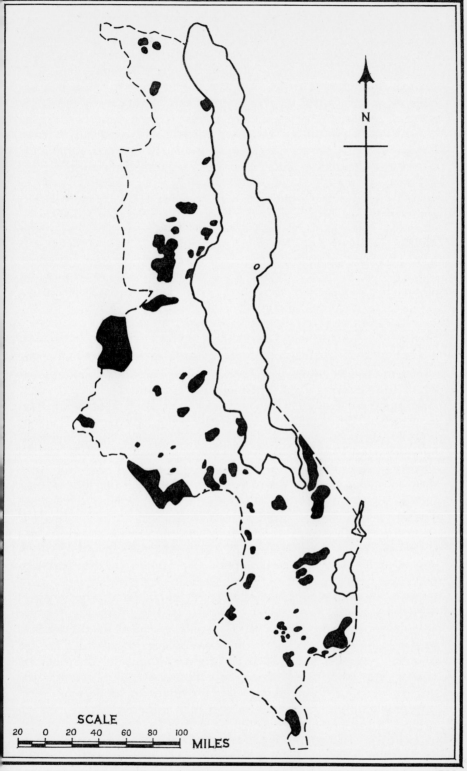

SCALE

20   0   20 40 60 80 100

MILES

JRM.

O²   Fig. 52.   The forest reserves of Malawi.

timber for constructional purposes, and resistance to termites, so that, although woodcutting is difficult and the tree stands often inaccessible, they have provided the bulk of timber for government purposes over many years. Over a twenty year period a concession resulted in the production of one million cubic feet from sixteen small stands totalling some 350 acres.

The hardwoods tend to occur singly or in small groups within other woodland communities, and are therefore of limited occurrence. *Pterocarpus angolensis* is the most widely distributed type, occurring mainly in the drier zones. It appears to achieve larger growth at lower altitudes, and where the soils are shallow, but overlying a fair depth of shattered rock.

Found in the many evergreen riverine forests are the *Adina microcephala*, while the *Khaya nyasica* grows commonly among the mountain evergreen forests of the southern part of the country, being absent north of Nkata Bay. Much investigation has been carried out on possible methods of regenerating trees of this kind, but as yet no answer has been found. One of the main problems of the Malawi forestry department is the production of hardwoods.

Of the hardwoods considered the *Pterocarpus* is in greater demand than any other. It is more suitable, because it is relatively light, soft, and of handsome appearance, for the making of furniture rather than for heavy constructional work.

Until 1953 demand for softwood timber required for building purposes was small and could be supplied from within the country. Increased demand after this year, however, made imports necessary. In 1957 imports exceeded £147,483 in value. With the rise in imports afforestation has taken place to reduce the reliance on other countries, for local timber production can take place at a much cheaper rate.

By 1960 state afforestation had utilized 25,000 acres and private afforestation 18,000 acres. Since most of the forests, however, consist of *Eucalyptus saligna*, state forests have concerned themselves with softwoods. It has been estimated that annual demand will be about 17 million cubic feet of round wood by 1990 produced from a planted acreage of softwood of 70,300. The present rate of planting is 2,300 acres per annum, and this is sufficient to supply the estimated future demand.

The areas being planted with softwood forest are the high mountain slopes and plateaux of Mlanje, Zomba, Dedza, Vipya, and the Nyika. Although the area available for plantations is comparatively small productivity tends to be higher than that apparent in cooler parts of the world. Fast and medium-fast growing pines on moderately good forest-land, and under a moist warm climate, yield a wood increment of about 250 cubic feet per annum; yields in Germany are 50 cubic feet, while in the U.S.A. they are as low as 7 cubic feet. Moreover, the profitability of softwood growth has been demonstrated in South Africa, where profits average 20 per cent. of the capital invested.

The main species of softwood grown in Malawi is *Pinus patula*, a species of pine native to Mexico. It has been introduced to many areas on the eastern side of Africa, especially in the summer rainfall areas at high altitudes. It was first introduced into Malawi in 1927, when small plantations were established on the Zomba plateau. The mature trees, now to be seen in the first plantations, yield timber of high quality for general building purposes.

No statistics are available for timber production on private estates, but returns in 1948–50 showed that the total area of plantations was about 18,000 acres, of which five-sixths were in the Southern Province. Almost all of these plantations consist of *Eucalyptus saligna*. Favourable climatic conditions make the growth of this species equal to similar plantations elsewhere in Africa.

In the tea-growing areas eucalyptus plantations were established originally for the supplying of firewood to the tea factories, and for general purposes on the estates. In addition to use on the estates the sale of poles has increased in importance recently. One company grows the wood exclusively for the manufacture of tobacco casks. Other poles are used for the roofing of buildings and for scaffolding.

Outside the valuable forests described above there are larger areas consisting of forest or woodland of much lesser value. The *Brachystegia* woodland which covers so much of the countryside has been described elsewhere. As with so many of the native trees the burning and dismemberment of young trees does not allow wood growth to develop normally, so that these are of no market value, although of importance in the village economy.

FISHING

The fishing industry and its potential development are of special importance because of an acute deficiency of animal protein in the diet of most of the African population. The industry is also important as a source of cash income for the lake-shore population, which is mainly concerned with subsistence in its agriculture.

The main centre of fishing consists of the two arms of the southern end of Lake Nyasa. Fishing is also important in Lakes Malombe and Chilwa and in the Shire River. In these areas a surplus exists for sale. Elsewhere fishing forms part of a subsistence economy, although a small quantity is caught and marketed in Tanganyika at the northern end of Lake Nyasa.

The lake and river fauna of Malawi is rich and varied. There are more than two hundred species and thirteen fish families represented. Eighty per cent. of all fish, however, belong to the *Cichlidae* family. It is probable that with long isolation from the waters of the Zambezi the original species have become differentiated into many forms, each becoming more specialized for a particular mode of life. Nearly nine-tenths of the fish cannot be found elsewhere in the world. The other more common species are all forms associated with inland swamp conditions, and can be found also in other parts of the Zambezi system and other rift valley lakes.

Species of the *Cichlidae*, *Cyprinidae*, *Bagridae*, and *Claridae* are commercially exploited, the majority of those netted being of the first named category. The *Cichlidae* are represented by six species of *Tilapia* (chambo)[1] and many species of *Haplochromids* (utaka).

Of the *Tilapia* species in Lake Nyasa the four main commercial species are known by the Nyanja name of *chambo*. In appearance they are rather like bream, but are more closely related to the perch family. It is thought that the ancestral species of *Tilapia* consisted of inshore-dwellers. The absence of large predators in these waters allowed variations to survive and propagate new species. Even today the *T. squamipinis* spawns in open water near to beaches and reedy shores, while *T. saka* spawns in one or two fathoms of water near to reedy shores and weed beds, and *T. karongae* lives near the northern Lake Nyasa shoreline at the point where the larger rivers flow into the lake. On the other hand *T. lidole* spurns the coastline and spawns in deep clear water, though even in this case often near to a point where the escarpment falls sheerly into the lake. *Tilapia* are normally caught by shore seine nets and river traps, or professionally by gill and ring nets.

Labeo mesops, a species of *Cyprinidae*, are abundant wherever there are areas of relatively shallow water. As mud-feeders they remain near to the bottom, being found down to depths of fifteen fathoms. Some are caught in seine nets, and others in gill nets, most being netted during the wet season during migration up the rivers to spawn.

Utaka is the Nyanja name given to a group of about six species of *Haplochromids*, which feed on zooplankton in the open waters of Lake Nyasa. Fishing for these is particularly important in the Northern Province, where there are few *Tilapia* or *Labeo mesops*.

Very little is known of *Utaka* movements, but they appear to move inshore when spawning and looking after young progeny, at which time they are often netted in large numbers in the southern lake waters. They are usually caught by means of an open water seine net worked from two canoes.

Two species of *Cyprinidae*, *Barilius microlepis* (mpasa) and *B. microcephalus* (sanjika), form the basis of important fisheries at the northern end of Lake Nyasa. They swim up the rivers to spawn between November and April, and are caught in large fish traps built across the main rivers. In June, when the river waters are low, box traps are often placed facing upstream to catch the fish descending after spawning. Large numbers of *B. microcephalus* are caught in the Luweya river near Nkata Bay when they attempt to ascend the Chiwandama falls and are caught by fishermen standing on the rocks below the falls with large hand manipulated scoop nets.

The main predators consist of *Bagrus meridionalis* (kampango) and various types of catfish. The larger predators live in deeper parts of

[1] Nyanja names in parentheses.

Lake Nyasa, and are fished only by commercial fishermen. They are normally caught in four-inch gill nets or by long lines set on the bottom at night. The smaller inshore predators are caught in a *saika*, a floating fish trap consisting of a lump of sudd bordered with reeds and backed by the hanging trap, into which the fish slide while searching for worms and smaller fish in the sudd.

Fish production amounts to less than half the estimated potential of the country's inland water fisheries. It is not easy, however, to increase the annual total by significant proportions. Most of the fishing carried out tends to be for subsistence, only small surpluses being sold. As fishermen are traditionally conservative and independent the formation of co-operatives for commercial purposes is not favoured.

Many fishermen work on a commercial basis for only short periods of the year, the rest of their time being used in cultivation of their land. Both these and the few full-time fishermen depend mainly on visiting African buyers for marketing facilities. The buyers usually operate on bicycles, purchasing dried fish cheaply and distributing them throughout the plateau villages where prices are higher.

Non-African commercial fishing is concentrated in the south-east arm of Lake Nyasa, near Fort Johnston. It is concerned mainly with *Tilapia*, but during December, when this type of fishing has a short close season, *Labeo mesops* and catfish are the main catch.

Commercial fishing production has risen rapidly from less than 500 tons in 1948 to 4,000 tons ten years later. The 1958 catch was valued at £207,360, more than half the estimated value of the total Nyasaland catch.

Distribution of fish is confined almost entirely to the larger urban centres, to some of the small administrative townships, and to the larger employers of labour in the Cholo and Mlanje tea estates. Transport is entirely by road, there being no direct rail connexion between Fort Johnston and the Shire Highlands. Unfortunately the lake-shore plains are not well provided with roads, and those which do exist are mainly seasonal. Since the heaviest catches are made during the rainy season much wastage occurs through roads being impassable.

BIBLIOGRAPHY

An Outline of Agrarian Problems and Policy in Nyasaland (Zomba, 1955).

C. K. R. Bertram, H. J. H. Borley, and E. Trewavas, *Report on the Fish and Fisheries of Lake Nyasa* (H.M.S.O., 1942).

F. N. Bonsma, *Livestock Production in Africa South of the Sahara* (1951).

——, 'Increasing Adaptibility by Breeding', *Farming in South Africa*, July 1948.

J. D. Chapman, 'Some Notes on Widdringtonia Whytei', *Nyasa. Jour.*, Vol. XIII (i).

H. A. Cox (Ed.), *Handbook of Empire Timbers* (1939).

I. J. Craib, 'State Afforestation after the War', *Journal of the South African Forestry Association*, No. 9 (1942).

D. E. Faulkner, 'A Paper on Problems of Beef Production in Nyasaland', *Nyasa. Far. and For.*, Vol. 4, No. 1.

M. C. Hoole, 'Notes on Fishing and Allied Industries as Practised among the Tonga of the West Nyasa District', *Nyasa. Jour.*, Vol. VIII (i).

R. H. Lowe, 'Report on the Tilapia and Other Fish and Fisheries of Lake Nyasa', *Fishery Publications*, Vol. 1, No. 2 (H.M.S.O., 1952).

The Natural Resources of Nyasaland (Zomba, 1961).

R. G. Willan, 'Indigenous Trees of Nyasaland', *Nyasa. Jour.*, Vol. XII (i).

CHAPTER XIII

OTHER NATURAL RESOURCES AND THEIR DEVELOPMENT

WATER SUPPLY

ALTHOUGH Malawi has a relatively high average rainfall by Central African standards and is bordered by the vast fresh water expanse of Lake Nyasa water supplies are a serious problem in many parts of the country. Length of dry season, sharp variations in the isohyetal pattern, and considerable fluctuations in total rainfall per annum bring about much unreliability of water sources and threaten human and animal life from time to time. This irregularity has been aggravated further by the tendency of a dense population relying on subsistence agriculture for its livelihood to denude the land of its natural vegetation, thus increasing wet season run-off. Some streams which are known to have been perennial now tend to dry up between wet seasons.

Rural water supplies are often gained by primitive means from shallow wells, or from small pits scraped daily in the beds of *dambos* and dried up river beds. In a minority of cases it is supplied from perennial streams or small reservoirs held up by earth dams. Since 1931 the Nyasaland Water Development Department has steadily exploited underground water resources by means of boreholes, of which there are now 900 in existence. At present their number is being increased at the rate of 130 per year. Varying in depth from 100 to 120 feet the average borehole is capable of producing some 700 gallons of water per hour.

Apart from the use of water for hydro-electric power and industrial purposes in the Blantyre, Zomba, and Mlanje areas, all consumption is for domestic and stock needs. Irrigation, except in a primitive and almost accidental manner for rice, and in a more developed sense on the tea estates, is rarely found. In the case of Africans it is probable that the small size of agricultural holdings and the migratory habits of many people have prevented the development of irrigation even in areas most suited to it. Where primitive irrigation has been practised it is observed that the strict water control necessary is not apparent, and crops tend to be spoiled through standing in too much water.

The recent rapid growth of Blantyre–Limbe has outstripped the availability of water supplies from reservoirs sited in the headwaters of the two local streams. In spite of a fairly heavy rainfall of between 40 and 55 inches local water supply is decreasing rather than increasing to meet the demand. Hydrological records confirm that there is a general depletion of dry season flow in local streams, and the increased sediment load indicates that this owes something to deforestation.

In order to solve the problem of water supply to Blantyre–Limbe recourse is to be made to using water from the Shire River. A detailed investigation has shown that by extending pipelines for 23 miles to the river a demand of 5·5 million gallons per day can be satisfied.

Water requirements inevitably tend to increase with the growth of population and a rising standard of living; water supplies tend to decrease with the removal of natural vegetation from catchment areas and the ensuing increased run-off. Both of these are evident in the country now, and unless the African people can be persuaded to place greater emphasis on the conservation and development of water resources adequate supplies will not be available in the future.

Areas of dense population at present inadequately served with water supplies are the Lilongwe district, whose *dambo* supplies become more polluted every year with the crowding of cattle and other animals on these damp grasslands, the Bwanje Valley, the Palombe Plain, and the Balaka area. All of these areas lie within the 30- and 35-inch isohyets, but rainfall is unevenly distributed throughout the year, evaporation rate is high, and perennial streams are few. The Chikwawa district, and the Rivi Rivi and Lisungwe valleys of the Middle Shire are areas with similar lack of surface water, and a sparse population which would become greater if water was available.

ELECTRIC POWER

As Malawi has little developed industrial capacity the development of electricity has lagged far behind the potential. Small demand has made it necessary in most areas to rely on diesel generators. Some of the larger administrative townships are lighted by this means. Of the larger urban centres, however, only Lilongwe has diesel generated electricity.

In Blantyre–Limbe the presence of the railway has encouraged the use of coal for the thermal power station there. This is the only one of its kind in the territory.

At Zomba a small hydro-electricity generator has been in operation for a number of years. Using water from a swift flowing mountain stream it produces about 1,000 kilowatts. There are similar hydro-electric developments on the tea estates of Mlanje and a number of mission stations.

In recent years, especially during the past decade, the growth of the European population and the rising standards of living of educated African people in the urban areas has resulted in a rapid increase in the demand for electricity supply. In 1950 the installed generating capacity in the country was only 755 kilowatts. By 1958 it had increased to 8,516 kilowatts. At present the Blantyre plant is loaded to its full capacity, and an increased supply is urgently needed.

Increased power supplies have been discussed for several years. The

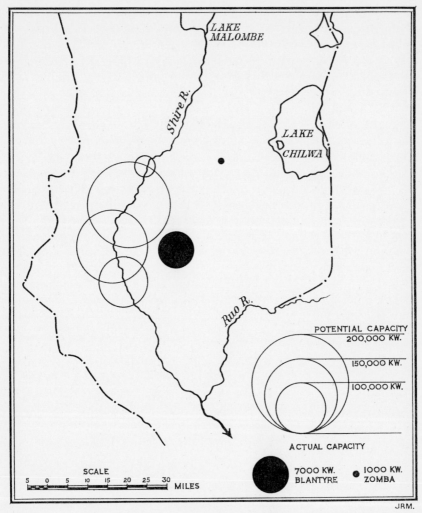

Fig. 53. Actual and potential development of electricity in the Southern Province.

hydro-electric potential of the country is estimated to be 400,000 kilowatts, of which 360,000 kilowatts could be generated in the series of falls and cataracts of the Shire river.

The potential power development of the Shire river has been examined in some detail, and the Shire Valley Project is a scheme for an integrated system with generators at Matope, Nkula, Mpatamanga, and Hamilton Falls. Table XVII summarizes the proposals.

Unfortunately the potential capacity is far greater than is likely to be needed for many years. In any case capital expenditure would be greater than a country with Malawi's modest assets could manage. To meet the estimated demand for the foreseeable future, a modest hydro-electric scheme is now being installed at Nkula Falls, where some

20,000 kilowatts will be generated, with an initial capital outlay of
£2·8 million. The average output of the fully developed generating capacity at the site is 67,000 kilowatts, which can be developed in stages as
demand increases. For the present the intention is to divert a proportion
of the Shire River's flow through a penstock tunnel alongside the falls
through a total head of 160 feet.

TABLE XVII

Potential Electricity Development in the Shire Valley

Station	Average output (kW.)	Peak output (kW.)	Installed capacity (kW.)
Matope	16,000	30,000	40,000
Nkula	67,000	135,000	180,000
Mpatamanga	96,000	120,000	150,000
Hamilton	61,000	75,000	100,000

Elsewhere in Malawi there are possibilities of developing hydro-
electricity on a smaller scale to provide a sustained supply, or for
seasonal augmentation of present installations. Sites can be found along
the rift valley margins on rivers such as the South Rukuru, Luweya,
Lilongwe, and Livulezi, and along the Ruo River, which has its source
on Mlanje massif. Unfortunately, although there is usually an adequate
head of water at many sites, the reduction of flow in the dry season and
the lack of appreciable storage sites is a discouraging factor. Nevertheless four tea estates have their own installations, one of which was
established as early as 1898. The modest needs of a tea estate and the
fact that most power is required during the rainy season are fortunate.

When the State forests of the Vipya Highlands begin production the
demand for power in that area will increase, so that a number of sites
along the eastern edge of the plateau in the Luweya catchment area
might be developed. These schemes will be small, the largest generating
capacity being about 1,000 kilowatts.

MINERALS

The mineral deposits of Malawi are, unfortunately, neither extensive enough for major exploitation nor often in areas which are easily
accessible. There are no large internal markets. Export often involves
transport over long distances to the coast. Moreover, the necessary
power supplies are not yet available. Nevertheless there are minerals of
some commercial importance. Corundum, galena, gold, kyanite, limestone, and mica have all been worked in the past. Others are expected
to be worked in the future.

Since 1924 large deposits of bauxite have been discovered as a result
of prospecting on the Mlanje massif. The deposit on Litchenya plateau
has been estimated as containing about 65 million tons of bauxite
averaging 42 per cent. alumina.

The bauxite deposits take the form of a capping to the various plateaux, having been formed *in situ* by the alteration of orthoclase–hornblende–syenite. Although this ore contains quantities of quartz derived from syenite this does not interfere with the Bayer process used in the smelting of alumina concentrate. This is fortunate for in many cases it is kaolin which is present, and this causes complications.

There is a possibility that Mlanje bauxite may be exploited within the next few years, the ore being carried down the mountainside by bucket lift, and then exported by railway to Beira. It is unlikely that a smelting works will be established, for there is no immediate possibility of producing the 70,000 kilowatts of hydro-electricity required to begin operations, and even less possibility of producing the 200,000 kilowatts needed later.

Coal occurs in four separate fields. They are associated with the Karoo sediments, and may be found near Chiromo in the Tangadzi valley, the Sumbu area, at Livingstonia on the north-western shores of Lake Nyasa, and at Nkana in the Songwe river area of Karonga district.

The Chiromo coalfield is the nearest deposit to the railway, and as such it received earlier attention than the others. Between 1923 and 1928 six boreholes were drilled, as a result of which it was discovered that the seams lie at a depth of 700 feet. Although the quality of the coal is good the complexity of faulting prevents economic exploitation.

West of the Chiromo coalfield lies the shallower Sumbu field, which covers a wider area than its neighbour. It has also been prospected, an estimated 45 million tons of coal of fair quality being present. Post-Karoo dolerite and basalt sills and dykes have resulted in some areas of anthracite. To what extent faulting is associated with these intrusions is not known, but it is possible there is some step-faulting of the beds, giving an exaggerated apparent thickness of the series. After considerable investigation it was considered that the field was unworkable, working costs being high because of the intense faulting. In any case considerable capital expenditure would be initially necessary in the extension of the railway over a distance of 50 miles through sparsely inhabited countryside.

The Livingstonia coalfield appears to be a continuation of the Ruhuhu coalfield of Tanganyika. Because of its proximity to the lake, and the possibility of cheap transport to the markets of the south it was once thought to be a probable mining centre. In spite of the possibility of relatively cheap adit mining, the adits to be driven into the rift valley escarpment, faulting is complex and the seams discontinuous, so that mining concerns are uninterested. There are probably some 24 million tons of workable coal.

Rather curiously the small Nkana coalfield seems to offer the greatest possibilities for commercial exploitation. Although there are only 14 million tons of medium quality workable coal in the Malawi section it must be considered as part of the larger coalfield over the Tanganyika border, with which it is continuous. The coal is shallow, and less faulted than elsewhere in Malawi, and a number of seams on the Tanganyika side have already been worked by individuals.

Corundum deposits are known to occur in the nepheline–syenite of Tambane in the Mwanza district, and also in the foothills of the Malawi hills of Port Herald district. The Tambane deposits were worked between 1942 and 1952, 1,450 tons valued at £20,000 being exported.

Iron ores are very common in Malawi, but rarely are deposits of workable size. The most important discoveries have been at Dzonze mountain in Ncheu district and at Mindale hill in Blantyre district. The latter deposits are sited close to the railway, and a sample 5,000 tons have been mined. It has been found, however, that the bands of iron ore are associated with larger quantities of gneiss than previously suspected and are not therefore of sufficiently high quality to make working economic. Dzonze mountain is in an area of poor communications, sufficient to prevent the mining of all but the highest quality ores. The ores in this case are easy to mine, but occur in very thin lenticular deposits.

Graphite is known to occur in a number of large deposits in the Central Province, where it is associated with the quartz–felspar–gneiss of the Moçambique series. In two ore bodies the graphite was found to be about 10 per cent. of the gneiss constituents. It is probable that some of the deposits in Dowa district are of economic importance.

Kyanite occurs as segregations and intrusions in kyanite–quartz–schist bands of the Moçambique series. Discoveries have been in the Ncheu district section of the Kirk Range, the largest deposit being located near to Kapiridimba hill. An aluminium silicate, the kyanite occurs as lenticular deposits in the gneiss, and, through weathering, as large detached boulders. In the boulders the iron has been largely removed by weathering, and the debris remaining consists of pure kyanite. Over 2,000 tons of a lump kyanite sample were exported between 1952 and 1954. Recent investigations suggest that ore reserves are in the region of 80,000 tons.

One of the most important mineral deposits to be exploited in the future is likely to be the apatites of Tundulu hill, south of Lake Chilwa. Recent prospecting indicates that reserves are not less than 3 million tons of apatite-rich rock, of a higher grade than the main phosphate deposits of Southern Africa so far exploited. A considerable demand for phosphate exists within Malawi, for the soils of the Northern Province are deficient, but development awaits transport improvement, the nearest point on the railway being 60 miles away.

There are small quantities of other minerals in widely scattered deposits, few of which are ever likely to be of the slightest economic importance. Even those discussed above are often of little importance. It is clear that Malawi can never be a major industrial country.

BIBLIOGRAPHY

K. Bloomfield, 'The Geology of the Nkana Coalfield', *Nyasaland Geological Survey Bulletin*, No. 8 (1957).

W. G. G. Cooper, 'The Geology and Mineral Resources of Nyasaland', *Nyasaland Geological Survey Bulletin*, No. 6 (1957).

W. G. G. Cooper and K. Bloomfield, 'The Geology of the Tambani–Salambidwe Area', *Nyasaland Geological Survey Bulletin*, No. 13 (1961).

W. G. G. Cooper and F. Habgood, 'The Geology of the Livingstonia Coalfield' *Nyasaland Geological Survey Bulletin*, No. 11 (1959).

Sir William Halcrow and Partners, *Report on the Shire Valley Project* (1956).

D. T. Jack *et al.*, *Report on an Economic Survey of Nyasaland*, (1958-59).

CHAPTER XIV

TRANSPORT AND THE EXPORT TRADE

I N the underdeveloped countries of Africa the development of communications and commerce depend on each other. Without the development of roads and railways trade cannot grow; without the existence of trade the development of transport facilities is often unjustified. In the case of Malawi the growth of communications and trade has been made difficult by the lack of *potential* commerce, for there are few mineral deposits of economic importance, cash crop production is in many areas limited by poor soils, and the mountainous nature of the country presents engineering problems. Even water transport has its problems, for the Shire River, formerly used as the main highway into the country, is not always navigable.

RAILWAY DEVELOPMENT

During the nineteenth century the Zambezi and Shire Rivers, together with Lake Nyasa, formed the most important means of communication. This route traversed the whole length of Malawi, and at first was interrupted only by the 60-mile long Murchison Rapids.

By the time that Johnston sailed up through the Chinde mouth of the Zambezi the level of Lake Nyasa, and therefore of the Shire, had begun to fall. Steamers found difficulty in proceeding upstream beyond Chiromo. Because of this and the growing importance of Blantyre a railway was planned to cover the distance between it and Chiromo. The next 50 miles to Katunga was traversed in a smaller boat. The Shire Highlands escarpment was climbed on foot.

By the time the railway was constructed the level of the Shire had fallen further, and the section between Chiromo and Port Herald had become navigable only with great difficulty. Thus when the railway was opened to traffic in 1908 its southern terminus was at Port Herald.

Further navigation difficulties encouraged the formation of a new railway company, the Central African Railway Company, to construct a new line linking Port Herald with the Zambezi at Chindio, by the confluence with the Shire. This section was completed in 1915.

In 1935 the railway was extended to the coast at Beira, following the building of a great bridge, 12,064 feet long, over the Zambezi river. The line from Beira to the Zambezi had been constructed some years earlier, the connexion between the two railheads being made by ferry across the river.

While the Zambezi bridge was being constructed work had also started on the northward extension from Blantyre to Lake Nyasa. It had been intended to develop the administrative township of Fort

Johnston as a railway port, but the rising of the lake level at that time resulted in a change of plan. The eventual route then followed, at much greater cost, the Bwanje valley and Dedza lake-shore plain to Salima. The railway port was developed at Chipoka, a few miles to the south of the northern terminal.

In recent years there has been some discussion about constructing an extension to Lilongwe. At present there is a tarred road linking the capital and marketing centre of the Central Province, but this is not adequate for the transport of the surplus maize, tobacco, groundnuts, and cattle to Blantyre. Although by no means an impossible task, and certainly an economic proposition in the long run,[1] a considerable infusion of capital would be required as costly engineering work can be anticipated in climbing the rift valley escarpment again and thereafter in traversing the Dowa hills.

Nevertheless it is expected that not only will the railway be extended to Lilongwe, but also to Fort Jameson.

WATER TRANSPORT

Mention has been made above of the difficulties experienced in the use of the Shire River for transport. Periodic reductions in flow and the Murchison Rapids have resulted in the discontinuance of river services as other forms of transport have been developed.

Only Lake Nyasa is permanently navigable; its use is essential for the transport of crops from the northern parts of the country, where skeletal roads limit links by land. Some places, such as Likoma Island, have no option but to rely on lake transport services.

Navigation on the lake has a long history, for the Arab *dhows* were sailing eastwards with their cargoes of slaves before the arrival of Livingstone. Although slaves are no longer carried the *dhows* sail on, owned and manned by Africans now. Examination of Fig. 54 will show that at the southern end of the lake alone there are many routes still in use.

From Hamisi Makanjira (near Fort Maguire) there is a trade route to Leopard Bay (near Salima). Often six or more *dhows* may be seen at anchorage at Hamisi. Each week a convoy of three sails across to Leopard Bay, setting out at dawn and often arriving a little before midday. On this journey there are many passengers seeking work on the western side of the lake, but on the return journey the *dhows* are loaded with provisions to be sold in the stores of the Fort Maguire area.

The most usual cargo carried in the *dhows* consists of foodstuffs. Many craft sail northward, picking up a cargo of cassava from Mtengula in Moçambique and selling it on Likoma and Chisamula Islands. Continuing northwards, with the aid of the *Mwera*[2] winds, they often drop anchor at Bandawe, Zirakoma, and the mouth of the Dwambazi

---

[1] It is estimated that during 1961 80,000 short tons of goods were handled at Salima originating from the Lilongwe Plain and the Fort Jameson area of Northern Rhodesia.

[2] South East Trade wind.

river on the north-western shores of the lake. From these they sail across to Likoma again, loaded with further supplies of cassava and maize. On continuing southwards from Likoma calls are often made at anchorages on both sides of the lake for rice cargoes, which are brought finally to Hamisi Makanjira.

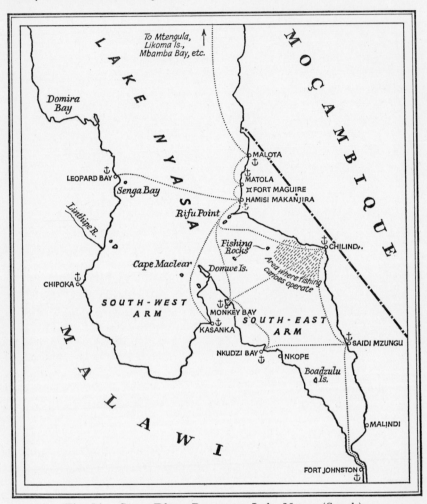

Fig. 54.   Some Dhow Routes on Lake Nyasa (South).
(From W. D. Talbot, 'Some Notes on the Dhows of Fort Johnson District', *The Nyasaland Journal*, Vol. XV(ii) Reproduced by kind permission of the Editor of *The Nyasaland Journal*.

From afar the *dhows* look graceful, but closer examination reveals them as crudely constructed and unreliable, even in the hands of experienced sailors. The frame and planks are made of hard wood, the planks fitting together clinker-fashion with numerous gaps plugged with kapok. The latter swells when wet. The sails are made of white drill (often patched with many other coloured pieces of cloth), and the ropes are made of locally collected lianas, often mixed with other fibres. The

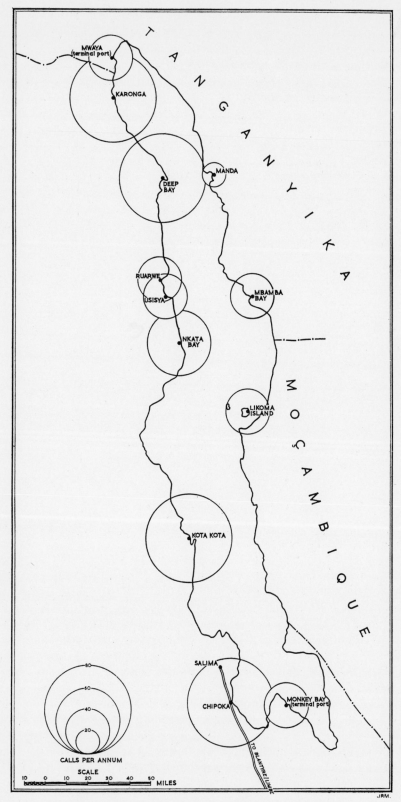

Fig. 55.   M.V. *Ilala II's* Ports of Call on Lake Nyasa.

latter tend only to last for about four weeks, after which they must be replaced.

With the greater use of motor vessels and the development of an improved road system the number of *dhows* is tending to diminish. However, because of the low operation costs and flexibility of movements (for they can anchor in places where larger vessels cannot do so) it will probably be many years before the last *dhow* is beached.

The use of motor vessels on Lake Nyasa was initiated by the *Ilala*, which was built in London, taken on board ship to the mouth of the Zambezi, re-assembled, and sailed up-river as far as the Murchison Rapids. At this point it was again dismantled, portered round the rapids, re-assembled at Matope, and sailed into the lake in 1875. The *Ilala* was owned by the Free Church of Scotland, and was intended to counter the slave traffic by intercepting Arab *dhows*.

TABLE XVIII

Lake Transport Statistics

Year	Passengers	Tonnage handled*	Revenue £	Operating expenditure £
1948	6	4,244	6,927	13,927
1949	2	6,754	8,911	14,125
1950	1	7,886	9,453	19,177
1951	3,629	8,255	17,096	37,553
1952	14,703	7,857	24,664	54,498
1953	25,693	11,059	39,465	61,816
1954	6,907	9,427	28,746	67,475
1955	23,664	9,917	40,647	71,199
1956	32,948	12,527	50,142	83,906
1957	44,480	12,790	55,750	94,291
1960	53,732	16,595	61,107	109,799

* Short tons (2,000 lb.).

(Information taken from H. W. Stevens, *Transportation in Nyasaland* (1962), published mimeograph, Nyasaland Railways Ltd.)

The *Ilala* was succeeded by other mission vessels, by boats belonging to trading companies also. Regular passenger and cargo traffic was established in 1931, when Nyasaland Railways began to operate vessels.

Even the sailing of motor vessels has its hazards, however, for in 1946 a new vessel on its third voyage, the *Vipya*, was blown over and sunk with large loss of life during a violent storm. Moreover, there are few sheltered harbours in which boats can take refuge.

Even at the most important ports docking facilities are scanty. A small jetty is evident at Chipoka, the railway port. A floating jetty was installed at Nkata Bay during 1958. In 1962 a new piled jetty, 1,200 feet long, came into use. Elsewhere there are only rudimentary facilities. One of the difficulties in improving harbour facilities, apart from the fact that as the lake service runs at a loss any infusion of capital is unlikely, is the tendency for the level of the lake to fluctuate.[1] Only at Monkey Bay has it been possible to find a sheltered spot with a sufficient depth of water in which to install a floating dock for repairs.

It will be seen from Table XVIII that although the revenue from both tonnage of goods handled and passengers has tended to increase rapidly in recent years, the operating expenditure has also increased rapidly. It is probable that a subsidy will always be necessary, for although commerce will certainly increase with the growing emphasis on a cash crop economy and a consequent decline in subsistence, it is likely that roads will also improve, and so come into greater use.

ROAD TRANSPORT

As in many other African countries the development of the road system has been subordinated to the cheaper forms of transport described above. Apart from the paths radiating from African villages and the incipient street patterns of Blantyre there were few roads in the later nineteenth century. An early route was the track which led up the Shire Highlands escarpment from the southern end of the Murchison Rapids to Blantyre. From Blantyre it continued northwards to Zomba, where it skirted the eastern slopes of Zomba plateau, and finally descended to the Shire River at Liwonde, where an early fort and *boma* was established.

The Katunga–Liwonde route not only linked navigable stretches of the Shire, but also passed through the commercial and administrative capitals. As a road in the true sense it was developed in 1893, when the amount of traffic between Blantyre and Zomba made construction of the section between these places essential. The section between Blantyre and the Shire to the south tended to atrophy with the development of the railway in 1908.

Another early development was the construction of the Stevenson road in 1883, which linked Karonga with the London Missionary Society's stations near Lake Tanganyika. This road followed an earlier slave route, for Mlozi's slave-trading centre at Karonga had tapped this hinterland.

The earliest roads were for missionary and trading purposes, and the contribution of both missionaries and traders has always been important. With the growth of the administrative services, however, there was a need for a network of roads linking, firstly, the administrative townships with each other, and secondly, the native authority courts with each district headquarters. Later, with the growth of trade, came the crop extraction roads linking with the main road system.

At the time of writing only 200 miles of roads have been covered with a tarred surface, and most of this is in strips wide enough for only one vehicle. From Blantyre the main road through Limbe to Cholo is tarred, as also is the road mentioned above from the same municipality to Zomba and on to the Liwonde Ferry. Outside the Southern Province

[1] For further information on fluctuations in lake level see above page 114.

tarred roads can be found in Lilongwe itself and along the stretch between the town and the railhead at Salima. Elsewhere only small strips can be found, as for instance through the trading estate at Ncheu.

From Liwonde northwards the main road to Lilongwe is being re-aligned and surfaced with gravel, which, although still very dusty during the dry season, is not muddy during the wet season as long as the clay beneath does not become exposed. Between Liwonde and Balaka and between Dedza and Lilongwe the road is well-surfaced and wide, but the intervening section between them has special problems, for it has to climb the escarpment north of Ncheu and follow the Moçambique border over a number of high syenitic intrusions. These factors prevent the re-alignment from being as straight as elsewhere, and widening operations are hampered by the need for much expensive blasting of rock. Nevertheless some improvement is expected to take place within the next two years. Thereafter it is probable that the road surface will be tarred as far as Lilongwe.

Beyond Lilongwe to the north piecemeal re-alignment has taken place, but no large scale works have yet been attempted. Those who enter Malawi from the north find that the roads are very much narrower than those of Tanganyika. From Fort Hill southwards the main road winds tortuously through hilly country until it reaches Rumpi. Five miles farther south the South Rukuru river is crossed by a bridge, at which point there is a junction with the road from Livingstonia to the east. Thereafter the road follows the watershed for a time and then continues in the lee of the Vipya plateau. Beyond Mzimba the plateau surface becomes flatter until it merges imperceptibly into the Lilongwe Plain. Over this section the road is narrow and sometimes difficult to traverse during the rainy season, but at present it is adequate, for the population density of the Northern Province is low and those areas bordering the lake can use water transport for export of crops.

Of the 5,800 miles of roads in Malawi some 3,000 miles are not maintained in all-weather conditions. Those which are in watershed areas are not usually impassable unless there has been a very heavy downpour of rain for a few days, but those in the rift valley are often put out of use even for four-wheel drive vehicles during long periods.

C. D. Twynam's account of the road between Mua and Ntakataka in the Dedza lake-shore area during 1927 is still true today. 'The route ran through a wide dambo of black cotton soil which flooded in the rains, and the track was carried across it on an embankment some 10 feet high with a big culvert in the middle. This had not been repaired, nor had a deviation been built, and we had to work our way down and up the steep sides slantwise in imminent danger of overturning.'

When traversing the lake-shore plains or the Shire valley during the dry season roads tend to dip down very steeply at frequent intervals into sandy hollows, the dried-up beds of streams. As the wet season arrives these deep hollows soon become filled to overflowing by raging torrents. Even where bridges are constructed they are often overtopped by water and washed downstream, disrupting road communications for several months. To improve these roads appreciably considerable infusions of capital not justified by the present economic output (or even in many cases the potential output) would be required.

THE EXPORT TRADE

The development of the export trade, with its beginnings in 1891, has been divided into five distinct periods. The first period, up to 1904, was marked by the export of ivory, rubber, and coffee. Between 1905 and 1921 ivory declined as elephants diminished rapidly in number. Coffee also declined, and was replaced by tobacco, cotton, and tea. During the third period, between 1922 and 1932 the same crops began to increase in production considerably. From being produced on a small scale in the Blantyre area, for instance, tobacco culture was spreading to the Central Province, and was being produced on African Trust Land as well as on European estates. While total exports for the second period were valued at £3·5 million, an annual average increase of £200,000, the third period showed an increase in total value to £7 million, an annual average of £660,000. More than 98 per cent. of the export trade before 1932 had been with the United Kingdom.

During the period between 1933 and 1951 tobacco began to decline in its percentage of the total exports. Earlier it had accounted for an average of 72 per cent. per annum, but now it dropped to 40 per cent. as tea rose in importance. Tung oil was also a new export. At the same time the British share in Malawi trade decreased to about 66 per cent., before the increasing interest of Sierra Leone, the Congo, and Egypt in tobacco. Total exports were valued at £38 million, an annual average of £2 million.

Since 1952 tobacco and tea have continued to be the most important export crops, each being worth more than 35 per cent. of all exports. Cotton, because of the recent higher incidence of stainers and red bollworm, has declined a little, while groundnuts have become important. Tung oil has continued to be an important commodity, in spite of a depression in the market. The total value of all exports between 1952 and 1960 was almost £70 million, an annual average of £7·7 million.

During the past seventy years the export trade has shown a number of changes. In the first place it was concerned with collected indigenous commodities, such as ivory and rubber. Then during the same period coffee rose in importance rapidly and declined in importance even more rapidly. Thereafter came the development of the two main commodities, tobacco and tea, which have remained paramount in importance up to the present time. The most marked changes in recent years have been concerned with increasing the diversity of export crops. Tung oil and groundnuts have become important. Cotton

P

and coffee have now survived their bad periods and seem to be holding their own, with the result that the share of the two main commodities will never be again as great as it was.

BIBLIOGRAPHY

C. W. B. Arnold, 'Lake Nyasa's Varying Level', *Nyasa. Jour.*, Vol. V (i).

C. A. Baker, 'Nyasaland, the History of its Export Trade', *Nyasa. Jour.*, Vol. XV (i).

C. A. Cardew, 'Notes re Mpimbe, Fort Sharpe and Liwonde', *Nyasa. Jour.*, Vol. IX (i).

F. Debenham, *Nyasaland, the Land of the Lake* (1955).

Sir H. H. Johnston, *British Central Africa* (1897).

H. W. Stevens, *Transportation in Nyasaland* (1962).

W. D. Talbot, 'Some Notes on the Dhows of Fort Johnston District', *Nyasa. Jour.*, Vol. XV (ii).

C. D. Twynam, 'The Original Blantyre–Zomba Road and the Half-way Rest House', *Nyasa. Jour.*, Vol. X (ii).

——, 'From Concession to Ntakataka in 1927', *Nyasa. Jour.*, Vol. VII (ii).

H. E. Whitehouse, 'Level of Lake Nyasa', *Nyasa. Jour.*, Vol. V (i).

S. G. Williams, 'Some Old Steamships of Nyasaland', *Nyasa. Jour.*, Vol. XI (i).

APPENDIXES

APPENDIX A
Annual Crop Produce Exports
(Nyasaland—1948–60)

	1948		1953		1960	
	Short tons	£	Short tons	£	Short tons	£
Tobacco	12,923	2,250,000	13,127	2,877,700	17,364	2,048,000
Tea	7,535	1,350,000	6,563	1,570,400	12,366	4,096,000
Cotton	2,453	369,100	3,209	788,400	13,566	644,000
Oilseeds	1,370	19,900	11,675	455,000	20,698	855,000
Tung Oil	400	67,000	903	127,300	1,191	122,000
Rice	11	300	1,572	100,500	7,080	118,000
Grain	860	15,700	41,545	966,600	16,613	112,000
Pulses	1,211	25,000	2,124	71,500	6,320	177,800
Roots	—	—	446	7,500	6,127	82,300
Coffee	—	—	5	1,700	179	—
	26,763	4,097,400	81,169	6,966,700	101,497	9,255,100

APPENDIX B
Tobacco Production, 1954–60

	Flue-cured		Dark-fired		Air-cured	
	Acreage	Production (mil. lb.)	Acreage	Production (mil. lb.)	Acreage	Production (mil. lb.)
1954	7,263	4·31	97,100	23·6	12,000	3·3
1955	6,791	3·7	84,971	14·8	8,700	2·3
1956	8,207	4·1	98,967	25·4	9,200	2·7
1957	5,878	3·0	114,897	25·5	9,400	3·0
1958	4,929	2·2	143,185	30·9	11,200	2·5
1959	4,261	2·2	133,100	26·4	12,200	5·4
1960	3,270	2·9	84,200	21·5	10,800	7·0

APPENDIX C
Tea Production, 1952–60

Year ending 31st March	Acreage	Export (mil. lb.)	Yields per acre (lb.)
1952–53	23,362	14·65	732
1953–54	24,726	15·03	683
1954–55	25,718	17·18	781
1955–56	26,186	18·39	766
1956–57	26,822	21·36	890
1957–58	27,381	16·74	700
1958–59	28,078	24·35	974
1959–60	28,728	24·73	975

APPENDIX D

Cotton Production. African Trust Land, 1952–60

Year	Acreage	Production Seed Cotton (short tons)	Yields per acre (lb.)
1952	40,588	7,702	385
1953	56,852	9,732	341
1954	42,489	7,179	342
1955	51,621	8,569	330
1956	36,826	3,233	174
1957	24,650	4,288	343
1958	32,112	5,513	344
1959	33,869	10,029	590
1960	51,236	12,515	556

Sources: Protectorate Annual Reports, 1952–60.
Economic Survey of Nyasaland, 1959.

APPENDIX E

Population Distribution and Densities by Districts

District	Population	Area in square miles	Population per square mile
SOUTHERN PROVINCE			
Fort Johnston	168,000	2,966	57
Zomba	271,000	2,723	100
Blantyre	280,000	1,880	149
Mlanje	273,000	1,291	211
Cholo	153,000	733	209
Chikwawa	78,000	1,874	42
Port Herald	87,000	741	117
Total	1,310,000	12,208	107
CENTRAL PROVINCE			
Kota Kota	89,000	2,426	37
Kasungu	67,000	3,335	20
Dowa	191,000	1,825	105
Fort Manning	64,000	950	67
Lilongwe	288,000	2,514	114
Dedza	175,000	1,747	100
Ncheu	114,000	1,210	94
Total	988,000	14,007	71
NORTHERN PROVINCE			
Karonga	107,000	3,120	34
Rumpi	33,000	1,546	21
Mzimba	183,000	4,086	45
Nkata Bay	57,000	1,912	30
Total	380,000	10,664	36

Figures taken from 1957 Estimate by Central African Statistical Office.

INDEX